Applied Stochastic A₁

Courant Lecture Notes in Mathematics

Executive Editor
Jalal Shatah

Miranda Holmes-Cerfon
University of British Columbia

33   **Applied Stochastic Analysis**

Courant Institute of Mathematical Sciences
New York University
New York, New York

American Mathematical Society
Providence, Rhode Island

2020 *Mathematics Subject Classification.* Primary 60J10, 60-01, 60G05, 60G07, 60H05, 60H10, 60H35, 60J25, 65C05, 65C30.

For additional information and updates on this book, visit
www.ams.org/bookpages/cln-33

Library of Congress Cataloging-in-Publication Data

Names: Holmes-Cerfon, Miranda, 1983- author.
Title: Applied stochastic analysis / Miranda Holmes-Cerfon, University of British Columbia.
Description: New York, New York : Courant Institute of Mathematical Sciences ; Providence, Rhode Island : American Mathematical Society, [2024] | Series: Courant lecture notes, 1529-9031; volume 33 | Includes bibliographical references and index.
Identifiers: LCCN 2024030698 | ISBN 9781470478391 (paperback) | ISBN 9781470478681 (ebook)
Subjects: LCSH: Stochastic analysis. | Stochastic integrals. | Markov processes. | AMS: Probability theory and stochastic processes – Markov processes – Markov chains (discrete-time Markov processes on discrete state spaces). | Probability theory and stochastic processes – Instructional exposition (textbooks, tutorial papers, etc.). | Probability theory and stochastic processes – Stochastic processes – Foundations of stochastic processes. | Probability theory and stochastic processes – Stochastic processes – General theory of processes. | Probability theory and stochastic processes – Stochastic analysis – Stochastic integrals. | Probability theory and stochastic processes – Stochastic analysis – Stochastic ordinary differential equations. | Probability theory and stochastic processes – Stochastic analysis – Computational methods for stochastic equations. | Probability theory and stochastic processes – Markov processes – Continuous-time Markov processes on general state spaces. | Numerical analysis – Probabilistic methods, simulation and stochastic differential equations – Monte Carlo methods. | Numerical analysis – Probabilistic methods, simulation and stochastic differential equations – Stochastic differential and integral equations.
Classification: LCC QA274.2 .H65 2024 | DDC 519.2/2–dc23/eng20241001
LC record available at https://lccn.loc.gov/2024030698
Courant Lecture Notes ISSN: 1529-9031 (print); 2472-4467 (online)
DOI: https://doi.org/10.1090/cln/33

To Antoine, Adrien, and Elodie

Contents

Preface

"Stochastic" is a fancy word for "random". Randomness plays a key role in the behavior of a great many physical, chemical, biological, engineering, and human systems. Yet "random" does not mean "unstructured"—randomness often has a lot of structure behind it. Stochastic analysis is a set of tools developed to understand and exploit this structure. Originally developed within the realm of probability theory, its wide applicability means it is becoming a foundational topic in applied mathematics.

This book introduces the major ideas of stochastic analysis to students and researchers in applied mathematics or related disciplines who wish to use these ideas to model or to simulate systems involving randomness. It builds the theoretical foundation required to solve concrete problems that arise in physically motivated models, and it introduces simulation techniques. The book should be accessible to those with a good upper-level undergraduate background in linear algebra, probability, ODEs, and PDEs. Because of the mathematical sophistication required to synthesize these topics, the book is best categorized as being at the graduate level. Indeed, this weaving together of many different mathematical topics is one of the beautiful aspects of stochastic analysis.

The book differs from others on the subject in that it takes a practical approach to introducing the major ideas of stochastic analysis, while retaining rigor in areas that are familiar to a typical applied math student. Measure theory is avoided because this theory is not always familiar to such students, and it sometimes obscures the key intuitions. Rigorous arguments are provided when doing so helps build techniques or intuition that will be useful later on, or when rigor does not detract too much from studying typical versions of the objects that are introduced. However, a fully rigorous treatment of stochastic analysis would require measure theory, so the treatment here is neither the most general nor the most complete—it does not always prove that the mathematical objects introduced actually exist, it does not worry about pathological cases that do not arise in applications, and it assumes all functions are as smooth as is necessary to perform calculations in the simplest possible way. I have found that this approach is sufficient to understand the behavior of stochastic phenomena using fairly standard calculations. For example, from the definition of a Brownian motion one can derive its full set of transition properties, as well as the forward and backward Kolmogorov equations, in just a few lines of calculus combined with some simple probabilistic reasoning. However, showing that a Brownian motion actually exists is a deep topic in probability theory. The book points out gaps in its arguments and provides references for readers who wish to delve into a topic more deeply.

The book is a compilation of lecture notes for a first year PhD course at the Courant Institute of Mathematics, and its structure follows that of the course. Each chapter corresponds to roughly a week of teaching (with the exception of Chapter 2, which spanned about two weeks including a brief review of probability theory). The book contains more material than was presented in class; for example, some proofs and examples were left as reading for interested students. I found myself removing topics each time I taught the course, but the corresponding sections are included in the book for completeness.[1] As with any area of mathematics, one can only learn by solving problems; therefore, the book contains many exercises, both embedded in the text, and at the end of each chapter. Some of these exercises are used to reinforce a concept, some are used to further develop an idea using arguments very similar to those in the book, and others were homework problems for the course, which extend the material, show applications of it, and ask students to implement simulation algorithms. Although simply writing up pseudocode as real code might sound like a trivial exercise, I have found that students gain a much deeper understanding of the algorithm and of the corresponding stochastic process once they simulate it. This exercise also helps them appreciate the inherent magnitude of randomness, and the frustratingly slow convergence of stochastic simulations—I cannot count the number of times have I seen students surprised to learn that 100 realizations is not a lot!

A variety of students took the course, which indicates the range of possibly interested readers. Most were applied mathematics graduate students, studying topics such as fluid dynamics, mathematical biology, materials science, atmosphere/ocean science, optimization, data science, and more recently, machine learning, where stochastic analysis is finding new applications. (Our finance students took a different course which related the ideas directly to finance; the core ideas are the same.) Some undergraduate students with unusual mathematical maturity also successfully completed the course. Occasionally, course participants included graduate students from other departments, including engineering, physics, and even sociology. Interestingly, sometimes PhD students specializing in probability took the course, simultaneously with probability courses which dealt with the same topics in name but placed them on a rigorous foundation (Limit Theorems I and II at Courant). These students told me that the courses complemented each other.

This book would not exist without the help of several other people. First of all, I would like to thank Chenqi (Dan) Jiang, for his careful proofreading, elegant calculations, and perceptive questions over the summer of 2022. I would also like to thank the several people who read and made detailed comments on sections of this book, notably Shanyin Tong, Shikun Nie, and Bill Holmes (my dad). I would like to thank Eric Vanden-Eijnden for creating the course on which this book is based and for his immensely helpful notes when I started teaching this course, and I am grateful to Jonathan Goodman and Robert Kohn for many insightful discussions related to the material in this book. I learned about the importance of detailed balance from Aleksandar Donev, who had much still left to teach us. Thanks to Oliver Büler for his continuing encouragement and support. Thanks also to the many people who emailed

---

[1] As an example of what could be omitted: most of Chapter 5, with the exception of Sections 5.5.1.2 and 5.5.3.1, which deal with the important topics of covariance functions and stationary processes; most of Chapter 12, with the exception of Section 12.12.1, which derives the structure of an SDE satisfying detailed balance, an important topic in applications. Some other sections that I have skipped on occasion include 3.3.3.4, 5.5.6, 6.6.6, 6.6.7, 9.9.3, 9.9.4, 11.11.3, and Chapter 13.

me with questions or encouraging comments; I appreciate your support and willingness to reach out. Finally, thanks to the many students of Applied Stochastic Analysis whose sharp intellects and astute questions have helped me refine both this text and my understanding over the years; our office hour discussions were a highlight of my day.

The material in this book is a reinterpretation of the work of previous authors. I am grateful for the many excellent books from which I have drawn, that are referenced frequently. I hope these references provide a starting point for those wishing to delve further into particular topics.

CHAPTER 1

Introduction

A great many systems evolve in ways that appear unpredictable, or random: the velocity in a turbulent fluid, the position of a grain of pollen in a glass of water, the mean temperature of the planet, the price of a stock, the number of bees in a bee hive, the number of molecules in the reactant state of a chemical reaction, the bond angles of a folding protein, the size of a self-assembling viral capsid, etc. For these and for many other systems it can be difficult or impossible to write down equations describing their exact evolution, so it is natural to model them as stochastic, or random, processes, using the tools of stochastic analysis. This chapter will give an overview of the types of stochastic processes we will encounter in this book and the tools and reasons for studying them. It is best read after familiarizing yourself with the key concepts of probability theory, which are reviewed in Appendix A.A.1.

1.1. What is a stochastic process?

A *stochastic process* is a random function of a single variable. Each instance, or realization, of the process, produces a different function. Here are examples of realizations of stochastic processes (Figure 1.1).

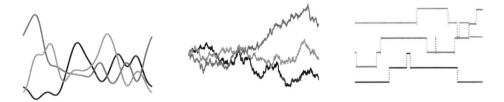

FIGURE 1.1. Realizations of three types of stochastic processes.

For each of the three types of processes we have shown three independent realizations of the process. For a given process, the realizations produce different functions but the functions resemble each other qualitatively. The first process produces functions that are smooth and vary about a common mean; the second produces functions that are jaggedy and appear to diverge from their starting point; and the third produces functions that are piecewise constant, with jumps at random times. Let us make this idea more precise. Let $(\Omega, \mathcal{F}, P)$ be a probability space (see Section A.A.1) and let T be an ordered set, called the *index set*. Usually we think of T as indexing time.

DEFINITION 1.1. A *stochastic process* is a collection of random variables $\{X_t, \ t \in T\}$, such that for each $t \in T$, X_t is a random variable on $(\Omega, \mathcal{F}, P)$.

We write a stochastic process as $X = (X_t)_{t \in T}$. We sometimes abbreviate this as X_t, when it is clear from the context what the index set is and that we refer to the process, not to a particular random variable.

When the index set is countable the process is called a *discrete-time* stochastic process. Examples include $T = \{\ldots, -1, 0, 1, \ldots, \}$, $T = \{0, 1, \ldots, N\}$. When the index set contains an interval of $\mathbb{R}$ the process is called *continuous-time*. Examples include $T = \mathbb{R}$, $T = [a, b]$. An index set may also be a mixture of continuous and discrete parts. All of the processes shown above are continuous-time processes. A stochastic process is actually a function of two arguments, a time $t \in T$ and an element in the probability space $\omega \in \Omega$. To highlight these two arguments we may write the process as $X(t, \omega)$ or $X_t(\omega)$. Fixing either of these arguments gives a different interpretation of a stochastic process.

(1) As a parametrized family of random variables. For each t, X_t is a random variable (producing the different values at each vertical slice in the examples above); over all t, we have a family of random variables, parameterized by t. These random variables are usually correlated with each other, in ways that depend on the particular process.

(2) As a probability distribution on path space. For each ω, $X_\omega(t) = X(t, \omega)$ is a function of $t \in T$. Therefore, each realization of the randomness produces a function of t, generated from some probability measure on the space of functions of t. Events in this space are sets of paths, e.g., "all paths that pass through $[x, x+h]$ at time t_0," "all paths whose maximum value is bigger than M," etc. It is impossible to construct a probability density on this probability space, because it is infinite-dimensional; however, we can still talk about probabilities of events and find ways to compute these probabilities.

1.2. What classes of stochastic processes will we learn about?

Without any more information about a stochastic process there is little to say. Therefore, we will turn our attention to classes of stochastic processes with some shared underlying structure, and learn tools that this structure provides to understand and make predictions about a process. The major classes of processes that we will study are the following

- *Markov chains* (Chapters 2–4). A Markov chain is a type of Markov process, which is, roughly, a stochastic process whose future evolution depends only on its current value, and not on any past values. It is a Markov chain if it has a discrete state space. We will spend the first half of the book studying Markov chains, partly because they are widely used as models, and partly because many of the ideas used to understand Markov chains can be generalized to study diffusion processes, which we will study in the second half of the book. In addition, one of the twentieth century's most powerful algorithms, Markov chain Monte Carlo (MCMC), is based on Markov chains. We will not study Markov chains exhaustively (you could take a whole course on them) but rather will focus on ideas we will build upon for diffusion processes: how to describe the evolution of probability density and statistics (via the Kolmogorov forward and backward equations), how to characterize a statistical steady-state (via stationary distributions), and how to determine how long it takes the process to reach a certain state (via mean first-passage times). We will show how to answer these questions using linear algebra by solving linear systems of equations.

- *Gaussian processes* (Chapter 5). These are models for a wide range of phenomena, such as velocities or waves in a fluid, the height of topography, or the uncertainty in a model. They are often smoother than Markov processes. Gaussian processes are studied because they have many statistical properties which are analytically tractable, and because the central limit theorem suggests they should arise generically whenever a process is the result of a superposition of random effects.

- *Stationary processes* (Chapter 5). Stationary processes are (roughly) those whose statistics do not change with time. They may occur for a stochastic system that has evolved for long enough to reach a statistical steady-state. Stationary Gaussian processes are studied particularly widely and are easy to simulate. We will look at the stochastic analogue of the Fourier transform, and will learn how to calculate the Fourier transform of functions which are not even integrable.

- *Brownian motion* (Chapter 6). This is perhaps the most famous stochastic process. It was originally invented to model the motion of pollen grains, and it now forms the foundation for studying diffusion processes, via stochastic calculus.

- *Diffusion processes* (Chapters 7–12). These are processes that are solutions to a stochastic differential equation, a stochastic analogue of an ordinary differential equation. They will be the focus of the second half of the book. We we ask questions such as:

  - How can we make sense of an equation with randomness in it? For example, how could we make sense of this equation:

$$
\underbrace{\frac{dx}{dt}}_{\substack{\text{velocity of}\\\text{particle in}\\\text{a fluid}}} = \underbrace{u(x,t)}_{\substack{\text{velocity of}\\\text{fluid}}} + \underbrace{\eta(t)}_{\substack{\text{noise term,}\\\text{e.g. unresolved velocity}}} ,
$$

or this one:

$$
\underbrace{\frac{dN}{dt}}_{\substack{\text{rate of change}\\\text{of population}}} = \big(\underbrace{a(t)}_{\substack{\text{average}\\\text{growth}\\\text{rate}}} + \underbrace{\eta(t)}_{\text{noise}} \big) \underbrace{N(t)}_{\substack{\text{population}\\\text{size}}} .
$$

Usually we want the noise term in a model to be "as random as possible," say, completely independent from timestep to timestep. It turns out this means we must choose the noise to be the "derivative" of Brownian motion, and furthermore, that the Riemann integral that we usually use for defining solutions to ODEs is no longer well defined. So, we will start with the fundamental issue of defining a new kind of integral, the Itô integral, and then show that this integral gives rise to new rules of calculus, such as a new kind of chain rule. These tools are collectively called *stochastic calculus*.

– How can we solve these equations? Both analytically and also numerically. For the latter, how can we measure how "close" we are to the true solution? We will see that adding randomness also adds many more ways of measuring the quality of a numerical scheme.

– How can we solve for statistical properties of the solution, such as its probability density at some time, or the average time it takes to reach a boundary? We can answer questions like these by solving elliptic or parabolic PDEs. We will spend a fair amount of time studying the link between diffusion processes and PDEs, since PDE theory provides an arsenal of applied math tools to make approximations when we cannot solve equations exactly.

This is not an exhaustive list of stochastic processes that arise in models. In particular, we will not study jump processes, point processes, or Levy processes. However, after reading this book you should have the tools to learn about these processes on your own.

Throughout the book we will pay careful attention to the principle of *detailed balance*, a fundamental principle that many physical systems satisfy, and hence that any models of them should satisfy too. Roughly, detailed balance is the principle that a stochastic process looks "the same" forwards and backwards in time. Since the laws of physics look the same when time is reversed, so should our models. It will turn out that systems that satisfy detailed balance also have an elegant mathematical structure, so there are reasons to understand this principle beyond its physical implications.

We make one final remark about why it is appropriate to model a system stochastically. Many of the systems we have mentioned are not inherently random—for example, in principle, one could write down the Navier–Stokes equations describing the flow of a turbulent fluid, and solve them to high precision to obtain the velocity at each location in the fluid—yet there can still be advantages in modelling a system as random even when it is not. One is that the governing equations could be too hard to simulate to high enough precision. In this case unresolved scales can be approximated by stochastic processes, which can help capture phenomena that depend on these scales and can help quantify the uncertainty of the simulation. This approach is used all the time in turbulence closures for fluids, stochastic parameterizations in climate models, or in coarse-graining the fluid molecules in a simulation of protein folding or of micron-scale physics. Relatedly, the governing equations may be chaotic, i.e., very sensitive to small perturbations, so any uncertainty in the initial condition or any discretization errors in a numerical method can be modeled stochastically. Furthermore, when approximating a discrete system as a continuous system, such as in replacing a finite collection of molecules by a density of molecules, or in replacing a finite number of individuals in a population by a continuum, the difference between the continuum and the discrete system is often effectively modelled as noise, capturing finite-size effects. Finally, even if we could simulate the exact deterministic equations, this wouldn't necessarily give us useful information: if we know where every atom is in a river at every point in time, what have we learned about the river? It is often more helpful to understand patterns, or large-scale, averaged behavior (such as the average velocity, or the scales over which it is correlated), which can be described statistically using stochastic processes, and are often more tractable to study.

CHAPTER 2

Markov Chains (I)

We will dive right in to the definition of a Markov chain in Section 2.2.1, and give an assortment of examples in Section 2.2.2. Sections 2.2.3–2.2.5 show how to use linear algebra to answer questions about the statistics of Markov chains.

2.1. What is a Markov chain?

Consider a stochastic process $(X_t)_{t \in T}$ with a discrete (finite or countable) state space S, which depends on discrete time $T = \{0, 1, 2, \ldots\}$. Since S is countable, we may index it with integers, as $S = \{1, 2, 3, \ldots\}$ or $S = \{\ldots, -1, 0, 1, \ldots\}$.

DEFINITION 2.1. The process $X_0, X_1, X_2, \ldots$ is a *discrete-time Markov chain* if it satisfies the *Markov property*:

$$(2.1) \qquad P(X_{n+1} = s | X_0 = x_0, X_1 = x_1, \ldots, X_n = x_n) = P(X_{n+1} = s | X_n = x_n)$$

or all $x_0, x_i, \ldots, s \in S$ and for all $n \geq 0$.

DEFINITION 2.2. The quantities $P(X_{n+1} = j | X_n = i)$ in (2.1) are called the *transition probabilities*. It is convenient to write them as

$$(2.2) \qquad\qquad P_{ij}(n) = P(X_{n+1} = j | X_n = i).$$

DEFINITION 2.3. The *transition matrix* at time n is the matrix $P(n)$ whose (i, j)th element is $P_{ij}(n)$.

We call P a matrix even if $|S| = \infty$. If the state space is infinite, then we interpret products such as PQ to mean infinite matrix with entries given by the infinite sum $(PQ)_{ij} = \sum_k P_{ik} Q_{kj}$.

Notice that the transition matrix has the following properties:

   (i) $P_{ij}(n) \geq 0 \quad \forall i, j \in S \quad$ (the entries are non-negative)
   (ii) $\sum_j P_{ij}(n) = 1 \quad \forall i \in S \quad$ (the rows sum to 1).

Any matrix that satisfies (i), (ii) above is called a *stochastic matrix*. Hence, the transition matrix is a stochastic matrix.

REMARK 2.4. Note that a "stochastic matrix" is *not* the same thing as a "random matrix"! Usually, "random" can be substituted for "stochastic" but not here. A random matrix is a matrix whose entries are random variables.

***Exercise* 2.1.** Show that the transition probabilities satisfy properties (i), (ii) above.

***Exercise* 2.2.** Show that if X_t is a discrete-time Markov chain, then

$$P(X_n = s | X_0 = x_0, X_1 = x_1, \ldots, X_m = x_m) = P(X_n = s | X_m = x_m)$$

for $0 \leq m < n$. That is, the probabilities at the current time, depend only on the most recent known state in the past, even if it is not exactly one step before.

DEFINITION 2.5. The Markov chain X_t is *time-homogeneous* if $P(X_{n+1} = j | X_n = i) = P(X_1 = j | X_0 = i)$. That is the transition probabilities do not depend on time n. Write $P_{ij} = P(X_1 = j | X_0 = i)$ for the probability to go from i to j in one step, and $P = P(1)$ for the transition matrix. If a Markov chain is not time-homogeneous then it is *time-inhomogeneous*.

We will mainly consider time-homogeneous Markov chains in this course, though we will occasionally remark on how some results may be generalized to the time-inhomogeneous case.

2.2. Examples of Markov chains

Here is a collection of examples to illustrate the breadth of situations that Markov chains might model.

Example 2.6 (Weather model). Let X_n be the state of the weather on day n in New York, which we assume is either *rainy* or *sunny*. We could use a Markov chain as a crude model for how the weather evolves day by day. The state space is $S = \{\text{rain}, \text{sun}\}$. One transition matrix might be

$$P = \begin{array}{c} \text{sun} \\ \text{rain} \end{array} \begin{array}{cc} \text{sun} & \text{rain} \\ \begin{pmatrix} 0.8 & 0.2 \\ 0.4 & 0.6 \end{pmatrix} \end{array}.$$

This says that if it is sunny today, then the chance it will be sunny tomorrow is 0.8, whereas if it is rainy today, then the chance it will be sunny tomorrow is 0.4.

Some questions you might be interested in include: if it is sunny today, what is the probability that it is sunny in two days? Or, what is the long-run fraction of sunny days in New York?

Example 2.7 (Coin flipping). Another two-state Markov chain is based on coin flips. Usually coin flips are used as the canonical example of independent Bernoulli trials. However, (**Diaconis et al., 2007**) studied sequences of coin tosses empirically, and found that outcomes are *not* independent. Rather, they are well modeled by a Markov chain with the following transition probabilities:

$$P = \begin{array}{c} \text{heads} \\ \text{tails} \end{array} \begin{array}{cc} \text{heads} & \text{tails} \\ \begin{pmatrix} 0.51 & 0.49 \\ 0.49 & 0.51 \end{pmatrix} \end{array}.$$

That is, if you throw a Heads on your first toss, there is a very slightly higher chance of throwing heads on your second, and similarly for Tails.

Example 2.8 (Random walk on the line). Suppose we perform a walk on the integers, starting at some integer k. At each step we move to one unit right with probability p or one unit left with probability $1 - p$. The position of the random walker is a Markov chain, which can be constructed explicitly as

$$X_n = \sum_{j=1}^{n} \xi_j, \qquad \xi_j = \begin{cases} +1 & \text{with probability } p \\ -1 & \text{with probability } 1-p \end{cases}, \qquad \xi_i \text{ i.i.d.}$$

The transition probabilities are

$$P_{i,i+1} = p, \quad P_{i,i-1} = 1-p, \quad P_{i,j} = 0 \quad (j \neq i \pm 1).$$

The state space is $S = \{\ldots, -1, 0, 1, \ldots\}$, which is countably infinite.

One canonical problem this models is a gambling game. A gambler starts with \$$k$, and at each game she either wins \$1 with probability p, or loses \$1 with probability $1-p$. We might be interested in questions such as: what is her average earnings after n games? What is the probability that she wins \$20, before she goes broke? On average, how long does it take for her to go broke? We will show the phenomenon called the *gambler's ruin*, which says that even for a fair game with $p = 1/2$, the gambler will go broke with probability 1.

Example 2.9 (Independent identically distributed (i.i.d.) random variables). A sequence of i.i.d. random variables is a Markov chain, albeit a somewhat trivial one. Consider a sequence of i.i.d. random variables $X_0, X_1, \ldots$ taking values in $S = \{1, 2, \ldots, k\}$ with probability $P(X_n = i) = p_i$. This is a Markov chain with transition matrix

$$P = \begin{array}{c} \\ 1 \\ 2 \\ \vdots \\ k \end{array} \begin{array}{cccc} 1 & 2 & \cdots & k \\ \begin{pmatrix} p_1 & p_2 & \cdots & p_k \\ p_1 & p_2 & \cdots & p_k \\ \vdots & \vdots & & \vdots \\ p_1 & p_2 & \cdots & p_k \end{pmatrix} \end{array}$$

Example 2.10 (Random walk on a graph (undirected, unweighted)). Suppose we have a graph: a set of N vertices, combined with a set of edges connecting them. We can perform a random walk on the graph as follows: if we are at vertex i, choose an edge uniformly at random from the set of edges leading out of it, and move along the edge to the other vertex. The process corresponding to the random walk on the vertices is a Markov chain with state space $S = \{1, 2, \ldots, N\}$, and with transition matrix $P_{ij} = 1/d_i$ if there is an edge between i, j, where d_i is the number of edges leading out of node i (the "degree" of node i).

Here is an example of an undirected graph and its corresponding transition matrix.

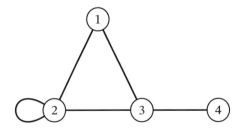

$$P = \begin{array}{c} \\ 1 \\ 2 \\ 3 \\ 4 \end{array} \begin{array}{cccc} 1 & 2 & 3 & 4 \\ \begin{pmatrix} 0 & \frac{1}{2} & \frac{1}{2} & 0 \\ \frac{1}{3} & \frac{1}{3} & \frac{1}{3} & 0 \\ \frac{1}{3} & \frac{1}{3} & 0 & \frac{1}{3} \\ 0 & 0 & 1 & 0 \end{pmatrix} \end{array}$$

Here is another example of an undirected graph, corresponding to a random walk on the vertices of a pentagon.

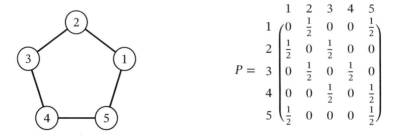

$$P = \begin{array}{c} \\ 1 \\ 2 \\ 3 \\ 4 \\ 5 \end{array} \begin{pmatrix} \begin{array}{ccccc} 1 & 2 & 3 & 4 & 5 \end{array} \\ 0 & \frac{1}{2} & 0 & 0 & \frac{1}{2} \\ \frac{1}{2} & 0 & \frac{1}{2} & 0 & 0 \\ 0 & \frac{1}{2} & 0 & \frac{1}{2} & 0 \\ 0 & 0 & \frac{1}{2} & 0 & \frac{1}{2} \\ \frac{1}{2} & 0 & 0 & 0 & \frac{1}{2} \end{pmatrix}$$

Example 2.11 (Random walk on a graph (weighted, directed)). Every Markov chain can be represented as a random walk on a weighted, directed graph. A weighted graph has a positive real number assigned to each edge, called the edge's "weight," and the random walker chooses an edge from the set of available edges, in proportion to each edge's weight. A directed graph assigns each edge a direction, and a walker can only move in that direction.

Here is an example of a weighted, directed graph, and the corresponding transition matrix:

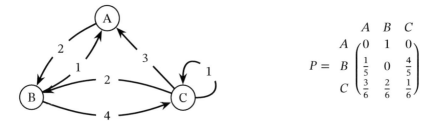

$$P = \begin{array}{c} \\ A \\ B \\ C \end{array} \begin{pmatrix} \begin{array}{ccc} A & B & C \end{array} \\ 0 & 1 & 0 \\ \frac{1}{5} & 0 & \frac{4}{5} \\ \frac{3}{6} & \frac{2}{6} & \frac{1}{6} \end{pmatrix}$$

The idea of Markov chains on directed graphs forms the foundation for Google's Page Rank algorithm, which has revolutionized internet searches. Page Rank constructs a directed graph of the internet, where nodes are webpages and there is a directed edge from webpage A to webpage B if A contains a link to B. Page Rank supposes an internet surfer clicks on links at random, and ranks pages according to the long-time average fraction of time that the surfer spends on each page.

Example 2.12 (Autoregressive model of order k, AR(k)). Given constants $a_1, \ldots, a_k \in \mathbb{R}$, let $Y_n = a_1 Y_{n-1} + a_2 Y_{n-2} + \ldots + a_k Y_{n-k} + W_n$, where W_n are i.i.d. random variables.

The process Y_n is *not* a Markov chain, because its next value depends on its past k values. However, we can form a Markov chain by defining $X_n = (Y_n, Y_{n-1}, \ldots, Y_{n-k+1})^T$. Then

$$X_n = A X_{n-1} + \underline{W}_n,$$

where

$$A = \begin{pmatrix} a_1 & a_2 & \cdots & & a_k \\ 1 & 0 & \cdots & & 0 \\ 0 & 1 & \cdots & & 0 \\ \cdots & \cdots & \cdots & 1 & 0 \end{pmatrix},$$

and $W_n = (W_n, 0, \ldots, 0)^T$. The vector-valued process X_n is a Markov chain.

Example 2.13 (Card shuffling). Shuffling a pack of cards can be modeled as a Markov chain. The state space S is the set of permutations of $\{1, 2, \ldots, 52\}$. A shuffle takes one permutation $\sigma \in S$, and outputs another permutation $\sigma' \in S$ with some probability.

A simple model is the top-to-random shuffle: at each step, take a card from the top of the deck, and put it back in at a random location. The transition matrix has elements

$$P(X_1 = \sigma' | X_0 = \sigma) = \begin{cases} \frac{1}{52} & \text{if } \sigma' \text{ is obtained by taking the top item in } \sigma \\ & \text{and moving it a random location,} \\ 0 & \text{otherwise.} \end{cases}$$

There are also Markov chain models for more complicated shuffles, such as the riffle shuffle. Using these models one can ask: How many shuffles are needed to make the deck "close to random"? It takes seven riffle shuffles to get close to random, but it takes 11 or 12 to get so close that a gambler in a casino cannot exploit the deviations from randomness to win a typical game. See the online essay (**Austin, 2010**) for an accessible introduction to these ideas, and (**Aldous and Diaconis, 1986**) for the mathematical proofs. (I first learned about the critical 7 riffle shuffles in the beautiful *Proofs from the Book*, by Aigner and Ziegler.)

Example 2.14 (Markov chains to approximate continuous processes). Sometimes a continuous stochastic process can be effectively modeled as a discrete one. Figure 2.4 shows data from an experiment (**Rogers et al., 2013**) where the authors measure the separation between two particles coated with velcro-like DNA strands.

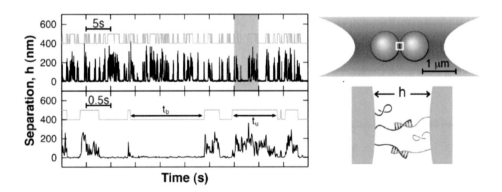

FIGURE 2.4. The separation between micron-scale particles (colloids) coated with sticky DNA strands can be modeled as a 2-state Markov chain. (Used with permission of the Royal Society of Chemistry, from Kinetics and nonexponential binding of DNA-coated colloids, W. Benjamin Rogers, Talid Sinno, and John C. Crocker, Soft Matter 9 (2013); permission conveyed through Copyright Clearance Center, Inc.)

The separation alternates between hovering near zero, and varying rapidly above zero. The authors found it effective to model the states of the particles as a two-state

Markov chain, with states "bound" and "unbound", depending on whether the distance between the particles was small or large. They then constructed a theory for the transition rates between these states based on their knowledge of the physics of the system.

Note that such a discrete approximation of a continuous process is rarely truly Markovian, but can nevertheless satisfy the Markov property approximately, provided the sets used in the discrete approximation are chosen appropriately.

Example 2.15 (Language and history of the Markov chain). Markov chains were first invented by Andrei Markov to analyze the distribution of letters in Russian poetry (**Hayes, 2013**). Markov was motivated not by a linguistic interest, but rather to disprove a colleague's statement that the law of large numbers (LLN) can only hold for independent sequences of random variables. (The colleague further claimed this implied the existence of free will but Markov took issue only with the mathematical content of his claim.) To this end, he meticulously counted the frequencies of vowel-consonant pairs in the first 20,000 letters of Pushkin's novel in verse, *Eugene Onegin*, and from this constructed a matrix representing the fraction of each kind of pair, reproduced here for an English translation of the poem:

$$
P = \begin{array}{c} \\ \text{vowel} \\ \text{consonant} \end{array}
\begin{array}{c} \text{vowel} \quad \text{consonant} \\ \left(\begin{array}{cc} 0.175 & 0.825 \\ 0.526 & 0.474 \end{array} \right). \end{array}
$$

First order

Theg sheso pa lyiklg ut. cout Scrpauscricre cobaives wingervet Ners, whe ilened te o wn taulie wom uld atimorerteansouroocono weveiknt hef ia ngry'sif farll t mmat and, tr iscond frnid riliofr th Gureckpeag

Third order

At oness, and no fall makestic to us, infessed Russion-bently our then a man thous always, and toops in he roguestill shoed to dispric! Is Olga's up. Italked fore declaimsel the Juan's conven night toget nothem,

Fifth order

Meanwhile with jealousy bench, and so it was his time. But she trick. Let message we visits at dared here bored my sweet, who sets no inclination, and Homer, so prose, weight, my goods and envy and kin.

Seventh order

My sorrow her breast, over the dumb torment of her veil, with our poor head is stooping. But now Aurora's crimson finger, your christening glow. Farewell. Evgeny loved one, honoured fate by calmly, not yet seeking?

FIGURE 2.5. Generating language using a Markov chain. From (**Hayes, 2013**), reprinted with permission of American Scientist, magazine of Sigma Xi, The Scientific Research Society.

Markov showed that from this matrix one can calculate the average fraction of vowels and consonants in the whole poem, (vowel, consonant) $\sim (0.39, 0.61)$, and, furthermore, that the distribution of vowels and consonants is not independent—there is a bias toward alternating between the two. When he realized how powerful his ideas were, he spent several years developing tools to analyze the properties of such random processes with memory.

Just for fun, Figure 2.5 is an example, from (**Hayes, 2013**), to show how Markov chains can be used to generate realistic-looking text. In each of these excerpts, a Markov chain was constructed by considering the frequencies of strings of $k = 1, 3, 5, 7$ letters from an English translation of the novel *Eugene Onegin* by Pushkin, and considering all the ways to transition between them. For example, for $k = 3$, the sequence *eau* appeared 27 times; in 18 of these occurences it was followed by *aut* as in *beauty*, so the probability of the transition *eau→aut* was set to 18/27. The chain was run from a randomly generated initial condition. When $k = 3$, there are English-looking syllables, when $k = 5$ there are English-looking words, and when $k = 7$ the words themselves almost fit together coherently.

2.3. Forward and backward Kolmogorov equations

Consider the gambler from Example 2.8. Suppose she has a 0.4 chance of winning each game, and a 0.6 chance of losing, and if she goes broke, she stops playing (so she doesn't go into debt). The transition matrix describing how her money evolves is the following.

$$(2.3) \qquad P = \begin{array}{c} \\ 0 \\ 1 \\ 2 \\ 3 \\ \vdots \end{array} \begin{array}{c} \begin{array}{cccccc} 0 & 1 & 2 & 3 & \cdots \end{array} \\ \left(\begin{array}{ccccc} 1 & 0 & 0 & 0 & \cdots \\ 0.6 & 0 & 0.4 & 0 & \cdots \\ 0 & 0.6 & 0 & 0.4 & \cdots \\ 0 & 0 & 0.6 & 0 & \cdots \\ \vdots & & & & \ddots \end{array} \right) \end{array}$$

We will answer questions such as: After playing n games, what is the probability she has gone broke? What is the average amount of money she can expect to have after n games? What is the variance of this amount? If she plays for a very very long time (and has some probability of earning money each game if she goes broke), what is the probability distribution of her earnings? How long does it take her, on average, to go broke for the first time? The answers to these questions can be estimated by simulating the Markov chain but we may obtain exact answers by solving linear systems of equations. In this section we derive the forward and backward Kolmogorov equations describing how the gambler's probability distribution and the average of a function evolve. In Section 2.2.4 we study the limiting distribution and stationary distribution, and in Section 2.2.5 we study mean first-passage times.

In general, suppose we have a Markov chain with transition probabilities $P(n)$, and let the probability distribution at time n be $\alpha^{(n)}$, as in

$$(2.4) \qquad X_n \sim \alpha^{(n)} = (\alpha_1^{(n)}, \alpha_2^{(n)}, \ldots), \qquad \text{where} \quad \alpha_i^{(n)} = P(X_n = i).$$

Here, $\alpha^{(n)}$ is a *row vector*, not a column vector—this is a convention for discrete probability distributions, whose utility will become apparent later. The initial state of the chain X_0 is also a random variable with probability distribution $\alpha^{(0)}$. We will consider how to calculate $\alpha^{(n)}$ from $\alpha^{(0)}$, and also how to calculate $\mathbb{E}f(X_n)$, the expectation of a function of X_n. We do this for a time-homogeneous Markov chain in Section 2.2.3.1, and extend these calculations to a time-inhomogeneous chain in Section 2.2.3.2.

2.3.1. Time-homogeneous Markov chain. Suppose we have a time-homogeneous Markov chain, so that $P(n) = P$, with initial condition $X_0 = i$. The probability distribution of X_1 is simply the ith row of P: $P(X_1 = j|X_0 = i) = P_{ij}$. At later times, we would like to know the n-step transition probabilities $P^{(n)}$, defined by

$$(2.5) \qquad\qquad P_{ij}^{(n)} = P(X_n = j|X_0 = i).$$

We will make frequent use of the law of total probability (LOTP), (A.3).

For $n = 2$, we calculate

$$
\begin{aligned}
P(X_2{=}j|X_0 = i) &= \sum_{k \in S} P(X_2{=}j|X_1{=}k, X_0{=}i)P(X_1{=}k|X_0{=}i) && \text{LOTP} \\
&= \sum_{k \in S} P(X_2{=}j|X_1{=}k)P(X_1{=}k|X_0{=}i) && \text{Markov Property} \\
&= \sum_{k \in S} P_{kj}P_{ik} && \text{time-homogeneity} \\
&= (P^2)_{ij}.
\end{aligned}
$$

That is, the two-step transition matrix is $P^{(2)} = P^2$. This calculation illustrates a technique called *first-step analysis*, where one conditions on the first step of the Markov chain and uses the law of total probability.

This calculation generalizes easily by induction.

THEOREM 2.16. *Let $X_0, X_1, \ldots$ be a time-homogeneous Markov chain with transition probabilities P. The n-step transition probabilities are $P^{(n)} = P^n$, i.e.,*

$$(2.6) \qquad\qquad P(X_n = j|X_0 = i) = (P^n)_{ij}.$$

To make the notation cleaner we will write $P_{ij}^n = (P^n)_{ij}$. Note that P_{ij}^n does *not* equal $(P_{ij})^n$.

Exercise 2.3. Prove this theorem, using a first-step analysis.

Example 2.17. Suppose the gambler with transition matrix (2.3) starts with \$2. Find the probability she has \$0 after three games.

SOLUTION. We start by calculating P^3. We could do this by hand, but the calculations below use a computer. To calculate P^3 on a computer we truncate the transition matrix at the rows and columns corresponding to \$5, to obtain matrix $\tilde{P}$. Then P^3 and $\tilde{P}^3$ will differ only in rows 3 and higher, not the row we are interested in. The 3-step transition probabilities are as follows.

$$
\tilde{P}^3 = \begin{array}{c c} & \begin{array}{c c c c c c} 0 & 1 & 2 & 3 & 4 & 5 \end{array} \\ \begin{array}{c} 0 \\ 1 \\ 2 \\ \vdots \end{array} & \left(\begin{array}{c c c c c c} 1 & 0 & 0 & 0 & 0 & 0 \\ 0.744 & 0 & 0.192 & 0 & 0.064 & 0 \\ 0.360 & 0.288 & 0 & 0.288 & 0 & 0.064 \\ \vdots & & & & & \vdots \end{array} \right) \end{array}
$$

Therefore, after three games the gambler's money has probability distribution (0.360, 0.288, 0, 0.288, 0, 0.064). That is, the probability she has \$0 is 0.36, the probability she has \$1 is 0.288, etc.   ⋈

From the n-step transition probabilities we can work out the probability distribution $\alpha^{(n)}$ of X_n. We use $\alpha_j^{(n)} = \sum_i P(X_n = j | X_0 = i) P(X_0 = i)$ to obtain

(2.7)
$$\alpha^{(n)} = \alpha^{(0)} P^n.$$

There is an evolution equation for $\alpha^{(n)}$ that will be useful in more general situations.

THEOREM 2.18 (Forward Kolmogorov equation).

(2.8)
$$\alpha^{(n+1)} = \alpha^{(n)} P.$$

PROOF. This follows from (2.7). Alternatively, we can show it directly using a first-step analysis:

$$\alpha_j^{(n+1)} = \sum_i P(X_{n+1} = j | X_n = i) P(X_n = i) \quad \text{LOTP}$$

$$= \sum_i P_{ij} \alpha_i^{(n)} \qquad\qquad \text{time-homogeneity and defn of } \alpha^{(n)}.$$

□

Now suppose we ask for the expected value of some function of the state of the Markov chain, such as $\mathbb{E}X_n^2$, $\mathbb{E}X_n^3$, $\mathbb{E}|X_n|$, etc. Can we solve a similar formula and evolution equation for this quantity?

Let $f : S \to \mathbb{R}$ be a function defined on state space, and let $u^{(n)} = (u_i^{(n)})_{i \in S}$ be a vector with components

(2.9)
$$u_i^{(n)} = \mathbb{E}^i f(X_n) = \mathbb{E}[f(X_n) | X_0 = i].$$

We should think of $u^{(n)}$ as a *column vector*; again this is a convention whose convenience will become more transparent later. We can solve for $u^{(n)}$ using the n-step transition probabilities and the definition of expectation as

(2.10)
$$u_i^{(n)} = \sum_j f(j) P(X_n = j | X_0 = i) = \sum_j u_j^{(0)} P_{ij}^n = (P^n u^{(0)})_i,$$

since $u_j^{(0)} = f(j)$. Hence,

(2.11)
$$u^{(n)} = P^n u^{(0)}.$$

Also useful will be the equation for how $u^{(n)}$ evolves in time.

THEOREM 2.19 (Backward Kolmogorov equation, time-homogeneous).

(2.12)
$$u^{(n+1)} = P u^{(n)}, \qquad u_i^{(0)} = f(i) \quad (i \in S).$$

PROOF. This follows from (2.11). A direct proof uses a first-step analysis:

$$u_i^{(n+1)} = \sum_j f(j)P(X_{n+1}{=}j|X_0 = i) \qquad\qquad \text{definition of expectation}$$

$$= \sum_j \sum_k f(j)P(X_{n+1}{=}j|X_1{=}k)P(X_1{=}k|X_0{=}i) \qquad \text{LOTP \& Markov property}$$

$$= \sum_j \sum_k f(j)P_{kj}^n P_{ik} \qquad\qquad \text{time-homogeneity}$$

$$= \sum_k \sum_j f(j)P_{kj}^n P_{ik} \qquad\qquad \text{switch order of summation}$$

$$= \sum_k u_k^{(n)} P_{ik} = (Pu^{(n)})_i \qquad\qquad \text{definition of } u^{(n)}.$$

We can switch the order of summation above if $|f|$ is bounded, since then the double sum is absolutely convergent. $\square$

Example 2.20. Returning to the gambler in Example 2.8 and with transition matrix (2.3), calculate the gambler's expected earnings after three games, assuming she starts with \$2. That is, calculate $u_2^{(3)} = \mathbb{E}[X_3|X_0 = 2]$.

SOLUTION. We have that $u^{(0)} = (0,1,2,3,\ldots)^T$. From the forward Kolmogorov equations, we calculate:

$$u^{(3)} = P^3 u^{(0)} = \begin{pmatrix} 0 \\ 0.64 \\ 1.472 \\ \vdots \end{pmatrix}.$$

Therefore, the gambler's expected earnings after three games are $u_2^{(3)} = 1.472$. $\boxtimes$

REMARK 2.21. What is so backward about the backward equation? It gets its name from the fact that it can be used to describe how conditional expectations propagate backward in time. To see this, suppose that instead of (2.9), which propagates the expectation of a function into the future given a fixed starting point, we choose a fixed time T and compute the expectation at that time, given an earlier, varying starting time. That is, for each $n \le T$, define a column vector $v^{(n)}$ with components

$$(2.13) \qquad\qquad v_i^{(n)} = \mathbb{E}[f(X_T)|X_n{=}i].$$

Such a quantity is studied frequently in financial applications, where X_n may represent the price of a stock at time n, f the value of an option to sell, T the time at which you decide (in advance) to sell a stock, and quantities of the form (2.13) represent the expected payout, conditional on being in state i at time n. One is interested in solving for $v^{(0)}$ and in finding the element which maximizes the expected payoff. One can show that the vector $v^{(n)}$ evolves according to

$$(2.14) \qquad\qquad v^{(n)} = P(n)v^{(n+1)}, \qquad v_i^{(T)} = f(i) \quad (i \in S).$$

That is, you find $v^{(n)}$ by evolving it *backward* in time—you are given a final condition at time T and you can solve for $v^{(n)}$ at all earlier times $n \le T$.

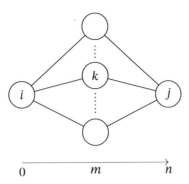

FIGURE 2.6. Schematic illustrating the Chapman–Kolmogorov equations, (2.15).

***Exercise* 2.4.** Derive (2.14) for a time-inhomogeneous Markov chain using a first-step analysis. (Another derivation is in the next section.)

2.3.2. Time-inhomogeneous Markov chain. The forward and backward Kolmogorov equations for a time-inhomogeneous Markov chain are derived from the Chapman–Kolmogorov equations, a relationship satisfied by all Markov chains and Markov processes more generally.[1]

THEOREM 2.22 (Chapman–Kolmogorov equations). *Given $i, j \in S$, and $n > m > 0$,*

$$(2.15) \qquad P(X_n = j | X_0 = i) = \sum_{k \in S} P(X_n = j | X_m = k) P(X_m = k | X_0 = i).$$

In words, to find the probability of transitioning from i to j in n steps, we may add up the probabilities of passing through all states $k \in S$ at some intermediate time m (Figure 2.6).

PROOF. We use an argument similar to a first-step analysis by using the law of total probability, then the fact that $P(A \cap B | C) = P(A | B \cap C) P(B | C)$, and finally the Markov property (see Example 2.2):

$$P(X_n = j | X_0 = i) = \sum_{k \in S} P(X_n = j, X_m = k | X_0 = i)$$

$$= \sum_{k \in S} P(X_n = j | X_m = k, X_0 = i) P(X_m = k | X_0 = i)$$

$$= \sum_{k \in S} P(X_n = j | X_m = k) P(X_m = k | X_0 = i).$$

$\square$

To use this relationship, define a function $P(j, t | i, s)$ to be the transition probability to be in state j at time t given the system started in state i at time s, i.e.,

$$(2.16) \qquad P(j, t | i, s) = P(X_t = j | X_s = i).$$

---

[1] Note that while all Markov processes satisfy a form of Chapman–Kolmogorov equations, from which many other equations can be derived, not all processes which satisfy Chapman–Kolmogorov equations are Markov processes. For a counterexample, see (**Grimmett and Stirzaker, 2001**, p. 218, Example 14).

The *forward Kolmogorov equation* comes from considering how $P(j, t|i, s)$ evolves in t, forward in time. The Chapman–Kolmogorov equations imply that

$$(2.17) \qquad P(j, t+1|i, s) = \sum_{k \in S} P(j, t+1|k, t)P(k, t|i, s) = \sum_{k \in S} P_{kj}(t)P(k, t|i, s).$$

We write $P_{kj}(t)_{kj} = P(j, t+1|k, t)$ to represent components of the 1-step transition matrix at time t, $P(t)$. In words, the transition matrix at time $t + 1$ equals the transition matrix at time t, multiplied on the left by the 1-step transition matrix at time t. Equation (2.17) is one version of the time-inhomogeneous forward equation; we can use it to show the forward equation involving the evolution of probability.

THEOREM 2.23 (Forward Komogorov equation, time-inhomogeneous). *Let $\alpha_j^{(t)} = P(X_t = j)$ be the probability mass function of the Markov chain at time t and let α_0 be the initial probability mass function. Then the vector $\alpha^{(t)}$ evolves as*

$$(2.18) \qquad \alpha^{(t+1)} = \alpha^{(t)}P(t), \qquad \alpha^{(0)} = \alpha_0.$$

In components, $\alpha_j^{(t+1)} = \sum_k \alpha_k^{(t)}P(j, t+1|k, t)$.

PROOF. Recall that $\alpha_j^{(t)} = \sum_i P(j, t|i, 0)\alpha_i^{(0)}$. Contract index i in (2.17) with $\alpha^{(0)}$, and evaluate at $s = 0$:

$$\begin{aligned} \alpha_j^{(t+1)} &= \sum_{i \in S} P(j, t+1|i, 0)\alpha_i^{(0)} \\ &= \sum_{i \in S} \sum_{k \in S} P_{kj}(t)P(k, t|i, 0)\alpha_i^{(0)} \\ &= \sum_{k \in S} P_{kj}(t)\alpha_k^{(t)}. \end{aligned}$$

We switched the order of summation in the last step because the sum is absolutely convergent. The initial condition follows by definition. □

The *backward Kolmogorov equation* comes from considering how $P(j, t|i, s)$ evolves in s, backward in time. The Chapman–Kolmogorov equations imply that

$$(2.19) \qquad P(i, t|i, s) = \sum_{k \in S} P(i, t|k, s+1)P(k, s+1|i, s) = \sum_{k \in S} P(j, t|k, s+1)P_{ik}(s).$$

In words, the transition matrix evolves backward in time in its starting state by multiplying by the 1-step transition matrix $P(s)$ on the right. Equation (2.19) is a version of the time-inhomogeneous backward equation for transition probabilities. From it we may obtain a version for the evolution of statistics.

THEOREM 2.24 (Backward Komogorov equation, time-inhomogeneous). *Let $f : S \to \mathbb{R}$ be a bounded function, let $T > 0$ be a fixed time, and let*

$$(2.20) \qquad u_i^{(s)} = \mathbb{E}[f(X_T)|X_s = i]$$

(recall (2.9),(2.13)). Then the vector $u^{(s)}$ evolves as

$$(2.21) \qquad u^{(s)} = P(s)u^{(s+1)} \quad (0 \le s < T), \qquad u_i^{(T)} = f(i).$$

In components, $u_i^{(s)} = \sum_k P(k, s+1|i, s)u_k^{(s+1)}$.

PROOF. Notice that $u_i^{(s)} = \sum_j f(j)P(j,T|i,s)$. Contract index j in (2.19) with the vector $(f(1), f(2), \ldots)$ and evaluate at $t = T$:

$$u_i^{(s)} = \sum_{j \in S} \sum_{k \in S} f(j)P(j,T|k,s+1)P_{ik}(s)$$

$$= \sum_{k \in S} \left(\sum_{j \in S} f(j)P(j,T|k,s+1) \right) P_{ik}(s)$$

$$= \sum_{k \in S} u_k^{(s+1)} P_{ik}(s).$$

We may switch the order of summation because f is bounded, so the sum is absolutely convergent. The terminal condition follows by definition (2.20). □

2.4. Long-time behavior and stationary distribution

Suppose we take a Markov chain and let it run for a long time. What happens? Clearly the random variable X_n does not generally converge to anything because it is continually jumping around, but its probability distribution might converge. Let us look at some examples.

Example 2.25. Consider the two-state weather model in Example 2.6. Suppose it is raining today. What is the probability distribution for the weather in the future? Let us calculate $\alpha^{(n)}$ from (2.7), using $\alpha^{(0)} = (0, 1)$.

n	P(sun)	P(rain)
0	0	1
1	0.4000	0.6000
2	0.5600	0.4400
3	0.6240	0.3760
4	0.6496	0.3504
5	0.6598	0.3402
6	0.6639	0.3361
7	0.6656	0.3344
8	0.6662	0.3338
9	0.6665	0.3335
10	0.6666	0.3334
11	0.6666	0.3334
12	0.6667	0.3333
13	0.6667	0.3333
14	0.6667	0.3333

The probability distribution seems to converge. After 12 days, the distribution does not change, to 4 digits. You can check that the distribution it converges to does not depend on the initial condition. For example, if we start with a sunny day, $\alpha^{(0)} = (1, 0)$, then $\alpha^{(10)} = (0.6667, 0.3333)$, $\alpha^{(11)} = (0.6667, 0.3333)$, etc.

Exercise 2.5. Work out the n-step transition probabilities for any initial condition analytically and show they converge to $(2/3, 1/3)$. (Hint: diagonalize the transition matrix.)

Does the probability always converge? Not necessarily. The following two examples illustrate situations where it doesn't converge.

Example 2.26. Consider a Markov chain on state space $\{0, 1\}$ with transition matrix

$$P = \begin{pmatrix} 0 & 1 \\ 1 & 0 \end{pmatrix}.$$

Suppose the random walker starts at state 0. Its distribution at time n is the following.

n	$P(0)$	$P(1)$
0	1	0
1	0	1
2	1	0
3	0	1
4	1	0
$\vdots$	$\vdots$	$\vdots$

Clearly the distribution does not converge. Yet, if we start with initial distribution $\alpha^{(0)} = (0.5, 0.5)$, we obtain the following.

n	$P(0)$	$P(1)$
0	0.5	0.5
1	0.5	0.5
2	0.5	0.5
$\vdots$	$\vdots$	$\vdots$

The distribution never changes!

Example 2.27. A *simple symmetric random walk* is a random walk on the integers with probability $p = 1/2$ to go left or right (see Example 2.8). The transition probabilities at time n are obtained by shifting the Binomial distribution:

$$P_{ij}^n = \begin{cases} \binom{n}{k}\left(\frac{1}{2}\right)^n & j = i + 2k - n, \quad k = 0, 1, \ldots, n \\ 0 & \text{otherwise.} \end{cases}$$

As $n \to \infty$, $P_{ij}^n \to 0$. So P^n converges—but not to a probability distribution, rather to the function that is identically zero. This is because probability eventually escapes to infinity, so any particular state eventually has zero probability.

2.4.1. Limiting and stationary distributions. When does the distribution of a Markov chain converge? And when it does, what does it converge to, and how can we find the limiting distribution? The answers are given by understanding the *limiting distribution* and *stationary distribution*. We consider only time-homogeneous Markov chains.

DEFINITION 2.28. Consider a time-homogeneous Markov chain with transition matrix P. A row vector λ is a *limiting distribution* if $\lambda_i \geq 0$, $\sum_j \lambda_j = 1$ (so that λ is a probability distribution), and if, for every i,

$$\lim_{n \to \infty} (P^n)_{ij} = \lambda_j \qquad \text{for all } j \in S.$$

In other words,

$$P^n \to \begin{pmatrix} \lambda_1 & \lambda_2 & \lambda_3 & \cdots \\ \lambda_1 & \lambda_2 & \lambda_3 & \cdots \\ \lambda_1 & \lambda_2 & \lambda_3 & \cdots \\ \vdots & \vdots & \vdots & \ddots \end{pmatrix} \qquad \text{as } n \to \infty .$$

As we saw in Examples 2.26 and 2.27, a limiting distribution doesn't have to exist. If it does exist, it is unique, by definition.

Exercise 2.6. Show that, if $|S| < \infty$, then λ is a limiting distribution if and only if $\lim_{n\to\infty} \alpha^{(0)} P^n = \lambda$ for any initial probability distribution $\alpha^{(0)}$.

If $|S| = \infty$, then we could have that $\lim_{n\to\infty} P^n$ exists but is not a probability distribution. For example, for the simple symmetric random walk in Example 2.27, $\lim_{n\to\infty} P^n = (\ldots, 0, 0, 0, \ldots)$—however, the zero vector is not a probability distribution.[2] What happens if we start a chain in a limiting distribution λ for a Markov chain with a *finite* state space ($|S| < \infty$)? Let us calculate the distribution $\alpha^{(1)}$ at the next step of the chain, starting from $\alpha^{(0)} = \lambda$. We have

$$\alpha_j^{(1)} = (\lambda P)_j = \sum_{k=1}^N (\lim_{n\to\infty} P_{ik}^n) P_{kj} = \lim_{n\to\infty} \sum_{k=1}^N P_{ik}^n P_{kj} = \lim_{n\to\infty} P_{ij}^{n+1} = \lambda_j.$$

We can interchange the sum and limit because the sum is finite. Therefore, if we start the chain in the limiting distribution, its distribution remains there forever. This motivates another definition.

DEFINITION 2.29. Given a Markov chain with transition matrix P, a *stationary distribution* is a probability distribution π which satisfies

$$(2.22) \qquad \pi = \pi P \qquad \Longleftrightarrow \qquad \pi_j = \sum_i \pi_i P_{ij} \quad \text{for all } j \in S.$$

REMARK 2.30. A stationary distribution may also be called an *invariant measure*, *invariant distribution*, *steady-state probability*, *equilibrium probability*, or *equilibrium distribution*.

The stationary distribution is stationary in the following sense: if we start the chain in the stationary distribution $X_0 \sim \pi$, the distribution does not change. $X_1 \sim \pi, X_2 \sim \pi$, etc. From its definition, it is clear that π is a left eigenvector of P corresponding to eigenvalue 1, and that it is normalized, $\sum_i \pi_i = 1$.

In applications we want to know the limiting distribution. We saw above that when $|S| < \infty$, a limiting distribution is a stationary distribution, but the converse is not always true. Indeed, in Example 2.26, a stationary distribution is $\pi = (0.5, 0.5)$, but this is not a limiting distribution.

Yet, the stationary distribution is easier to calculate than a limiting distribution, since we can find it by solving a linear system of equations. Therefore, we will restrict our focus to the stationary distribution. Some questions we might ask about it include:

---

[2]The problem is that we cannot interchange a limit and sum in general: although $\sum_j P_{ij}^n = 1$, hence $\lim_{n\to\infty} \sum_j P_{ij}^n = 1$; we have $\sum_j \lim_{n\to\infty} P_{ij}^n = 0$, hence, $\lim_{n\to\infty} \sum_j P_{ij}^n \neq \sum_j \lim_{n\to\infty} P_{ij}^n$.

(i) Does it exist?

(ii) Is it unique?

(iii) When is it a limiting distribution, i.e., when does an arbitrary distribution converge to it?

This is the subject of a rich body of work on the limiting behavior of Markov chains. In general, there are two broad approaches to answering such questions. One approach is probabilistic, using tools such as recurrence times and coupling properties. Another approach uses linear algebra to study the transition matrix, which is possible for Markov chains with a finite state space. We will survey some results using this second approach, which should be more familiar to students from a range of applied backgrounds.

Exercise 2.7. (a) Solve for the stationary distribution for the gambler in the example at the beginning of Section 2.2.3. (b) Solve again, but this time assume that if the gambler loses all her money, there is some small probability 0.1 per game that she finds \$1 on the ground and can play again (if she does not find money on the ground, she does not play that game).

Exercise 2.8. Calculate the eigenvalues and the eigenvectors of the transition matrices in Examples 2.25, 2.26.

2.4.2. Stationary distributions and linear algebra.

Let us focus on Markov chains with a finite state space, $|S| = N < \infty$, and ask what linear algebra tells us about the stationary and limiting distributions associated with the transition matrix P. We know that P has an eigenvalue $\lambda = 1$, since the rows of P sum to 1, so we have

$$
P \begin{pmatrix} 1 \\ 1 \\ \vdots \\ 1 \end{pmatrix} = \begin{pmatrix} 1 \\ 1 \\ \vdots \\ 1 \end{pmatrix},
$$

and therefore $(1, 1, \ldots, 1)^T$ is a right eigenvector. To ensure that the corresponding left eigenvector π is a stationary distribution, we need to know that its entries are nonnegative. (We also need $\sum_i \pi_i = 1$, but we can impose this by multiplying by a suitable constant.) Let us put the issue of the nonnegativity of π on hold for a moment and ask if P has a limiting distribution. We do this by calculating P^n. Suppose that P can be diagonalized, so we can write it as

$$
(2.23) \qquad P = B\Lambda B^{-1}, \qquad \text{or, equivalently,} \qquad P = \sum_{i=1}^{n} \lambda_i v_i u_i^T.
$$

The vectors $\{v_i\}_{i=1}^n$ are the right eigenvectors of P and form the columns of B; the vectors $\{u_i\}_{i=1}^n$ are the left eigenvectors of P and form the rows of B^{-1}. The matrix Λ is a diagonal matrix with diagonals equal to the eigenvalues of P, $\lambda_1, \ldots, \lambda_N$; let us order the eigenvalues so that $\lambda_1 = 1$. Then P^n is

$$
(2.24) \qquad P^n = B\Lambda^n B^{-1} = \sum_{i=1}^{n} \lambda_i^n v_i u_i^T
$$

where Λ^n has diagonal elements $\Lambda_{ii} = \lambda_i^n$. What happens as $n \to \infty$? For the first eigenvalue we have $\lambda_1^n = 1$. Any eigenvalue such that $|\lambda_i| < 1$ will converge to zero, $\lambda_i^n \to 0$ as $n \to \infty$. Therefore, if $|\lambda_i| < 1$ for $i \geq 2$, we have, using our knowledge of the right and left eigenvectors corresponding to λ_1,

$$\lim_{n \to \infty} P^n = B \begin{pmatrix} 1 & 0 & \cdots & 0 \\ 0 & 0 & \cdots & 0 \\ \vdots & \vdots & \vdots & \vdots \\ 0 & 0 & \cdots & 0 \end{pmatrix} B^{-1}$$

$$= \begin{pmatrix} 1 \\ 1 \\ \vdots \\ 1 \end{pmatrix} \begin{pmatrix} \pi_1 & \pi_2 & \cdots & \pi_N \end{pmatrix}$$

$$= \begin{pmatrix} \pi_1 & \pi_2 & \cdots & \pi_N \\ \pi_1 & \pi_2 & \cdots & \pi_N \\ \vdots & \vdots & \vdots & \vdots \\ \pi_1 & \pi_2 & \cdots & \pi_N \end{pmatrix}.$$

We argue that π must be a probability distribution: since P has nonnegative entries, so does P^n, so π must be nonnegative. Furthermore, $\sum_j \pi_j = 1$, since $\sum_j P_{ij}^n = 1$, so taking the limit as $n \to \infty$ and interchanging sum and limit (for a finite sum) gives $\sum_j \lim_{n \to \infty} P_{ij}^n = 1$.

We have just shown that if P is diagonalizable, such that all eigenvalues except λ_1 have $|\lambda_i| < 1$, then the left eigenvector π corresponding to λ_1 is a limiting distribution, and therefore it is also a stationary distribution. (If P is not diagonalizable, then we can do a similar calculation using the Jordan canonical form of the matrix and obtain the same conclusion given similar conditions on the generalized eigenvalues.)

It remains to ask: When do all eigenvalues (or generalized eigenvalues) satisfy $|\lambda_i| < 1$ for $i \neq 1$? We can show quite easily that all eigenvalues must have norm less than or equal to 1.

LEMMA 2.31. *The spectral radius of a stochastic matrix P is 1, i.e., $\rho(P) = \max_\lambda |\lambda| = 1$, where $|\cdot|$ is the complex norm and the maximum is over all eigenvalues of P.*

PROOF. Let η be a left eigenvector with eigenvalue λ, so that $\lambda \eta_i = \sum_{j=1}^N \eta_j P_{ji}$. Since the complex norms of complex numbers satisfy $|\lambda \eta_i| = |\lambda||\eta_i|$, we have, taking the L^1-norm and then using the triangle inequality,

$$\sum_{i=1}^N |\lambda \eta_i| = |\lambda| \sum_{i=1}^N |\eta_i| = \sum_{i=1}^N |\sum_{j=1}^N \eta_i P_{ji}| \leq \sum_{i=1}^N \sum_{j=1}^N |\eta_i| P_{ji} = \sum_{i=1}^N |\eta_i|.$$

Dividing through $\sum_{i=1}^N |\eta_i|$ gives that $|\lambda| \leq 1$. $\square$

REMARK 2.32. Lemma 2.31 is a special case of the Gershgorin circle theorem.

Whew! This is good news—it shows that no eigenvalue of P has complex norm greater than 1—but it still does not rule out the possibility that there are other eigenvalues with complex norm equal to 1. To handle this possibility we turn to a powerful theorem from linear algebra, the Perron–Frobenius theorem.

DEFINITION 2.33. A matrix A is *positive* if it has all positive entries: $A_{ij} > 0$ for all i, j.

REMARK 2.34. A is positive is *not* the same as A being positive-definite.

THEOREM 2.35. (Perron–Frobenius theorem.) *Let M be a positive $k \times k$ matrix, with $k < \infty$. Then the following statements hold:*

(i) *There is a positive real number λ_1 which is an eigenvalue of M. All other eigenvalues λ of M satisfy $|\lambda| < \lambda_1$.*

(ii) *The eigenspace of eigenvectors associated with λ_1 is one-dimensional.*

(iii) *There exists a positive right eigenvector v and a positive left eigenvector w associated with λ_1. Furthermore,*

$$\lim_{n \to \infty} \frac{1}{\lambda_1^n} M^n = v w^T,$$

where the eigenvectors are normalized so that $w^T v = 1$.

(iv) *M has no other eigenvectors with nonnegative entries.*

For a proof, see an advanced linear algebra textbook, such as (**Lax, 1997**, Chapter 16) or (**Horn and Johnson, 2013**, Theorem 8.2.8). There is also a brief description of the proof in (**Strang, 1988**, Section 5.3).

We can combine the Perron–Frobenius theorem with Lemma 2.31 to obtain a statement about Markov chains.

THEOREM 2.36. *Let $X_0, X_1, X_2, \ldots$ be a time-homogeneous Markov chain with a finite state space. Suppose the transition matrix P is positive. Then there exists a unique stationary probability distribution π such that π is positive. Furthermore, π is also a limiting distribution.*

PROOF. From Lemma 2.31, the spectral radius of P is 1. The Perron–Frobenius theorem tells us there is a one-dimensional eigenspace associated with the eigenvalue $\lambda_1 = 1$, and the corresponding left eigenvector π is positive. Therefore, π is the unique stationary distribution. All other eigenvalues have complex norm less than 1. Furthermore, since the corresponding right eigenvector is $v = (1, \ldots, 1)^T$, we obtain that $\lim_{n \to \infty} P_{ij}^n = \pi_j$, which is the definition of a limiting distribution. $\square$

We obtain a similar result for Markov chains such that P^s is positive for some integer $s > 0$. This means that there is a time s such that, no matter where you start, there is a nonzero probability of being at any other state.

THEOREM 2.37. *Let $X_0, X_1, X_2, \ldots$ be a time-homogeneous Markov chain with a finite state space and transition matrix P. Suppose there exists some integer $s > 0$ such that P^s is positive. Then there exists a unique stationary probability distribution π such that π is positive. Furthermore, π is also a limiting distribution.*

For a direct proof that analyzes the evolution of probability and shows it converges exponentially quickly to the stationary distribution, see (**Koralov and Sinai, 2007**, p. 72). The proof using linear algebra can be pieced together[3] from theorems and definitions in (**Horn and Johnson, 2013**). This theorem can be weakened slightly by

---

[3]Since P and P^s are positive, P is irreducible and has only one nonzero eigenvalue of maximum complex norm (**Horn and Johnson, 2013**, Definitions 6.2.22, 8.5.0, Theorem 8.5.2). Theorem 8.4.4 (another

allowing for Markov chains with some kind of periodicity. We need to consider a chain which can move between any two states (i, j), but not necessarily at a time s that is the same for all pairs.

DEFINITION 2.38. A stochastic matrix and the corresponding Markov chain is *irreducible* if, for every pair (i, j) there exists an $s > 0$ such that $(P^s)_{ij} > 0$.

The difference between an irreducible matrix and a matrix such that P^s is positive, is that for an irreducible matrix, the value of s for which $(P^s)_{ij} > 0$ can be different from each pair (i, j). For example, the transition matrix from Example 2.26

$$(2.25) \qquad P = \begin{pmatrix} 0 & 1 \\ 1 & 0 \end{pmatrix}$$

is irreducible but there is no s such that P^s is positive, since $P^{2n} = I$, $P^{2n+1} = P$.

THEOREM 2.39. *Let $X_0, X_1, X_2, \ldots$ be a time-homogeneous Markov chain with a finite state space and irreducible transition matrix P. Then there is a unique stationary distribution π such that π is positive. Furthermore, the time-averaged probability distribution converges to it:*

$$\alpha^{(0)} \bar{P}^{(n)} \to \pi \quad as\ n \to \infty, \qquad where\ \bar{P}^{(n)} = \frac{1}{n} \sum_{k=1}^{n} P^k .$$

We need to form the average because there may be a built-in periodicity, as in Equation (2.25), where $\alpha^{(n)}$ can oscillate between two distributions instead of converging to a fixed limit.

The proof is again obtained from linear algebra; see (**Horn and Johnson, 2013**, Theorem 8.4.4) for a proof of the uniqueness of the stationary distribution, and (**Horn and Johnson, 2013**, Theorem 8.6.1) for a proof that the average distribution converges.

REMARK 2.40. So far we have analyzed only Markov chains with a finite state space. There are also results for Markov chains with infinite state spaces, which are often proved using probabilistic approaches. To state the results, one is interested in the mean recurrence time μ_i of each state i, defined by

$$(2.26) \qquad \mu_i = \mathbb{E}(T_i | X_0 = i),$$

where $T_i = \min\{n \geq 1 : X_n = i\}$ is the first return time to i. We could have that μ_i is finite or infinite. If a Markov chain is irreducible and $\mu_i < \infty$ for all states i, then there is a unique stationary distribution π given by $\pi_i = \mu_i^{-1}$ ((**Grimmett and Stirzaker, 2001**, Section 6.5, Theorem 3) or (**Norris, 1998**, Theorem 1.7.7)). Furthermore, if the chain is irreducible, has stationary distribution π, and is *aperiodic* (there exists a t such that $P_{ii}^s > 0$ for all $s \geq t$, and for some state i), then π is a limiting distribution ((**Grimmett and Stirzaker, 2001**, Section 6.4, Theorem 17) or (**Norris, 1998**, Theorem 1.8.3)).

---

version of the Perron–Frobenius theorem) shows that since P is irreducible and nonnegative, there is a one-dimensional eigenspace associated with the eigenvalue $\lambda_1 = 1$, and the corresponding left eigenvector π is positive. Theorem 8.5.1 shows that $\lim_{n \to \infty} P_{ij}^n = \pi_j$, so π is a limiting distribution.

2.5. Mean first-passage time

Sometimes we want to know how long it takes a Markov chain to do something—how long will it be until the weather turns sunny again, how long does it take a gambler to go broke, etc.? We can handle questions about such random times using tools from linear algebra.

DEFINITION 2.41. The *first-passage time* to a set $A \subset S$ is defined by

$$T_A = \min\{n \geq 0 : X_n \in A\}.$$

The first-passage time is a random variable whose distribution depends on the distribution of X_0 and on the transition probabilities for the Markov chain.

DEFINITION 2.42. The *mean first-passage time* (mfpt) to set A starting at state i is

(2.27) $\tau_i = \mathbb{E}[T_A | X_0 = i].$

Example 2.43 (Random walk on a line segment). Consider a Markov chain on 3 states with transition probabilities given on the arrows.

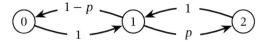

Suppose $X_0 = 0$ and $p = 1/2$, and we run the chain 5 times until it hits state $A = \{2\}$. Here is an example sequence of states for the different realizations and the corresponding values of T_A.

realization	T_A
0, 1, 2	2
0, 1, 0, 1, 2	4
0, 1, 0, 1, 0, 1, 2	6
0, 1, 2	2
0, 1, 0, 1, 2	4

An estimate for the mean first-passage time starting from state 0 would be

$$\tau_0 \approx \frac{2+4+6+2+4}{5} = 3.6.$$

Let us compute τ_i using a first-step analysis, assuming (for now) that $P(T_A < \infty | X_0 = i) = 1$ for all $i \in S$. We consider only a time-homogeneous Markov chain.

For $i \in A$, we have $T_A = 0$ so $\tau_i = 0$. Consider $i \notin A$. Then

$$\tau_i = \sum_{t=1}^{\infty} t P(T_A = t | X_0 = i) \qquad\qquad \text{defn of expectation}$$

$$= \sum_{t=1}^{\infty} \sum_{j \in S} t P(T_A = t | X_1 = j) P(X_1 = j | X_0 = i) \qquad \text{LOTP \& Markov property.}$$

Because the chain is time-homogeneous, we expect that $P(T_A=t|X_1=j) = P(T_A=t-1|X_0=j)$ by changing the change of variables $t \to t-1$. To show this explicitly, write

$$P(T_A=t|X_1=j) = P(X_2 \in A^c, \ldots, X_{t-1} \in A^c, X_t \in A|X_1 = j) \qquad \text{by defn}$$
$$= P(X_1 \in A^c, \ldots, X_{t-2} \in A^c, X_{t-1} \in A|X_0 = j) \quad \text{time-homogeneity}$$
$$= P(T_A=t-1|X_0=j).$$

Substituting this result and changing the index $t \to t+1$, we have

$$\tau_i = \sum_{t=0}^{\infty} \sum_{j \in S} (t+1) P(T_A=t|X_0=j) P_{ij}$$

$$= \sum_{j \in S} \sum_{t=0}^{\infty} t P(T_A=t|X_0=j) P_{ij} + \sum_{j \in S} \sum_{t=0}^{\infty} P(T_A=t|X_0=j) P_{ij}.$$

We can interchange the order of summation because all terms are nonnegative. Now, we have that

$$\sum_{t=0}^{\infty} t P(T_A=t|X_0=j) = \tau_j,$$

by definition. We also observe that $\sum_{t=0}^{\infty} P(T_A=t|X_0=j) = P(T_A < \infty) = 1$, so

$$\sum_{j \in S} \sum_{t=0}^{\infty} P(T_A=t|X_0=j) P_{ij} = \sum_{j \in S} P_{ij} = 1.$$

We obtain the following.

THEOREM 2.44 (Mean first-passage time). *Let $\tau = (\tau_i)_{i \in S}$ be a vector of mean first-passage times from each state $i \in S$. Then τ is nonnegative and solves the system of linear equations:*

(2.28)
$$\begin{cases} \tau_i = 0 & i \in A \\ \tau_i = 1 + \sum_j P_{ij}\tau_j & i \notin A. \end{cases}$$

REMARK 2.45. If $|S| = \infty$, then there could be multiple solutions to (2.28), and τ can be shown to be the minimal nonnegative solution to these equations. This means that any other nonnegative solution y to (2.28) has $y_i \geq \tau_i$ for all i (see (**Norris, 1998**, Theorem 1.3.5)).

REMARK 2.46. We showed Theorem 2.44 assuming $P(T_A < \infty|X_0 = i) = 1$. One can carry through the same calculations without this assumption, starting from the identity $\tau_i = \sum_{t=1}^{\infty} t P(T_A=t|X_0=i) + \infty P(T_a = \infty|X_0=i)$, and obtain the same system of equations (2.28). If $\tau_i = \infty$ (which can happen even when $P(T_A < \infty|X_0=i)=1$), then there will not exist a nonnegative solution to (2.28).

Equation (2.28) gives a way to find the mean first-passage time by solving a linear system of equations. We can write (2.28) as

(2.29)
$$(P' - I)\tau' = -1,$$

where P' is P with the rows and columns corresponding to elements in A removed, and τ' is τ with the elements in A removed. We would use this form of the equations to solve for τ on a computer. Note that we cannot find the mfpt from state i in isolation; we have to solve for the mfpt from all states i simultaneously. For systems that are not too large, this means we can use built-in linear algebra solvers to calculate mfpts. If the problem has some extra structure we can sometimes find analytical solutions.

Example 2.47 (Random walk on a line segment, continued). Let us use this result to calculate the mean first-passage time τ_0 from Example 2.43. We must solve the system of equations

$$\begin{aligned} \tau_0 &= 1 + P_{01}\tau_1 \\ \tau_1 &= 1 + P_{12}\tau_2 + P_{10}\tau_0 \end{aligned} \quad \Rightarrow \quad \begin{aligned} \tau_0 &= 1 + \tau_1 \\ \tau_1 &= 1 + (1-p)\tau_0 \end{aligned} \ .$$

Solving gives $\tau_0 = 2/p$, $\tau_1 = 2/p - 1$. For example, for $p = 1/2$, we have $\tau_0 = 4, \tau_1 = 3$.

Example 2.48. Consider the gambler from Example 2.8. Let $A = \{0\}$, the event that she has \$0. Show that if $p < 1/2$, then the average time it takes her to go broke, starting from \$k, is $\tau_k = \frac{k}{1-2p}$.

SOLUTION. Solved by verifying that (2.28) is satisfied. Note that if the gambler were to stop when she wins some amount \$M, then the mfpt to the set $B = \{0, M\}$ can be found by solving the inhomogeneous recurrence relation in (2.28) to be[4]

$$\tau_k^M = \frac{k}{1-2p} - \frac{M}{1-2p} \cdot \frac{\left(\frac{1-p}{p}\right)^k - 1}{\left(\frac{1-p}{p}\right)^M - 1} \quad (p \neq 1/2), \qquad \tau_k^M = Mk - k^2 \quad (p = 1/2).$$

For $p < 1/2$, as $M \to \infty$, $\tau_k^M \to \tau_k$. (For $p \geq 1/2$, $\tau_k^M \to \infty$ as $M \to \infty$.) ◻

We can calculate the probability that T_A is finite by solving a similar system of equations.

DEFINITION 2.49. The *hitting probability* of set A starting at state i is

(2.30) $h_i = P(T_A < \infty | X_0 = i).$

THEOREM 2.50. *The vector of hitting probabilities $h = (h_i)_{i \in S}$ is the minimal non-negative solution to the system of linear equations*

(2.31) $$\begin{cases} h_i = 1 & i \in A \\ h_i = \sum_j P_{ij} h_j & i \notin A. \end{cases}$$

Exercise 2.9. Prove the above theorem using a first-step analysis (see (**Norris, 1998**, Theorem 1.3.2)).

Example 2.51. Consider the gambler from the beginning of Section 2.2.3. Calculate the probability she eventually goes broke, starting from \$k.

SOLUTION. (See (**Norris, 1998**, Example 1.3.3).) We must solve the recurrence relation

$$h_0 = 1, \qquad h_i = p h_{i+1} + (1-p) h_{i-1}, \quad i = 1, 2, \dots.$$

If $p \neq 1/2$ the general solution is

$$h_i = C + D \left(\frac{1-p}{p} \right)^i$$

---

[4]See https://web.mit.edu/neboat/Public/6.042/randomwalks.pdf

for some constants C, D. For $p < 1/2$, the condition $h_i \leq 1$ requires $D = 0$ so $h_i = 1$ for all i—the gambler will always end up broke. If $p = 1/2$, the recurrence relation has a general solution

$$h_i = C + Di,$$

and again $D = 0$ so $h_i = 1$ for all i. Therefore, even if the gambler is playing a fair game, no matter how much money she starts with she is certain to end up broke. This phenomenon is called the *gambler's ruin*. ◻

2.6. Additional exercises

Exercise 2.10. A die is rolled repeatedly. Which of the following are Markov chains? For those that are, supply the transition matrix.
   (i) The largest number X_n shown up to the nth roll.
   (ii) The largest number Z_n shown in the past 6 rolls.
   (iii) The number N_n of sixes in n rolls.
   (iv) At time r, the time C_r since the most recent six.
   (v) At time r, the time B_r until the next six.
   (vi) $X_n = (Y_{n-1}, Y_n)$, where Y_n is the value of the die on the nth roll.

Exercise 2.11. Construct a Markov chain that has at least 2 stationary distributions.

Exercise 2.12. A particle performs a random walk on the vertex set of an undirected connected graph G, which, for simplicity we assume to have neither loops (vertices connected to themselves) nor multiple edges (two or more edges between the same vertices). At each stage it moves to a neighbor of its current position, each such neighbor being chosen with equal probability. If G has η ($< \infty$) edges, show that the stationary distribution is $\pi_i = d_i/(2\eta)$, where d_i is the degree of vertex i (the number of edges coming out of it.)

Exercise 2.13. Suppose a knight performs a random walk on a chessboard, choosing a square to move to uniformly from the set of allowable moves. Use Exercise 2.12 and theorems from the lecture to estimate the probability of finding the knight in a given corner square, after a large amount of time has passed.

Exercise 2.14. Consider a time-inhomogeneous Markov chain X_t. Let $\alpha^{(t)}$ be the probability distribution of X_t as in (2.4), and let $u^{(t)} = \mathbb{E}[f(X_T)|X_t = i]$ as in (2.20). Consider the inner product $\alpha^{(t)}u^{(t)} = \sum_i \alpha_i^{(t)}u_i^{(t)} = \sum_i P(X_t = i)\mathbb{E}[f(X_T)|X_t = i]$. Show that $\alpha^{(t)}u^{(t)} = \mathbb{E}f(X_T)$. Hence, conclude that $\alpha^{(t)}u^{(t)}$ is constant in t.

Exercise 2.15. Suppose you perform a random walk on the integers where at each step you jump left or right with equal probability, and let X_n be your position at time n. Calculate (either analytically or on a computer) the mean first-passage time τ_0 to leave the interval $(-6, 6)$, starting at $X_0 = 0$.

Exercise 2.16. Consider a time-homogeneous Markov chain X with state space S and transition matrix P. Let $A, B \subset S$ be two disjoint subsets of the state space and define a function $q : S \to \mathbb{R}$ by

$$q_i = P(X \text{ hits } B \text{ before } A | X_0 = i).$$

Another way to write it is $q_i = P(T_B < T_A | X_0 = i)$ where T_A, T_B are the hitting times of sets A, B. Show that q solves the following linear system of equations:

$$q_i = \sum_{k \in S} P_{ik} q_k \ \ (i \notin A \cup B), \qquad q_i = 0 \ \ (i \in A), \quad q_i = 1 \ \ (i \in B).$$

Comment: The function q_i is called the *committor* function. The committor function is widely studied in chemistry, and related areas like protein folding, because it can be used to measure the rate of a chemical reaction, and to say something about the mechanism of the reaction. It has a lot of nice mathematical properties and can also be used to coarse-grain a Markov chain.

Exercise 2.17. What happens if we run a Markov chain backward? Suppose we take a Markov chain with a regular transition matrix, start it in the stationary distribution π, and let it run, to get $X_0, X_1, X_2, \dots, X_N$, each of these with distribution $X_i \sim \pi$. Let $Y_n = X_{N-n}$ be the "reversed" chain. Show that $Y_0, Y_1, \dots, Y_N$ is a Markov chain with transition probabilities $P(Y_{n+1} = j | Y_n = i) = \frac{\pi_j}{\pi_i} P_{ji}$.

Do not forget that in addition to having the correct transition probabilities, you also need to show the sequence of random variables satisfies the Markov property.

Exercise 2.18 (*Hitting distribution*). The aim of this question is to determine *which* particular state in A a Markov chain hits, the first time it hits set of states A. Let $X_0, X_1, \dots$ be an irreducible Markov chain with finite state space S, and transition matrix P, and let $A \subseteq S$ be some set of states. Let T_A be the first-passage time to set A, and let $G_{ij} = P(X_{T_A} = j | X_0 = i)$ be the probability of hitting state $j \in A$, given the chain started in $i \in A^c$. Show that G satisfies the matrix equation

$$G_{ij} = P_{ij} + \sum_{l \notin A} G_{lj} P_{il} \qquad \Longleftrightarrow \qquad G = QG + R,$$

where Q is the matrix obtained from P by removing all the rows and columns representing states in A, and R is the matrix obtained from P by deleting the rows corresponding to A and the columns corresponding to A^c.

Exercise 2.19 (*Computation required*). A simple game of Snakes and Ladders is played on a board of 9 squares; see Figure 2.7.

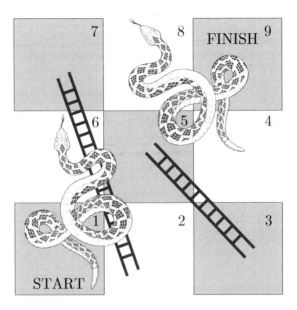

FIGURE 2.7. A simple game of snakes and ladders

At each turn a player tosses a fair coin and advances one or two places according to whether the coin lands Heads or Tails. If you land at the foot of a ladder you immediately climb to the top, but if you land at the head of a snake, you immediately slide down to the tail. If you reach square 9 you win, and you stay there. Let X_n be the value of the square you are at on turn n. You start at $X_0 = 1$.

You will need to write code to solve the following questions. For (i)–(iv) you should solve an appropriate system of linear equations.

(i) Compute and plot the probability of having won the game by turn n, $P(X_n = 9|X_0 = 1)$, for $n = 1$ to 20.

(ii) Compute and plot your average square number, $\mathbb{E}[X_n|X_0 = 1]$, for $n = 1$ to 20.

(iii) How many turns on average does it take to complete the game, starting from square 1?

(iv) Suppose you start on square 5. What is the probability that you win the game before you slip back and hit square 1? Evaluate this using linear algebra.

(v) Simulate the above Markov chain many times and estimate the mean first-passage time in (iii) from your simulations. Verify that this agrees with your calculation in (iii).

(vi) If you had a real game, which has 100 squares, which method do you think you would use to solve for the mean first-passage time: the method from (iii) or from (v)? What if a game had 1,000,000 squares? Give advantages and disadvantages of each method for large games.

CHAPTER 3

Markov Chains (II): Detailed Balance and Markov Chain Monte Carlo (MCMC)

3.1. Detailed balance

Detailed balance is an important property of certain Markov chains. It must be satisfied in models of many physical systems, and when satisfied, it leads to powerful tools for studying Markov chains theoretically.

DEFINITION 3.1. Let $X_0, X_1, \ldots$ be a time-homogeneous Markov chain with stationary distribution π. The chain is said to satisfy *detailed balance with respect to π* if

$$(3.1) \qquad \pi_i P_{ij} = \pi_j P_{ji} \qquad \text{for all } i, j \in S.$$

Equations (3.1) are called the *detailed balance equations*.

What do equations (3.1) imply about the dynamics of the chain? Suppose we start a chain in the stationary distribution, so that $X_0 \sim \pi$. Then $\pi_i P_{ij}$ is the amount of probability that flows from i to j in one time step. If (3.1) holds, then the amount of probability flowing from i to j, equals the amount that flows from j to i. Therefore, there is no *net* flux of probability between $i \leftrightarrow j$ during one time step. Compare (3.1) with the condition for a stationary distribution:

$$(3.2) \qquad \pi_i = \sum_{j \in S} \pi_j P_{ji}, \qquad \text{for all } i \in S.$$

For a finite system with N states, equations (3.2) require solving a system of N equations, whereas the detailed balance equations (3.1) require solving a system of $N(N-1)/2$ equations. Therefore detailed balance is a much *stronger* condition than the condition that π be a stationary distribution; a general Markov chain will not satisfy detailed balance. Indeed, equations (3.2) for the stationary distribution require the flow of probability to be balanced *globally*: at each *state* or vertex, the amount of probability that flows in in one step equals the amount that flows out. The detailed balance equations require the flow to be balanced *locally*: at each *edge*, the amount of probability that flows across in one direction in one step equals the amount that flows in the opposite direction.

An analogy[1] comes from thinking about traffic flow in New York City: let each borough be a node of a Markov chain and join two nodes if there is a road or bridge connecting the boroughs directly. For example, the node corresponding to Manhattan would be connected to Queens (via the Queensboro bridge), to Brooklyn (via the Brooklyn bridge), etc. (Figure 3.1).

---

[1] Thanks to Oliver Bühler for this idea.

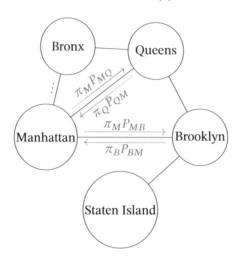

FIGURE 3.1. A simple schematic of traffic flow in New York City.

Suppose that cars driving around represent little elements of probability, and the transition matrix describes the fraction of cars that cross from one borough to another each day. The traffic is in the stationary distribution if the number of cars in Manhattan—and in all other boroughs—does not change each day. This is possible even when cars are constantly driving around in circles, such as if all cars leave Manhattan to Queens via the Queensboro bridge, drive to Brooklyn on roads, and reenter Manhattan via the Brooklyn bridge. As long as the number of cars per unit time leaving Manhattan across the Queensboro bridge equals the number per unit time entering Manhattan via the Brooklyn bridge, the number of cars in Manhattan does not change, and the traffic can be stationary. The traffic is in detailed balance only if the number of cars that leaves *each bridge* (or road) per unit time equals the number that enter that *same* bridge (or road). For example, the flux of cars entering Manhattan through the Brooklyn bridge ($\pi_B P_{BM}$) must equal the flux of cars exiting Manhattan through the Brooklyn bridge ($\pi_M P_{MB}$), and similarly for every other bridge. Not only does the number of cars in Manhattan remain constant with time, but the fluxes of cars across each bridge separately must be equal in each direction.

Detailed balance is a powerful concept because it gives a tractable way to find a stationary distribution, and it allows us to construct a system that has a desired stationary distribution.

THEOREM 3.2. *Let P be the transition matrix of a Markov chain X_n, and suppose there exists a distribution π such that $\pi_i P_{ij} = \pi_j P_{ji}$ for all $i, j \in S$. Then π is a stationary distribution of the chain.*

PROOF. Suppose that π satisfies the conditions of the theorem. Then

$$\sum_i \pi_i P_{ij} = \underbrace{\sum_i \pi_j P_{ji}}_{\text{by detailed balance}} = \pi_j \underbrace{\sum_i P_{ji}}_{=1} = \pi_j.$$

Therefore, $\pi = \pi P$, so π is a stationary distribution.   □

Theorem 3.2 gives a useful way of finding the stationary distribution, since it is often easier to solve the detailed balance equations (3.1), which are local, than the equations for the stationary distribution (3.2), which are global. Here are two examples to illustrate how one uses detailed balance to find a stationary distribution.

Example 3.3 (Random walk on a graph). Consider a random walk on an unweighted, undirected graph (Example 2.10). Recall that the transition matrix is $P_{ij} = 1/d_i$ if there is an edge between i, j, where d_i is the degree of node i. We look for a stationary distribution satisfying detailed balance, which requires that, for each edge (i, j),

$$\frac{\pi_i}{d_i} = \frac{\pi_j}{d_j}.$$

Clearly, this condition is satisfied if $\pi_i \propto d_i$. Therefore, a stationary distribution is $\pi_i = Z^{-1}/d_i$ with $Z = \sum_i d_i = 2\eta$, where η is the total number of edges in the graph, and, furthermore, this Markov chain satisfies detailed balance.

Example 3.4 (Ehrenfest model of diffusion). Consider a container with a membrane (real or imagined) in the middle and a total of m particles distributed in some way between the left and right sides of the container. For example, suppose we have a room, and the particles are air molecules occupying either the left or right sides of the room. At each step we pick one particle at random and move it to the other side. Let X_n be the number of particles in the left side at time n. Then X_n is a Markov chain, with transition probabilities $P_{i,i+1} = 1 - \frac{i}{m}$, $P_{i,i-1} = \frac{i}{m}$. What is the stationary distribution of this chain?

Let us look for a probability distribution π that satisfies (3.1). If we find a solution, we know by Theorem 3.2 that it is a stationary distribution. We also know it is a unique such stationary distribution, since the transition matrix P is irreducible (Theorem 2.39). Notice that all edges are between nodes $i \leftrightarrow i+1$ for $i = 0, 1, \ldots, m-1$, so we only have to solve the equations

$$\pi_i P_{i,i+1} = \pi_{i+1} P_{i+1,i} \quad \Leftrightarrow \quad \pi_i \left(1 - \frac{i}{m}\right) = \pi_{i+1} \left(\frac{i+1}{m}\right) \quad \Leftrightarrow \quad \pi_{i+1} = \pi_i \frac{m-i}{i+1}.$$

One way to solve this is to (temporarily) set $\pi_0 = 1$, and then solve recursively for $\pi_1, \pi_2, \ldots$. It is not hard to derive the (again, temporary) formula $\pi_i = \binom{m}{i}$. Now, normalize π to make it a probability distribution:

$$\pi_i = \frac{1}{2^m} \binom{m}{i}, \qquad i = 0, 1, \ldots, m.$$

Therefore, the stationary distribution for the number of particles in one side of the container is Binomial$(m, \frac{1}{2})$. Although this is a crude model for the motion of air molecules in a room, it nevertheless explains why we never find ourselves in a room with all the air molecules on one side of the room. The number of air molecules in a room is $m \sim O(10^{26})$, so the probability that they are all on one side is roughly $2^{-10^{26}}$ —not something to hold your breath for.

Markov chains that satisfy detailed balance have another important property, namely, that they are time reversible: they are indistinguishable whether they are run forward or backward in time when started in the stationary distribution. Consider a Markov chain initialized in the stationary distribution and let it run to get $X_0 \sim \pi, X_1 \sim \pi, \ldots, X_N \sim \pi$. Let $Y_n = X_{N-n}$ be the "reversed" chain.

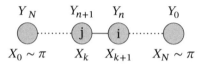

Exercise 2.17 showed that $Y_0, Y_1, \ldots, Y_N$ is a Markov chain with transition probabilities

$$P(Y_{n+1} = j | Y_n = i) = \frac{\pi_j}{\pi_i} P_{ji}.$$

When are the transition probabilities for Y_n the same as those for X_n? Exactly when X_n satisfies detailed balance! In this case, the chain is statistically indistinguishable whether it is run forward or backward in time—given a trajectory, no statistical test can be applied to tell if it came from running the forward-in-time chain X_n or the backward-in-time chain Y_n.

Detailed balance is a critical concept in physics and chemistry. Any system that is an *equilibrium system*—meaning that it is a closed system that is not acted upon by external forces—must satisfy detailed balance, and, conversely, detailed balance defines an equilibrium system. This is because, for such a system, the laws of physics, such as Newton's laws of motion,[2] are time-reversible, so any statistical model that comes from coarse-graining the laws of motion by representing them stochastically must also be time-reversible. Therefore, if we are constructing a model of a physical system and there is no external forcing that could cause it to be time-irreversible, *we must construct a model that satisfies detailed balance*.

If a system does not satisfy detailed balance, it is called a *nonequilibrium system*. In this case, there are nonzero fluxes in steady-state, which is only possible if the system has forces acting on it. The statistical mechanics of such forced systems is vastly more complicated, and is an active area of research.

If you like fluid dynamics, one way to picture detailed balance is to imagine a turbulent fluid in a box. If the fluid is forced and dissipated isotropically (e.g., by some external heat bath), then the mean flow over long enough timescales should be zero. However, if we stir the fluid in one direction, then there will be a mean circulation in the box.

Here are some examples of physical systems that do/do not satisfy detailed balance.

---

[2]This is not quite true. If a system has velocities or other "odd" variables, then the concept of reversibility has to be modified; we return to this in Section 12.12.5 when we discuss detailed balance for diffusion processes.

| Detailed balance | No detailed balance |

Detailed balance
- passive particle diffusing in a fluid
- protein binding and unbinding to a receptor on a cell
- Ising model with dynamics to be described
- ideal gas in an insulated box
- system in contact with one heat bath
- covered, insulated coffee cup with liquid/vapour equilibrium
- crystal with no external forces

No detailed balance
- self-propelled (e.g., swimming) particles, (such as a collection of bacteria)
- molecular motor
- atmospheric circulation patterns
- plasma with non-Maxwellian velocities
- system in contact with two heat baths at different temperatures
- snowflake melting in a coffee cup
- sheared crystal

3.2. Spectral decomposition for a Markov chain that satisfies detailed balance

The transition matrix P for a Markov chain satisfying detailed balance can be symmetrized by a similarity transformation. Let

$$(3.3) \qquad V = \Lambda P \Lambda^{-1}, \qquad \text{where} \quad \Lambda = \begin{pmatrix} \sqrt{\pi_1} & & & \\ & \sqrt{\pi_2} & & \\ & & \ddots & \\ & & & \sqrt{\pi_N} \end{pmatrix}.$$

All off-diagonal elements of Λ are 0. We claim that when P satisfies detailed balance, then V is symmetric. Let us check:

$$V_{ij} = \frac{\sqrt{\pi_i}}{\sqrt{\pi_j}} P_{ij} = \underbrace{\frac{\sqrt{\pi_i}}{\sqrt{\pi_j}} \frac{\pi_j}{\pi_i} P_{ji}}_{\text{detailed balance}} = \frac{\sqrt{\pi_j}}{\sqrt{\pi_i}} P_{ji} = V_{ji}.$$

Therefore, we can use our knowledge of the spectrum of symmetric matrices to characterize the spectrum of P. Since V is symmetric, it has a full set of real eigenvalues $\{\lambda_j\}_{j=1}^N \subset \mathbb{R}$, and an orthonormal set of eigenvectors $\{w^{(j)}\}_{j=1}^N$ that are both the left and right eigenvectors (we think of both of these as columns vectors in this section). Therefore, P has the same eigenvalues $\{\lambda_j\}_{j=1}^N$, and it has the following eigenvectors

left eigenvectors $\quad \psi^{(j)} = \Lambda w^{(j)} \quad \Leftrightarrow \quad \psi_i^{(j)} = w_i^{(j)} \sqrt{\pi_i},$

right eigenvectors $\quad \phi^{(j)} = \Lambda^{-1} w^{(j)} \quad \Leftrightarrow \quad \phi_i^{(j)} = w_i^{(j)} (\sqrt{\pi_i})^{-1}.$

The relationship above between the left and right eigenvectors implies that

$$\psi^{(j)} = \Lambda^2 \phi^{(j)} \quad \Leftrightarrow \quad \psi_i^{(j)} = \pi_i \phi_i^{(j)},$$

i.e., the left eigenvector equals the right eigenvector multiplied (component-wise) by π. We already knew this was true for the eigenvectors corresponding to $\lambda_1 = 1$, since $\phi^{(1)} = (1, \ldots, 1)^T$ and $\psi^{(1)} = \pi$, but for a chain that satisfies detailed balance it is true for all the other eigenvectors as well.

Note that the orthonormality condition $|w^{(j)}|^2 = 1$ in an L^2-norm, implies that neither $\psi^{(j)}$ nor $\phi^{(j)}$ are orthonormal in the L^2-norm; however, they are orthonormal in weighted L^2-spaces:

$$(3.4) \qquad \sum_i (\phi_i^{(j)})^2 \pi_i = 1, \qquad \sum_i (\psi_i^{(j)})^2 \pi_i^{-1} = 1.$$

We can write P using its spectral decomposition (assuming $|w^{(j)}| = 1$) as

$$(3.5) \qquad P = \sum_{k=1}^N \lambda_k \phi^{(k)} (\psi^{(k)})^T = \sum_{k=1}^N \lambda_k \phi^{(k)} (\phi^{(k)})^T \Lambda^2.$$

In components: $P_{ij} = \sum_{k=1}^N \lambda_k \phi_i^{(k)} \psi_j^{(k)} = \sum_{k=1}^N \lambda_k \phi_i^{(k)} \phi_j^{(k)} \pi_j$. Therefore, the n-step transition matrix is

$$(3.6) \qquad P^n = \sum_{k=1}^N \lambda_k^n \phi^{(k)} (\psi^{(k)})^T.$$

If n is large, then the main contributions to P^n come from the eigenvectors corresponding to eigenvalues with norms close to 1; these eigenvectors are therefore related to the long-time dynamics of the chain.

REMARK 3.5. The spectral decomposition (3.5) is sometimes used to approximate P by truncating the sum after a small number of eigenvectors, which effectively keeps only the dynamics that evolve on longer time scales, as we will see shortly. However, if you truncate (3.5), then you typically do not obtain a stochastic matrix. In fact, if you evolve the probability with the truncated matrix, the probability can even become negative. The spectral decomposition hides the fact that P is stochastic.

The spectral decomposition gives insight into the timescales associated with the Markov chain. Let us take a look at an example.

Example 3.6. Consider the following transition matrix and corresponding graph representation of the Markov chain.

$$P = \begin{pmatrix} 1 - \frac{1}{2m} & \frac{1}{2m} & 0 & 0 & 0 \\ \frac{1}{2} & 0 & \frac{1}{2} & 0 & 0 \\ 0 & \frac{1}{2} & 0 & \frac{1}{2} & 0 \\ 0 & 0 & \frac{1}{2} & 0 & \frac{1}{2} \\ 0 & 0 & 0 & \frac{1}{2m} & 1 - \frac{1}{2m} \end{pmatrix}$$

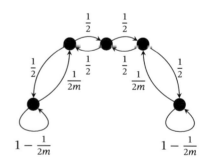

This Markov chain describes a particle moving on a state space with 5 sites. It undergoes an unbiased random walk along the middle 3 nodes but when it hits an endpoint, it tends to stay there for a time proportional to parameter m before escaping. We are interested in the dynamics for large m.

You can check that the chain satisfies detailed balance, with stationary distribution $\pi = Z^{-1}(m, 1, 1, 1, m)$ where $Z = 2m + 3$.

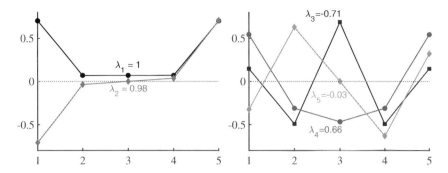

FIGURE 3.3. Left eigenvectors of the transition matrix in Example 3.6, with $m = 10$.

Let us calculate the eigenvalues.

$$m = 2 : \quad \lambda = \{1, \quad 0.89, \quad -0.75, \quad 0.5, \quad -0.14\}$$
$$m = 5 : \quad \lambda = \{1, \quad 0.95, \quad -0.72, \quad 0.62, \quad -0.05\}$$
$$m = 20 : \quad \lambda = \{1, \quad 0.99, \quad -0.71, \quad 0.68, \quad -0.01\}$$
$$m = 100 : \quad \lambda = \{1, \quad 0.999, \quad -0.71, \quad 0.70, \quad -0.03\}$$

There is a spectral gap between the second eigenvalue λ_2, which approaches 1 as $m \to \infty$, and the third eigenvalue λ_3, which appears bounded in absolute value away from 1.

What do the eigenvectors represent? Figure 3.3 shows a plot of the left eigenvectors for $m = 10$. The eigenvector corresponding to λ_1 is the stationary distribution (as expected), while the eigenvector corresponding to λ_2 captures transitions between the endpoints—it corrects the stationary distribution to account for the imbalance of probability between the endpoints. The timescale of transition is controlled by $-1/\log|\lambda_2|$. The other eigenvectors describe the diffusive, random walk–like motion across the nodes in the middle.

3.3. Markov chain Monte Carlo

Markov chain Monte Carlo (MCMC) refers to a collection of algorithms to generate a random variable X whose probability distribution is π,

$$X \sim \pi.$$

Usually, the goal is to estimate the average of a function of the random variable,

$$(3.7) \qquad \mathbb{E}_\pi f(X) = \int f(x)\pi(dx).$$

The reader might already know about methods for generating independent samples from a probability distribution, such as the inverse transform method, the acceptance/rejection method, etc. However, these methods are totally infeasible when the dimensionality of the system is high. Markov chain Monte Carlo algorithms are feasible even in high dimensions, leading to insight into otherwise intractable problems. Indeed, the Metropolis–Hasting algorithm (a particular MCMC method) has been named on of the top ten most influential algorithms of the twentieth century.[3] They are so widespread that (**Diaconis, 2009**) says that,

> "To someone working in my part of the world, asking about applications of Markov chain Monte Carlo is a little like asking about applications of the quadratic formula."

Yet, a Monte Carlo researcher, Alan Sokal, starts his popular set of lecture notes with this warning (**Sokal, 1989**):

> "Monte Carlo is an extremely *bad* method; it should be used only when all alternative methods are worse."

How can such an influential algorithm also be bad? Hopefully by the end of this short section you will also understand the power and the pitfalls of MCMC. For now, let us start by looking at a few examples where "all else is worse."

3.3.1. Examples.

Example 3.7 (Ising model). This is a model that was initially invented to study magnetism, but it has since been been used in an enormous variety of applications, including ice, gases, spin glasses, cancer, ion channels, neuroscience, and urban segregation.

Consider a 2d lattice with $N = m \times m$ sites (the magnet), where each square on the lattice is assigned a "spin" $\sigma_j \in \{+1, -1\}$, called an up spin or a down spin. Each configuration of spins $\sigma = (\sigma_1, \dots, \sigma_N)$ has an energy

$$(3.8) \qquad H(\sigma) = - \sum_{\langle i,j \rangle} \sigma_i \sigma_j,$$

where $\langle i, j \rangle$ means i, j are neighbors on the lattice. The energy is lower when neighboring spins are the same.

The stationary distribution we wish to sample is the Boltzmann distribution:

$$(3.9) \qquad \pi(\sigma) = Z^{-1} e^{-\beta H(\sigma)}.$$

Here, $Z = \sum_\sigma e^{-\beta H(\sigma)}$ is a normalization constant, which is rarely known except in problems with special structure, and β is a parameter, called the *inverse temperature*. It is related to the actual temperature T as $\beta = (k_B T)^{-1}$, where k_B is Boltzmann's constant.

For large β (low temperature), $\pi(\sigma)$ is bimodal—it is highly peaked near configurations with mostly $+1$s or mostly -1s. Physically, the system is magnetized. For small β (high temperature), $\pi(\sigma)$ gives most weight to systems with nearly equal $+1$s and -1s; the system is disordered and loses its magnetization. One question of interest is: At which temperature (which β) does this transition occur?

We can answer this by calculating the average magnetization $M(\sigma) = |\frac{1}{N} \sum_{i=1}^{N} \sigma_i|$ when the system is in its stationary distribution. That is, we calculate $\mathbb{E}_\pi M = \sum_\sigma \pi(\sigma) M(\sigma)$.

---

[3]See `http://www.siam.org/news/news.php?id=637`, and also Nick Higham's blog `https://nickhigham.wordpress.com/2016/03/29/the-top-10-algorithms-in-applied-mathematics/`. The other 9 include the simplex method of linear programming, Krylov subspace iteration methods, the decompositional approach to matrix computations, the Fortran optimizing compiler, the QR algorithm for computing eigenvalues, Quicksort, Fast Fourier transform, Integer relation detection, and the Fast multipole method (invented in part by Courant's own Leslie Greengard!).

One way to do this is to generate random variables $\sigma^{(1)}, \sigma^{(2)}, \cdots, \sigma^{(n)} \sim \pi$, and average their corresponding values of M,

$$\hat{M} = \frac{1}{n} \sum_{i=1}^{n} M(\sigma^{(i)}).$$

As β increases, $\hat{M} \approx \mathbb{E}_\pi M$ transitions from 0 (not magnetized) to 1 (magnetized), with a sharper transition as the system gets larger.

Example 3.8 (Particles interacting with a pairwise potential). A widely studied model is a collection of point particles with positions $x_i \in \mathbb{R}^3$ that interact with a pair potential $V(r)$, where r is the distance between a pair. The total energy of a system of n particles is the sum over all the pair interactions

$$U(x) = \sum_{i,j=1}^{n} V(|x_i - x_j|),$$

where $x = (x_1, x_2, \ldots, x_n) \in \mathbb{R}^{3n}$ is the vector of particle positions; we may also restrict positions to a lattice so that $x_i \in \mathbb{Z}^3$. For example, one may be interested in the Lennard–Jones potential

$$V(r) = \epsilon \left[\left(\frac{\sigma}{r} \right)^6 - \left(\frac{\sigma}{r} \right)^{12} \right]$$

where σ, ϵ are parameters. Such models arise in numerous systems to describe the interactions between atoms in a crystal or noble gas cluster, between amino acids in a protein, between jammed particles such as sand grains, and even in studies of pedestrian flows.

The stationary distribution is again the Boltzmann distribution—

$$\pi(x) = Z^{-1} e^{-\beta U(x)},$$

where again, β is the inverse temperature, and we rarely know the normalization constant $Z = \int_{\mathbb{R}^{3n}} e^{-\beta U(x)}$.

Depending on β, the system could prefer to be in a number of different states such as a solid, crystal, liquid, gas, or other phase. To calculate the phase diagram we must generate samples from $\pi(x)$ and compute averages of some function (called an order parameter) that characterizes the system's phase.

Example 3.9 (Likelihood functions). In Bayesian statistics one must generate samples of parameter values $\theta = (\theta_1, \theta_2, \ldots, \theta_p)$ from a probability distribution proportional to a likelihood function $L(\theta|x)$, where $x = (x_1, x_2, \ldots, x_M)$ is observed data. The likelihood function can be calculated from a probability model as $L(\theta|x) = p_\theta(x)$, where $(p_\theta(x))_\theta$ is a family of probability densities for observing data x; or it can be calculated through a Bayesian procedure. Usually, this function is very complicated (**Kaipio and Somersalo, 2005**). One area where this kind of inference problem is widely used is in astronomy (**Sharma, 2017**); for example, Courant's Jonathan Goodman and collaborators used the radial velocity data of a star to determine how many planets are in its orbit (**Hou et al., 2014**). Another is in Bayesian inverse problems; for example, Courant's Georg Stadler and collaborators used such a framework to determine how ice sheets flow (**Petra et al., 2014**).

There are several difficulties in sampling from π for these examples and a vast number of related ones:

- The size of the state space is often **huge**!

  For example, the $m \times m$ Ising model has $N = 2^{m^2}$ elements in the state space. Even for small m, say $m = 10$, we have over 10^{30} configurations; there is no way one could list them all. For a system of particles the dimension increases beyond reach of deterministic means even for a handful of particles—e.g., a system of 100 particles lives in 300-dimensional space. There is no way one could adequately sample every region in this space—if we divided it into boxes with only 10 points per dimension, we would still have 10^{300} boxes to sample from.

- Often, we do not know the normalization constant for π, only a function it is proportional to, $g(x) = Z\pi(x)$. That is, we know g but not Z, so we do not have a formula for π.

  For example, the Boltzmann distribution $Z^{-1}e^{-\beta U(x)}$ arises frequently. We usually know the potential energy $U(x)$ but can almost never calculate Z analytically or through any deterministic procedure (you can calculate Z in some cases by a randomized procedure that involves generating random variables $X \sim \pi$; see, e.g., (**Frenkel and Ladd, 1984**)). Likelihood functions are similarly complicated and cannot generally be integrated analytically or by using deterministic numerical techniques.

- While we could simulate the *dynamics* of the system until it reaches steady-state, we may not know the system's true dynamics, or these may have widely separated time scales so cannot be efficiently simulated. Yet, we still often know the steady-state distribution π and would like to sample from it.

  For example, for the Ising model, the true dynamics of a magnet are given by quantum mechanics via the Schrödinger equation, but these dynamics cannot be solved for any but the smallest systems. For particles in a box, the heat bath that thermalizes the system often has much faster timescales than the ones we are interested in. For example, a protein that folds jiggles randomly because of the fluctuations of the solvent (usually water), but the dynamics of water atoms occur on timescales that are orders of magnitude faster than the timescale of protein folding, and, additionally, there are far too many water atoms to simulate. For likelihood functions, there are not even any dynamics to simulate.

3.3.2. Metropolis–Hastings algorithm. To overcome these challenges, MCMC generates samples from π by creating a Markov chain that has π as its stationary distribution and that is easy to simulate. The most common MCMC algorithm is the Metropolis–Hastings algorithm.

METROPOLIS–HASTINGS ALGORITHM. Let π be a discrete probability distribution and let H be the transition matrix for *any* irreducible Markov chain whose state space contains the support of π. Construct a Markov chain $X_0, X_1, \ldots$ as follows. Suppose $X_n = i$. Generate X_{n+1} in the following steps:

(1) Choose a *proposal state* Y according to the probability distribution given by the ith row of H, so that $P(Y = j | X_n = i) = H_{ij}$.

(2) Calculate the *acceptance probability*

$$(3.10) \qquad\qquad a_{ij} = \min\left(1, \frac{\pi_j H_{ji}}{\pi_i H_{ij}}\right).$$

(3) Accept the proposal $Y=j$ with probability a_{ij}. That is, let $U \sim \text{Uniform}([0,1])$, and:
  - If $U \le a_{ij}$ then *accept* the move: set $X_{n+1} = Y$;
  - If $U > a_{ij}$ then *reject* the move: set $X_{n+1} = X_n$.

Then repeat.

The result of the Metropolis–Hastings algorithm is a Markov chain with transition probabilities

$$(3.11) \qquad\qquad P_{ij} = \begin{cases} H_{ij}a_{ij} & (i \ne j) \\ 1 - \sum_{i \ne j} H_{ij}a_{ij} & (i = j) \end{cases}$$

We will show shortly (Lemma 3.14) that this Markov chain has stationary distribution π. Provided the Markov chain is irreducible, if the chain is simulated for a long time, its averaged distribution will approach π (recall Theorem 2.39). Therefore, we can estimate averages such as (3.7) by averaging our empirical observations:[4]

$$(3.12) \qquad\qquad \mathbb{E}_\pi f \approx \hat{f}_n = \frac{1}{n}(f(X_1) + \cdots + f(X_n)).$$

REMARK 3.10. This algorithm works equally well in a continuous state space, provided we interpret the transition probability h as a density: $h(y|x)$ is the probability density of jumping to y, given we start at x. The Metropolis–Hastings acceptance ratio is $a(y|x) = \min\left(1, \frac{\pi(y)h(x|y)}{\pi(x)h(y|x)}\right)$.

REMARK 3.11. There are other ways to calculate the acceptance probability a_{ij}, leading to algorithms with other names (see Exercise 3.6). The Metropolis-Hastings formula (3.10) can be shown to be statistically optimal, in the sense that it has the smallest correlation time (see (3.13) below) for a class of statistics f (e.g., (**Liu, 2001**, Section 13.3.1)).

REMARK 3.12. This algorithm was first developed first by Nicholas Metropolis, Arianna Rosenbluth, Marshall Rosenbluth, Augusta Teller, and Edward Teller, for the case when $H_{ij} = H_{ji}$ (**Metropolis et al., 1953**). It is not clear why Metropolis got the credit; some accounts suggest that Marshall and Arianna Rosenbluth did most of the work (**Gubernatis, 2005**). The formula was later generalized by Wilfred Hastings to allow for nonsymmetric proposals (**Hastings, 1970**).

Example 3.13. Suppose we wish to generate a random variable X on state space $S = \{1, 2, 3\}$ with distribution

$$\pi_1 = \frac{1}{6}, \quad \pi_2 = \frac{1}{3}, \quad \pi_3 = \frac{1}{2}.$$

---

[4]This result, that time-averages converge to the expectation, is something we have not shown and is a form of ergodic theorem, which generalizes the law of large numbers to correlated sequences of random variables.

Let us do this by rolling a die D, and if $D = 1, 2$ we move right by one step, and if $D = 3, 4, 5, 6$ we move left. Our proposal matrix is $H_{i,i+1} = 1/3$, $H_{i,i-1} = 2/3$, and $H_{ij} = 0$ if $i \neq j$.

Suppose $X_0 = 2$, and the algorithm plays out as follows.

(1) $D = 4$ so the proposal is $Y = 1$. The acceptance probability is

$$a_{21} = \min\left(\frac{\pi_1 H_{12}}{\pi_2 H_{21}}, 1\right) = 1/4.$$

We generate $U = 0.7341$. Since $U > a_{21}$, we reject the proposal, and set $X_1 = 2$.

(2) $D = 1$ so the proposal is $Y = 3$. The acceptance probability is

$$a_{23} = \min\left(\frac{\pi_3 H_{32}}{\pi_2 H_{23}}, 1\right) = \min(3, 1) = 1.$$

Therefore, we always accept the move, so we set $X_2 = 3$.

(3) $D = 2$ so the proposal is $Y = 4$. Now

$$a_{34} = \min\left(\frac{\pi_4 H_{43}}{\pi_3 H_{34}}, 1\right) = 0,$$

since $\pi_4 = 0$. Therefore, we reject the move and set $X_3 = 3$.

The example above illustrates a general feature of the algorithm—we may propose moves outside the support of π, as we did in step (3), but if we do they must be immediately rejected. It also gives insight into why (3.10) helps "correct" the Markov chain we would have obtained from H to make it have the right stationary distribution. If we tend to propose moves to lower-probability regions with a relatively high probability, as in step (1) where H_{ij} was large compared to H_{ji} but π_j was small compared to π_i, then the acceptance probability $a_{ij} = \pi_j H_{ji}/\pi_i H_{ij}$ will be small. Therefore, we will tend to refrain from actually moving there and will repeat the state i, which should occur with higher probability than it would with H alone.

LEMMA 3.14. *The Markov chain constructed by the Metropolis–Hastings algorithm has stationary distribution π.*

PROOF. We prove this by showing the chain satisfies detailed balance with respect to π.

Suppose that $\pi_j H_{ji} \leq \pi_i H_{ij}$. Then $P_{ij} = H_{ij} \min\left(1, \frac{\pi_j H_{ji}}{\pi_i H_{ij}}\right) = \frac{\pi_j}{\pi_i} H_{ji}$, and $P_{ji} = H_{ji} \min\left(1, \frac{\pi_i H_{ij}}{\pi_j H_{ji}}\right) = H_{ji}$. Therefore

$$\pi_i P_{ij} = \pi_i \frac{\pi_j}{\pi_i} H_{ji} = \pi_j H_{ji} = \pi_j P_{ji}.$$

A similar calculation holds if $\pi_j H_{ji} > \pi_i H_{ij}$. Therefore, the chain satisfies detailed balance with respect to π, so, by Theorem 3.2, π is the stationary distribution. □

One feature of the Metropolis–Hastings algorithm which makes it so powerful is that the proposal matrix H can be absolutely anything (in theory), as long as it is irreducible and has the right state space. In particular, the proposals do not have to bear any relation to moves that are physically plausible. This gives a lot of freedom to choose proposals based on what is convenient and efficient for the problem at hand. Here are some possible proposals for the examples in Section 3.3.3.1:

(1) (Ising model)
  - pick a random spin, flip it: $\sigma_j \to -\sigma_j$.
  - pick a random pair of neighboring spins, exchange their values: $\sigma_i = \sigma_j$, $\sigma_j = \sigma_i$.
  - pick a spin or a cluster of spins, change the value(s) depending on the environment surrounding them, e.g., set the value to be the one that minimizes the energy in the spin's local neighborhood.

(2) (Particles)
  - pick a single particle, move it some random displacement in a random direction: $x_i \to x_i + \xi$, where ξ is a random variable, often Gaussian.
  - move all particles in the direction of the gradient of the potential, plus some random amount: $x \to x - s\nabla U(x) + \xi$, where s is a parameter and ξ is a random variable.

Another powerful feature of the algorithm is that you do not need to know π, the normalized probability distribution, but rather only a function $g(x)$ it is proportional to: $g(x) = Z\pi(x)$, where $Z = \sum_x g(x)$. The normalization constant Z cancels out in the acceptance ratio (3.10), so you do not need to calculate it. This makes it feasible to apply in high-dimensional problems where we almost never know Z.

3.3.3. Practical considerations of the Metropolis–Hastings algorithm.

Here is a brief summary of some of the issues one must consider when implementing the Metropolis–Hastings algorithm in practice.

3.3.3.1. *Constructing the proposals.* While, in theory, one can use any proposal matrix H, in practice, the efficiency of the algorithm depends critically on H. Constructing *good* proposals is an art that requires taking into account the structure of individual problems; there are few general theories.

Once the basic form of the proposals has been decided, there are usually parameters governing the average sizes of the proposed moves, i.e., how close they are on average to the current point. If proposals are too close to the current point, then almost every move is accepted but it takes a long time to explore the whole space. If proposals are too far from the current point, then almost all moves are rejected, which also slows convergence. Proposals should be large enough to explore the whole space quickly but not so large that they are often rejected.

A rule of thumb is to choose parameters to achieve a desired average acceptance ratio. Results for idealized problems suggest this should be $\approx$ 25% (**Gelman et al., 1996**; **Roberts et al., 1997**). In practice, for a complex problem, one does not know the optimal acceptance ratio, but would aim for something in the neighborhood of results for idealized problems. Alternatively, one can tune parameters to minimize the correlation time of a statistic, described below.

3.3.3.2. *Burn-in time.* Since the chain starts from an initial condition X_0 that is *not* drawn from the stationary distribution, it will take some time before it reaches the stationary distribution. This time is called the *burn-in time.* If the chain is run for long enough this initial transient will not significantly affect the measured statistics. In some situations it is not possible to run the chain for such long times, such as in PDE-constrained optimization problems which require solving an expensive PDE at each step of the chain, so practitioners may only run the chain for twice the estimated burn-in time and then discard the first half of the data.

Theoretically, the time it takes the chain to reach its stationary distribution is controlled by $-\log|\lambda_2|$, where λ_2 is the eigenvalue of P with the second-largest norm. In practice, we almost never know λ_2, so one must estimate the burn-in time empirically. A simple (but crude) way to do this is to plot the current running average $\hat{f}_n$ (see (3.12)) as a function of n. Initially, this will vary quite a lot, but eventually it will settle down and will not change much; the time where it appears to settle down is the burn-in time. More sophisticated measures of convergence are discussed in (**Cowles and Carlin, 1996**).

3.3.3.3. *Correlation time.* A common way to measure the efficiency of the algorithm is by the correlation time of a statistic. The correlation time associated with function f is

$$(3.13) \qquad \tau_f = \frac{1}{C_f(0)} \sum_{t=-\infty}^{\infty} C_f(t)dt,$$

where $C_f(t) = \mathbb{E}_\pi f(X_t)f(X_0) - (\mathbb{E}_\pi f(X_t))^2$. The function $C_f(t)$ is the covariance function of $f(X_t)$, assuming $X_0 \sim \pi$. (We will study covariance functions in more detail in Chapter 5.) The quantity τ_f characterizes the time it takes the chain X_t to forget its given state—when τ_f is large, we need to generate many more steps of the chain to forget the last step, whereas when τ_f is small, we do not need to generate as many points. Therefore, we would like to choose our proposals H so the resulting Markov chain has a small correlation time.

The correlation time has a geometric interpretation: if the area under the covariance function is rearranged to form a rectangle with the same height $C_f(0)$ as the covariance function, then the width of the rectangle is τ_f.

Correlation times can be estimated empirically from an empirical estimate of the covariance function, though one has to be careful not to truncate the infinite sum in (3.13) at too high a time, or the estimate will be corrupted by noise. A controlled truncation may be obtained using the "self-consistent window method" (**Goodman and Sokal, 1989**; **Goodman and Weare, 2010**).

3.3.3.4. *Variance of the estimator $\hat{f}_n$.* To characterize how close the estimator $\hat{f}_n$ in (3.12) should be to the true value $\mathbb{E}_\pi f(X)$, we can calculate the variance of the estimator, $\text{Var}(\hat{f}_n)$. A typical "statistician's" error bar is

$$\hat{f}_n \pm \sqrt{\text{Var}(\hat{f}_n)}.$$

If the random variables $X_1, X_2, \ldots, X_n$ were independent, then (Exercise 3.1)

$$(3.14) \qquad \text{Var}(\hat{f}_n) = \frac{\text{Var}(f(X))}{n}.$$

The random variables output by an MCMC method are typically *not* independent; their correlation increases the variance. One can show (Exercise 5.12) that when the X_i are correlated, the variance approaches

$$(3.15) \qquad \text{Var}(\hat{f}_n) \to \frac{\text{Var}_\pi(f(X))}{n_{\text{eff}}} \quad \text{as } n \to \infty, \qquad \text{where } n_{\text{eff}} = \frac{n}{\tau_f}.$$

The quantity n_{eff} is the "effective" number of points in the sample, sometimes called the *effective sample size*. Since points remain correlated for a timescale measured by τ_f,

FIGURE 3.4. Example of a rugged function $U(x)$ with lots of local minima.

it is reasonable that the effective number of points is decreased by a factor of τ_f from the actual number of points.

To estimate $\mathrm{Var}(\hat{f}_n)$ empirically, one could estimate τ_f as discussed in the section above and use (3.15) (**Zappa et al., 2018**). Alternatively, a "poor man's method" for estimating the variance is to run M independent chains, producing estimates $\hat{f}_n^{(1)}, \ldots, \hat{f}_n^{(M)}$, and construct an estimator and its variance as

$$\hat{f}_n = \frac{1}{M}(\hat{f}_n^{(1)} + \cdots + \hat{f}_n^{(M)}), \qquad \mathrm{Var}(\hat{f}_n) \approx \frac{\mathrm{Var}(\hat{f}_n^{(1)}, \ldots, \hat{f}_n^{(M)})}{M}.$$

***Exercise* 3.1.** Let $X_1, X_2, \ldots, X_n$ be independent, identically distributed random variables, and let $\hat{f}_n = \frac{1}{n} \sum_{i=1}^{n} f(X_i)$. Show that $\mathrm{Var}(\hat{f}_n) = \frac{\mathrm{Var}(f(X_1))}{n}$ (Equation (3.14)).

3.3.4. MCMC methods in optimization. A widespread use of MCMC methods is in optimization. Suppose you have a nonconvex, possibly very rugged function $U(x)$, e.g., as shown in Figure 3.4. How can you find the global minimum?

Deterministic methods (e.g., steepest-descent, Gauss–Newton, Levenberg–Marquadt, BFGS, etc.) are good at finding a *local* minimum. To find a *global* minimum, or one that is close to optimal, one must search the landscape stochastically.

One way to do this is to create a stationary distribution π that puts high probability on the lowest-energy parts of the landscape, such as the Boltzmann distribution $Z^{-1}e^{-\beta U(x)}$ for some inverse temperature β. Then, one constructs a Markov chain to sample this stationary distribution, and keeps track of the smallest value the chain has seen.

The choice of β is critical to have some hope of finding a global minimum. When β is large, the global minimum will be the most likely place to be in equilibrium, but it will take a very long time to reach equilibrium because the system will get trapped in local minima. When β is small, the chain moves about on the landscape much more quickly but does not spend as much time near the local minima. Therefore, it seems reasonable to start with a large value of β and slowly decrease it, a technique known as *simulated annealing*. For example, one can vary β with time t as $\beta = \log t$ or as $\beta = (1.001)^t$. As $t \to \infty$, it can be shown that for some choices of $\beta(t)$ the stationary distribution converges to a delta function at the global minimum (**Kirkpatrick et al., 1983**). In practice, it takes an exponentially long time to do so, but this method still gives good results for many problems.

Example 3.15 (Cryptography). Here is an example of how this optimization method has been used in cryptography to decode ciphers (**Diaconis, 2009**). A cipher is a function $\phi : S \to A$, where S is a set of symbols (e.g., a permutation of the alphabet, the Greek letters, a collection of squiggles, etc.), and $A = \{a, b, c, \ldots\}$ is a set of letters and other symbols used in writing. A code is a string of symbols $x_1 x_2 x_3 \ldots x_n$, where $x_i \in S$. Here is an example of a code, used by inmates in a prison in California (Figure 3.5).

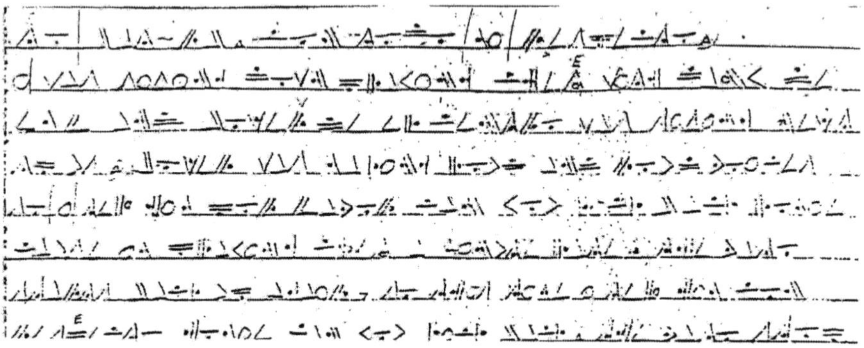

FIGURE 3.5. A code used by inmates in a prison. Image from (**Diaconis, 2009**); reused with permission of the American Mathematical Society.

How can we decipher this code? To start, one could look at the frequencies of each symbol and compared them to the known frequencies of letters in a particular language. Suppose $f_1(a_i)$ is the frequency of letter $a_i \in A$, which could be found empirically by counting the frequency of letters in an excerpt of English text. One can then construct a likelihood function for seeing a particular code as

$$L_1(x_1, x_2, \ldots, x_n; \phi) = \prod_{i=1}^{n} f_1(\phi(x_i)).$$

The likelihood function $L_1(\phi)$ is high when the code obtained from cipher ϕ contains letter frequencies that are similar to those in English. Therefore if we define a probability distribution by

$$\pi(\phi) = \frac{L(\phi)}{\sum_{\phi} L(\phi)},$$

then $\pi(\phi)$ will be large for ciphers that give "likely" letter frequencies, and small for codes that give unlikely letter frequencies. One strategy for deciphering a code is find the cipher ϕ that gives the largest value of $L_1(\phi)$.

Optimizing ϕ by evaluating it for all possible ciphers ϕ is impossible—even if the set of letters contains only lower-case letters and the space, there are $27! \approx 10^{28}$ possible ciphers. However, one can generate samples from $\pi(\phi)$ using an MCMC method, and keep track of the running best value ϕ.

This method was used by statisticians at Stanford to decode the prisoners' message above. It did not work initially; the output was nonsense. So the statisticians tried again using a more sophisticated likelihood function, that included information about the frequencies of pairs of letters $f_2(a_i, a_j)$, which can also be estimated empirically (they estimated it from the novel *War and Peace*). The new likelihood function for seeing a particular code is

$$L_2(x_1, x_2, \ldots, x_n; \phi) = \prod_{i=1}^{n} f_2(\phi(x_i), \phi(x_{i+1})).$$

Optimizing L_2 over all codes using an MCMC method *did* work, and the researchers learned about daily life in prison (in a mixture of English, Spanish, and prison slang) (Figure 3.6).

```
    to bat-rb. con todo mi respeto. i was sitting down playing chess with
danny de emf and boxer de el centro was sitting next to us. boxer was
making loud and loud voices so i tell him por favor can you kick back
homie cause im playing chess a minute later the vato starts back up again
so this time i tell him con respecto homie can you kick back.  the vato
stop for a minute and he starts up again so i tell him check this out shut
the f**k up cause im tired of your voice and if you got a problem with it
we can go to celda and handle it. i really felt disrespected thats why i
told him. anyways after i tell him that the next thing I know that vato
slashes me and leaves. dy the time i figure im hit i try to get away but
the c.o. is walking in my direction and he gets me right dy a celda. so i
go to the hole. when im in the hole my home boys hit doxer so now "b" is
also in the hole. while im in the hole im getting schoold wrong and
```

FIGURE 3.6. Decoded code from Figure 3.5. (Image from (**Diaconis, 2009**); reused with permission of the American Mathematical Society.)

3.4. Additional exercises

Exercise **3.2.** Show that every two-state Markov chain except one has a unique stationary distribution and is reversible with respect to this stationary distribution.

Exercise **3.3.** Construct a three-state Markov chain that is not reversible and such that none of the transition probabilities is exactly 1.

Exercise **3.4** (*Another diffusion model*). N black balls and N white balls are placed in two urns so that each contains N balls. After each unit of time one ball is selected at random from each urn and the two balls are interchanged. Let X_n equal the number of black balls in the first urn at step n. Write down the transition probabilities of this Markov chain and find the unique stationary distribution (you do not need to know the normalizing constant). Does the chain satisfy detailed balance?

Exercise **3.5.** Let P be the transition matrix for a Markov chain with k states that satisfies detailed balance whose stationary distribution is π. Suppose we define an inner product on $\mathbb{R}^k$ as $\langle u, v \rangle_\pi = \sum_i u_i v_i \pi_i$. Show that P is self-adjoint with respect to this inner product, i.e., that $\langle Pu, v \rangle_\pi = \langle u, Pv \rangle_\pi$ for all $u, v \in \mathbb{R}^k$.

Exercise 3.6. Show that if you set the acceptance probability for an MCMC algorithm with proposal matrix $H = (h_{ij})$ to be

$$a_{ij} = \frac{\frac{\pi_j h_{ji}}{\pi_i h_{ij}}}{1 + \frac{\pi_j h_{ji}}{\pi_i h_{ij}}},$$

then the Markov chain you generate satisfies detailed balance with respect to π. (This choice of acceptance probability is called *Glauber dynamics*.)

Exercise 3.7 (*Network analysis and low-dimensional embeddings*). Suppose you are given a data set in the form of a weighted network: you have a set of N nodes, such as points embedded in a high-dimensional space, and weights $w_{ij} \geq 0$ between each node. Let us assume the weights are symmetric, i.e., $w_{ij} = w_{ji}$. We define a Markov chain on the network with transition probabilities

$$p_{ij} = \frac{w_{ij}}{d_i}, \qquad d_i = \sum_j w_{ij}.$$

(We assume that $d_i > 0$ for all i.) For example, if all the weights are either 1 or 0, then this describes a random walk on a graph where the random walker chooses the next edge with equal probability from all the available edges.

   (i) Show that $\pi_i = \frac{d_i}{\sum_k d_k}$ is the stationary distribution for the chain above and that the transition matrix P satisfies detailed balance. You can assume the graph is connected.
   (ii) Explain why P has a full set of real eigenvalues.

One way to put a metric on this network is via the *diffusion distance* D_t:

$$(3.16) \qquad D_t^2(i, j) = \|P_{i,\cdot}^t - P_{j,\cdot}^t\|_{1/\pi}^2 = \sum_k \frac{(P_{i,k}^t - P_{j,k}^t)^2}{\pi_k}.$$

This says the distance between two nodes i, j is small if the corresponding conditional distributions at time t, starting at each node, are close in the L^2 norm. The weight $1/\pi$ penalizes discrepancies on domains of low density more than those of high density.

   (iii) Express the diffusion distance in terms of the right eigenvectors $\{\phi_k\}$ and eigenvalues λ_k of P.
   (iv) Consider an embedding of the network in $\mathbb{R}^m$ where $m < N$ is a fixed integer, given by

$$(3.17) \qquad \Phi_t(i) = \begin{pmatrix} \lambda_0^t \phi_0(i) \\ \lambda_1^t \phi_1(i) \\ \vdots \\ \lambda_m^t \phi_m(i) \end{pmatrix}.$$

That is, $\Phi_t : S \to \mathbb{R}^m$ is a map from the state space of the Markov chain (e.g., a collection of points, each living in a high-dimensional space), to an m-dimensional space, where m is often chosen quite small (e.g., $m = 2$ or $m = 3$).

   Explain (heuristically) when and why you expect Euclidean distances between embedded points $|\Phi_t(i) - \Phi_t(j)|$ to be close to the diffusion distance between these points $D_t^2(i, j)$.

Comment: The diffusion distance (3.16) and the corresponding embedding (3.17) together give a powerful method for mapping a high-dimensional data set to a lower-dimensional one, called a *diffusion map*, introduced in (**Coifman, 2005**).

Exercise 3.8 (*MCMC; computing required*). Suppose you want to sample a random variable X from a Poisson distribution with parameter λ, which has probability mass function

$$\pi(i) = e^{-\lambda} \frac{\lambda^i}{i!}, \qquad i = 0, 1, 2, \dots .$$

You wish to do this using the Metropolis–Hastings algorithm.[5] Your proposed move is constructed in the following way:

$$y = x + \Delta x, \qquad \Delta x = \begin{cases} \text{Unif}(1, 2, \dots, M) & \text{with probability 2/3} \\ \text{Unif}(-1, -2, \dots, -M) & \text{with probability 1/3} \end{cases}$$

That is, your step size is chosen uniformly from the integers $\{1, 2, \dots, M\}$ where M is a parameter and the step direction is to the right with probability 2/3, and to the left with probability 1/3.

(i) Suppose the current value of the chain is $X_n = x$ and you propose a value $Y = y$. Calculate (by hand) the acceptance probability a_{xy}. (Remember to consider the cases $x < y, y < x, y < 0$.)

(ii) Implement an MCMC method with the proposal described above using $\lambda = 5$. Test the correctness of your function by sampling `npts` points with some M and comparing your empirical histogram to the known probability mass function. How large does `npts` have to be so that you cannot distinguish the two by eye?

(iii) Calculate the running average of your Markov chain, $\bar{X}_n = \frac{1}{n} \sum_{i=1}^n X_i$, plot this, and estimate the burn-in time when $X_0 = 0$.

(iv) Calculate the covariance functions $C(t) = \mathbb{E} X_s X_{s+t} - \mathbb{E} X_s \mathbb{E} X_{s+t}$ for different M. Plot these on the same graph. Comment on the differences in the decay rates of $C(t)$ for different M. Which values of M lead to the fastest decay? How large does M have to be to have approximately the same decay rate as $M = 1$?

---

[5]You should only want to do it this way because your teacher asked you to; there are better ways to do it otherwise.

CHAPTER 4

Continuous-Time Markov Chains

Many random processes have a discrete state space but can change their values at any instant of time rather than at fixed time points. Examples include radioactive atoms decaying, the number of reactant molecules in a chemical reaction, populations with birth/death/immigration/emigration, the number of emails in an inbox, the number of people in the checkout counter at Trader Joe's, the number of sick individuals in a population, etc. Such processes are piecewise constant, with jumps that occur at continuous times, as in this example showing an unbiased random walk on the integers $\{1, 2, 3, 4, 5\}$ with a constant jump rate.

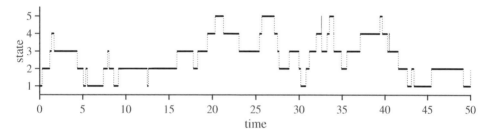

We will look at such processes which satisfy a continuous version of the Markov property, and hence are called continuous-time Markov chains (ctMC). This chapter will introduce tools to describe continuous-time Markov chains, which are variants of the tools we learned to handle discrete-time chains.

4.1. Definition and transition probabilities

DEFINITION 4.1. Let $X = (X_t)_{t \geq 0}$ be a stochastic process taking values in a finite or countable state space S. X is a *continuous-time Markov chain* (ctMC) if it satisfies the *Markov property*:[1]

$$(4.1) \qquad P(X_{t_n} = i_n | X_{t_1} = i_1, \ldots, X_{t_{n-1}} = i_{n-1}) = P(X_{t_n} = i_n | X_{t_{n-1}} = i_{n-1})$$

for all $i_1, \ldots, i_n \in S$ and any sequence $0 \leq t_1 < t_2 < \cdots < t_n$ of times. Additionally, the process is assumed to be right-continuous.

---

[1]The Markov property in continuous time can be formulated more rigorously in terms of σ-algebras. Let $(\Omega, \mathcal{F}, P)$ be a probability space and let $\{\mathcal{F}_t\}_{t \geq 0}$ be a filtration: an increasing sequence of σ-algebras such that $\mathcal{F}_t \subseteq \mathcal{F}$ for each t, and $t_1 \leq t_2 \Rightarrow \mathcal{F}_{t_1} \subseteq \mathcal{F}_{t_2}$. We suppose the process X_t is *adapted* to the filtration $\{\mathcal{F}_t\}_{t \geq 0}$: each X_t is measurable with respect to $\mathcal{F}_t$. For example, this will be true if we let $\mathcal{F}_t$ be the σ-algebra generated by $(X_s)_{0 \leq s \leq t}$, i.e. generated by the pre-images $X_s^{-1}(B)$ for Borel sets $B \subset \mathbb{R}$ and $0 \leq s \leq t$. Then X_t has the Markov property if

$$\mathbb{E}[f(X_t)|\mathcal{F}_s] = \mathbb{E}[f(X_t)|\sigma(X_s)]$$

for all $0 \leq s \leq t$ and bounded, measurable functions f. Another way to say this is $P(X_t \in A|\mathcal{F}_s) = P(X_t \in A|\sigma(X_s))$, where $P(\cdot|\cdot)$ is a *regular conditional probability* (see (**Koralov and Sinai, 2007**, p. 184)).

The Markov property (4.1) says that the distribution of the chain at some time in the future only depends on the current state of the chain, and not on its history. The difference from the Markov property that we learned for discrete processes is that now the set of times that we condition on is continuous—the chain can jump between states at any time, not just at integer times. In fact, the Markov property combined with right-continuity of the process allows us to condition on a continuum of times, as (written somewhat heuristically)

$$(4.2) \qquad P(X_{s+t} = j | X_s = i, X_u = x_u, 0 \le u < s) = P(X_{t+s} = j | X_s = i),$$

where $i, j \in S$ and $(x_u)_{0 \le u < s} \subset S$ is a right-continuous path. This latter result follows from a standard result of measure theory (e.g., (**Norris, 1998**, Section 6.6)), which says that the probability of any event depending on a right-continuous process is determined by the finite-dimensional distributions of the process (see Chapter 5).

DEFINITION 4.2. A continuous-time Markov chain is *time-homogeneous* if the conditional probability does not depend on the current time, so that:

$$(4.3) \qquad P(X_{s+t} = j | X_s = i) = P(X_t = j | X_0 = i), \qquad s \ge 0.$$

We will consider only time-homogeneous processes in this lecture.

There is no exact analogue of the transition matrix P, since there is no natural unit of time. Therefore we consider the transition probabilities as a function of time.

DEFINITION 4.3. The *transition probability* for a time-homogeneous chain is

$$(4.4) \qquad P_{ij}(t) = P(X_{s+t} = j | X_s = i), \qquad s, t \ge 0.$$

Write $P(t) = (P_{ij}(t))_{i,j \in S}$ for the matrix of transition probabilities at time t. Clearly, $P(t)$ is a stochastic matrix.

REMARK 4.4. For a time-inhomogeneous chain, the transition probability would be a function of two times, as $P_{ij}(s, t) = P(X_t = j | X_s = i)$.

A fundamental relationship from which most other relationships can be derived is the Chapman–Kolmogorov equations.

THEOREM 4.5 (Chapman–Kolmogorov equations, time-homogeneous).

$$(4.5) \qquad P(t + s) = P(t)P(s) \quad \Longleftrightarrow \quad P_{ij}(t + s) = \sum_{k \in S} P_{ik}(t) P_{kj}(s).$$

PROOF.

$$
\begin{aligned}
P_{ij}(s + t) &= P(X_{s+t} = j | X_0 = i) \\
&= \sum_{k \in S} P(X_{s+t} = j | X_t = k, X_0 = i) P(X_t = k | X_0 = i) && \text{(LOTP)} \\
&= \sum_{k \in S} P(X_{s+t} = j | X_t = k) P(X_t = k | X_0 = i) && \text{(Markov property)} \\
&= \sum_{k \in S} P_{ik}(t) P_{kj}(s) && \text{(time-homogeneity).}
\end{aligned}
$$

□

The transition probabilities characterize the evolution of probability for a continuous-time Markov chain, but they give too much information. We do not need to know $P(t)$ for all times t to understand the dynamics of the chain. Rather, we will consider two equivalent ways of characterizing the dynamics of a ctMC:

(i) Through the *generator Q*, which gives its infinitesimal transition rates.

(ii) By the times at which the chain jumps and the states that it jumps to.

For the rest of the chapter we will assume that $|S| = N < \infty$; without loss of generality we let $S = \{1, 2, \dots, N\}$. Most of the results we derive will also be true when $|S| = \infty$ under certain additional, not-very-restrictive assumptions, but they are much harder to prove; see (**Norris, 1998**) for a rigorous discussion that includes the case $|S| = \infty$.

4.2. Infinitesimal generator

A fundamental characterization of a ctMC is by its generator. To define the generator, let us make the following assumption:

$$P(t) \text{ is right-differentiable at } t = 0.$$

This assumption will be true in applications and it makes the subsequent theory much easier to derive.[2] It implies (from the Chapman–Kolmogorov equations) that $P(t)$ is differentiable for all $t > 0$.

Exercise 4.1. Show that if $P(t)$ is right-differentiable at $t = 0$ and if it is continuous for $t > 0$, then it is differentiable for $t > 0$.

DEFINITION 4.6. Let $X = (X_t)_{t \geq 0}$ be a ctMC with transition probabilities $P(t)$. The *generator* or *infinitesimal generator* of the Markov chain is the matrix

$$(4.6) \qquad Q = \lim_{h \to 0^+} \frac{P(h) - I}{h}.$$

Write its entries as $q_{ij} = Q_{ij}$.

In virtually all applications, one is given the *generator* (or one constructs it as a model) and not the set of transition probabilities. The generator is therefore the fundamental object of interest, while (4.6) is used to compute the transition probabilities from the generator, as we will see in Section 4.4.4.

Some properties of the generator that follow immediately from its definition are:

(i) Its rows sum to 0: $\sum_j q_{ij} = 0$.

(ii) $q_{ij} \geq 0$ for $i \neq j$.

(iii) $q_{ii} \leq 0$.

PROOF.

(i) $\sum_j P_{ij}(h) = 1$, since $P(h)$ is a transition matrix and $\sum_j I_{ij} = 1$. Pass to the limit using the finiteness of S to interchange limit and sum.

---

[2] The weaker assumption $P(t) \to I$ uniformly as $t \searrow 0$ is sufficient to derive the results in this section; see (**Grimmett and Stirzaker, 2001**, Section 6.10) or (**Norris, 1998**, Chapter 2). If $P(t)$ is merely continuous at 0, then it is possible that some diagonal elements of the generator, defined via the limit in (4.6), are $q_{ii} = -\infty$, meaning the process is immediately killed and removed from the system when it hits state i. See (**Grimmett and Stirzaker, 2001**, Section 6.10).

(ii) For $i \neq j$, $P_{ij}(h) \geq 0$, so this is true in the limit.

(iii) Follows from (i) and (ii), since $q_{ii} = -\sum_j q_{ij}$.   □

There is a more general way to define the generator, which generalizes to arbitrary Markov processes. We leave showing its equivalence to Definition 4.6 as an exercise.

Exercise **4.2.** Show that Definition 4.6 is equivalent to defining the generator as the matrix Q such that

$$(4.7) \qquad (Qf)_i = \lim_{h \to 0} \frac{\mathbb{E}^i f(X_h) - f(i)}{h}$$

for all functions $f : S \to \mathbb{R}$, where $\mathbb{E}^i$ means the expectation with initial condition $X_0 = i$, and where Qf is a vector with components $(Qf)_i = \sum_j Q_{ij} f(j)$.

(Hint: multiply (4.6) on the right by an arbitrary vector $\underline{f} \in \mathbb{R}^{|S|}$.)

If $|S| = \infty$, then most of what follows will be true under the assumption that $\sup_i |q_{ii}| < \infty$ (**Norris, 1998**, Theorem 2.7.1). This condition ensures the chain cannot blow up to ∞ in finite time. Therefore, we will consider examples with $|S| = \infty$, even though we will not prove that the theory still works.

REMARK 4.7. Another way to construct a ctMC is to take a matrix Q satisfying properties (i)–(iii) above and then assume the transition probabilities satisfy for all $i, j \in S$,

$$P(X_{t+h} = j | X_t = i) = \delta_{ij} + q_{ij}h + o(h)$$

as $h \downarrow 0$, uniformly in t, together with the Markov property. See (**Norris, 1998**, Theorem 2.8.2).

How should the entries of the generator be interpreted? Each entry q_{ij} with $i \neq j$ is the *rate* of jumping from i to j. The diagonal entries $-q_{ii}$ are the overall rates of leaving each state i. One way to see this is to consider the transition probabilities after a small amount of time h has elapsed:

$$(4.8) \qquad \begin{aligned} P_{ij}(h) &= q_{ij}h + o(h) & (j \neq i) \\ P_{ii}(h) &= 1 + q_{ii}h + o(h) & (j = i). \end{aligned}$$

Then q_{ij} gives the rate at which probability flow from state i to state j over a small time and $-q_{ii}$ is the rate at which probability leaves i.

Another interpretation comes from recalling that a rate measures the average number of events (event in the colloquial, not probabilistic, sense) per unit time. In our case an event is a transition from i to j. So, we could estimate the rate of transitioning from i to j by starting the chain in state i, letting it run for a small time h, checking whether or not the chain is in j, and repeating many times. The rate can be estimated as

$$\text{rate}(i \to j) \approx \frac{\# \text{ of times } X_h = j | X_0 = i}{(\# \text{ of experiments}) \cdot h} \approx \frac{P(X_h = j | X_0 = i)}{h} = q_{ij}.$$

Similar reasoning shows the overall rate of leaving is $-q_{ii} = \sum_j q_{ij}$ because the overall rate of leaving is the rate at which *any* transition happens, so it is the sum of the individual rates.

This argument ignores the possibility of transitioning more than once to j in the interval $(0, h]$. This probability is $o(h)$, as we will argue later in Lemma 4.18.

Here are some examples of ctMCs and their corresponding generators.

Example 4.8 (Two-state chain). A generic two-state ctMC has generator

$$Q = \begin{pmatrix} -\lambda & \lambda \\ \mu & -\mu \end{pmatrix},$$

where $\lambda, \mu \geq 0$ are parameters. For example, suppose you wish to model a ligand that can bind and unbind to a protein. You are told the rate of binding is 10 binding events per second and the rate of unbinding is 2 binding events per second. Your model for the ligand is a continuous-time Markov chain X_t on the state space $S = \{\text{unbound,bound}\}$ with generator, when t is measured in seconds,

$$Q = \begin{array}{c} \\ \text{unbound} \\ \text{bound} \end{array} \begin{array}{cc} \text{unbound} & \text{bound} \\ \begin{pmatrix} -10 & 10 \\ 2 & -2 \end{pmatrix} \end{array}.$$

Example 4.9 (Birth-death process). Consider a model for the population of black bears in the Catskills. Assume that bears are born at a rate of 30 bears per year and die at a rate of 25 bears per year. (If there are no more bears, we may still assume they are "born" with rate 25; for example, this could model immigration from another location.) Let X_t be the number of bears at time t, where time is measured in units of years. If X_t is a Markov process, then its generator is, writing $\lambda = 30, \mu = 25$,

$$Q = \begin{array}{c} 0 \\ 1 \\ 2 \\ 3 \\ \vdots \end{array} \begin{array}{ccccc} 0 & 1 & 2 & 3 & \\ \begin{pmatrix} -\lambda & \lambda & 0 & 0 & \cdots \\ \mu & -(\lambda + \mu) & \lambda & 0 & \cdot \\ 0 & \mu & -(\lambda + \mu) & \lambda & \cdots \\ 0 & 0 & \mu & -(\lambda + \mu) & \cdots \\ \vdots & \vdots & \vdots & \vdots & \ddots \end{pmatrix} \end{array}.$$

The generator above is an example of a *birth-death process* with birth rate λ and death rate μ. For a general birth-death process, the birth and death rates can be state-dependent, so that transitions from $i \to i + 1$ occur with rate λ_i, and transitions from $i \to i-1$ occur with rate μ_i. Such a process is used to model a wide variety of situations, such as people arriving at and leaving from a lineup, search requests arriving at and being processed from a Google server, emails arriving in and being deleted from an inbox, the number of individuals infected with and recovering from a given virus, etc.

Example 4.10 (Poisson process). A *Poisson process with rate λ* (see Figure 4.1) is a continuous-time Markov chain $N = (N_t)_{t \geq 0}$ on $S = \{0, 1, 2, \ldots\}$ with initial condition $N_0 = 0$ and generator

$$Q = \begin{pmatrix} -\lambda & \lambda & 0 & 0 & \cdots \\ 0 & -\lambda & \lambda & 0 & \cdots \\ 0 & 0 & -\lambda & \lambda & \cdots \\ \vdots & \vdots & \vdots & \vdots & \vdots \end{pmatrix}.$$

The Poisson process is often used to count the number of events that have happened at time t if the events occur completely independently of each other with rate λ.

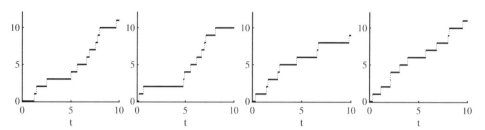

FIGURE 4.1. Realizations of the Poisson process with rate $\lambda = 1$, over 10 time units.

For example, it could count the number of buses that pass a bus stop in a certain time t if the drivers have absolutely no idea where the other drivers are, and are so delayed by bad traffic that their arrival times are random and independent. Other examples include the number of radioactive atoms that have decayed, the number of telephone calls that arrive at a call center, the number of search requests received by Google's servers, or the number of large waves that arrive at an oil platform.

REMARK 4.11. Another definition of the Poisson process, which is sometimes more useful in practical calculations and does not require the theory of continuous-time Markov chains, is as a process $N = (N_t)_{t \geq 0}$ taking values in $S = \{0, 1, 2, \ldots\}$ such that
   (i) $N_0 = 0$;
   (ii) N_t has *stationary and independent increments*: for any $0 \leq t_1 < t_2 < \cdots < t_n$, the random variables
$$N_{t_2} - N_{t_1},\ N_{t_3} - N_{t_2},\ \ldots, N_{t_n} - N_{t_{n-1}}$$
   are independent, and for any $t \geq 0$, $s \geq 0$, the distribution of $N_{t+s} - N_t$ is independent of t;
   (iii) $N_t \sim \text{Poisson}(\lambda t)$.

4.3. Transition times and jumps

A continuous time Markov chain stays in one state for a certain amount of time, then jumps immediately to another state where it stays for another amount of time, etc. A natural way to characterize this process is by the times at which it jumps, and the probabilities of the states it jumps to. Such a characterization will also lead to a method to simulate exact realizations of the process.

DEFINITION 4.12. Let us define the following (see Figure 4.2 for an illustration):
   • The *jump time* J_m is the time of mth jump. It is defined recursively by
$$J_{m+1} = \inf\{t > J_m : X_t \neq X_{J_m}\}, \qquad J_0 = 0.$$
   • The *holding time* S_m is the length of time a ctMC stays in its state, before jumping for the mth time. It is calculated from the jump times as $S_m = J_m - J_{m-1}$, for $m = 1, 2, \ldots$.
   • The discrete-time process $(Y_n)_{n=0}^{\infty}$ given by $Y_n = X_{J_n}$ is called the *jump process, jump chain*, or *embedded chain*.

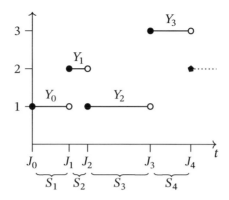

FIGURE 4.2. Example illustrating the jump times J_m, holding times S_m, and jump process Y_n. In this example, the jump process is $Y_0 = 1, Y_1 = 2, Y_2 = 1, Y_3 = 3, \ldots$.

We wish to determine the probability distributions of J_m and Y_m. First, we need a couple of technical results.

DEFINITION 4.13. A random variable T with values in $[0, \infty]$ is a *stopping time*[3] for a continuous-time process X, if, for each $t \in [0, \infty)$, the event $\{T \leq t\}$ depends only on $(X_s)_{0 \leq s \leq t}$.

THEOREM 4.14. *The jump time J_m is a stopping time of $(X_t)_{t \geq 0}$ for all m.*

For a proof, see (**Norris, 1998**, Lemma 6.5.2, p. 226).

THEOREM 4.15 (Strong Markov property). *Let $X = (X_t)_{t \geq 0}$ be a ctMC with generator Q and let T be a stopping time with $P(T < \infty) = 1$. Let $Y_t = X_{t+t}$. Then $(Y_t)_{t \geq 0}$ is a continuous-time Markov chain with generator Q, and initial distribution $Y_0 \sim X_T$. Furthermore $(X_{T+t})_{t \geq 0}$ is independent of $(X_t)_{0 \leq t < T}$.*

The strong Markov property says that if we consider X only beginning at a stopping time, the subsequent process has the same transition probabilities as the original process and is independent of previous values of the original process. In other words,

$$(4.9) \qquad P(X_{T+t} = j \mid X_T = i, \ X_s = x_s, \ 0 \leq s < T) = P(X_t = j \mid X_0 = i).$$

Proving this theorem (and even properly making sense of a stopping time in the continuous-time case) requires measure theory, so we will not do this. See (**Norris, 1998**, Theorem 6.5.4).

Let us use these results to compute the distributions of the jump times and jump chain. We start with the jump times. First, the strong Markov property implies that $S_1, S_2, S_3, \ldots$ is an independent sequence of random variables. Next, suppose we are in state i after the $(m-1)$th jump, and we wish to know the distribution of S_m, the time we wait until we jump again.

LEMMA 4.16. *Conditioned on $X_{J_{m-1}} = i$, the holding time S_m is an exponentially distributed random variable.*

---

[3]The rigorous definition is: T is a stopping time (with respect to a filtration $\mathcal{F} = (\mathcal{F}_t)_{t \geq 0}$) if $\{T \leq t\} \in \mathcal{F}_t$ for all $t \geq 0$.

REMARK 4.17. Recall that a random variable Y is exponentially distributed with parameter $\lambda > 0$ if it has probability density function $p(y) = \lambda e^{-\lambda y}$ for $y \geq 0$, or, equivalently, if $P(Y > y) = e^{-\lambda y}$. Exponential random variables have the "lack-of-memory" property: $P(Y > y + x | Y > y) = P(Y > x)$, and one can show they are the only continuous random variables with this property ((**Grimmett and Stirzaker, 2001**, pp. 140 & 259), (**Norris, 1998**, Theorem 2.3.1, p. 70)).

PROOF OF LEMMA 4.16. Our approach will be to show that S_m is memoryless. We also know that $S_m > 0$ with probability 1, since X_t is right-continuous; we also expect S_m to be a continuous random variable by the strong Markov property. Therefore, Remark 4.17 will imply that S_m has an exponential distribution.

Write the event $\{S_m > r\}$ as (recalling $X_{J_{m-1}} = i$),

$$\{S_m > r\} = \{X_{J_{m-1}+u} = i \text{ for all } 0 \leq u \leq r\}.$$

Therefore,

$$
\begin{aligned}
P(S_m > r + t \mid S_m > r, X_{J_{m-1}}=i) &= P(S_m > r + t \mid X_{J_{m-1}+u}=i, \ 0 \leq u \leq r) \\
&= P(S_m > r + t \mid X_{J_{m-1}+r}=i) \\
&= P(S_m > t \mid X_{J_{m-1}}=i).
\end{aligned}
$$

The first step follows because we are conditioning on the same event, the second from the strong Markov property, and the third from time-homogeneity. The final step shows that S_m is memoryless. Since S_m is continuous it must have an exponential distribution: $P(S_m > t \mid X_{J_{m-1}}=i) = e^{-\lambda_i t}$ for some parameter $0 \leq \lambda_i < \infty$. $\qquad \square$

Calculating the parameter λ_i is most easily done after showing that the probability of jumping two or more times in a small interval is sufficiently small.

LEMMA 4.18. *The probability that a continuous-time Markov chain jumps more than once in a time interval of length h is $o(h)$.*

PROOF. Lemma 4.16 showed that $P(S_i \leq h) \leq \lambda h + o(h)$, where λ is the maximum over all parameters λ_i (which we assume is $< \infty$). Since holding times are independent,

$$P(S_1 \mid S_2 \leq h) \leq P(S_1 \leq h, S_2 \leq h) - P(S_1 \leq h)P(S_2 \leq h) = o(h) \qquad \square$$

THEOREM 4.19. *Suppose $X_{J_{m-1}} = i$. The holding time S_m is an exponentially distributed random variable with parameter $-q_{ii}$.*

We remark that it is possible for the parameter in the exponential distribution to be $\lambda_i = -q_{ii} = 0$ when the state i is absorbing, but otherwise $\lambda_i = -q_{ii} > 0$.

PROOF. Lemma 4.16 showed the distribution is exponential, so the cdf is $P(S_m \leq t | X_{J_{m-1}}=i) = 1 - e^{-\lambda_i t}$. It remains to calculate the parameter λ_i, which may be obtained as

$$\lambda_i = -\frac{d}{dt}\Big|_{t=0} P(S_m > t \mid X_{J_{m-1}}=i) = \lim_{h \to 0} \frac{1 - P(S_m > h | X_{J_{m-1}}=i)}{h}.$$

Lemma 4.18 implies that

$$P(S_m > h | X_{J_{m-1}}=i) = P(X_h=i | X_0=i) + o(h),$$

where the $o(h)$ term represents the possibility that there were two or more jumps in the interval $(0, h]$ such that the process returns to i. Therefore,

$$\lambda_i = \lim_{h \to 0} \frac{1 - P(X_h=i|X_0=i) + o(h)}{h} = \lim_{h \to 0} \frac{-q_{ii}h + o(h)}{h} = -q_{ii}. \qquad \square$$

REMARK 4.20. The same proof can be straightforwardly adapted to show that, if $X_s = i$ for some *deterministic* time s, then the waiting time until the next jump is exponential with parameter $-q_{ii}$. Just replace J_{m-1} with s in the proofs above and use the regular Markov property. In words, because the exponential distribution is memoryless, the waiting time distribution does not depend on the time at which we start counting.

Now we consider the jump process $Y_0, Y_1, \ldots$. By the strong Markov property and the fact that J_m is a stopping time, this process is a discrete-time Markov chain. It is time-homogeneous because X is time-homogeneous. Therefore, we can characterize the jump chain by its transition matrix, which we will call $\tilde{P}$, and which has elements

(4.10) $$\tilde{P}_{ij} = P(Y_m = j|Y_{m-1} = i) = P(X_{J_m} = j \mid X_{J_{m-1}} = i).$$

By definition, the diagonal elements are $\tilde{P}_{ii} = 0$ if $q_{ii} \neq 0$, and $\tilde{P}_{ii} = 1$ if $q_{ii} = 0$.

THEOREM 4.21. *The transition matrix of the embedded chain has elements $\tilde{P}_{ij} = -q_{ij}/q_{ii}$ for $i \neq j$. Furthermore, Y_m is independent of S_m.*

Here is a sketch, in words, of the proof that follows. Suppose that $X_{J_{m-1}} = i$ and that $t < S_m \leq t+h$, and suppose that h is small enough that the chain jumps only once in $(t, t+h]$. Then

$$P(\text{it jumps to } j | \text{it first jumps in } (t, t+h], X_{J_{m-1}}=i)$$
$$= P(\text{it jumps to } j | \text{it first jumps in } (t, t+h], X_t=i)$$
$$= \frac{P(\text{it jumps to } j \cap \text{it first jumps in } (t, t+h]|X_t=i)}{P(\text{it first jumps in } (t, t+h]|X_t=i)}$$
$$\approx \frac{P(X_{t+h} = j|X_t=i)}{1 - P_{ii}(h)} \approx \frac{P_{ij}(h)}{1 - pP_{ii}(h)} \to -\frac{q_{ij}}{q_{ii}} \quad \text{as} \quad h \searrow 0.$$

Since this probability does not depend on time, Y_m, S_m are independent, and therefore this also gives the probability distribution of Y_m.

PROOF. To show this statement in more detail we need to condition on each possible value of S_m and work out the embedded chain's transition probability using known behavior of $P(t)$. Additionally, we must show that this transition probability does not depend on the value of S_m. However, a conditional probability such as $P(Y_m = j|Y_{m-1}=i, S_m=t)$ does not make sense, since we cannot condition on an event of measure zero, so instead we condition on the jump occurring in a small interval $(t, t+h]$, and then let $h \to 0$.

That is, let us define

$$\tilde{P}_{ij}^t = \lim_{h \to 0+} P(X_{J_{m-1}+t+h}=j|X_{J_{m-1}}=i, t < S_m \leq t+h)$$

to be the probability that the next state is j, given the holding time is $S_m = t$. By the strong Markov property and the definition of S_m, we may shift the time argument of

$X_{J_{m-1}}$ to write this as

$$\tilde{P}^t_{ij} = \lim_{h \to 0+} P(X_{J_{m-1}+t+h}{=}j|X_{J_{m-1}+t}{=}i, t < S_m \le t + h).$$

Now we want to shift time by J_{m-1}. To handle S_m, we define $U = \inf\{s > t : X_s \ne i\}$ to be the first time after time t that the process is not in state i, and calculate, by time-homogeneity and then by the definition of conditional probability,

$$\tilde{P}^t_{ij} = \lim_{h \to 0+} P(X_{t+h}{=}j|X_t{=}i, t < U \le t + h) = \lim_{h \to 0+} \frac{P(X_{t+h}{=}j, t < U \le t + h|X_t{=}i)}{P(t < U \le t + h|X_t{=}i)}.$$

Now we use two facts:

- $P(X_{t+h}{=}j, t < U \le t + h|X_t{=}i) = P(X_{t+h}{=}j|X_t{=}i)$; and
- $P(t < U \le t + h|X_t{=}i) = -q_{ii}h + o(h)$, since $U \sim \mathrm{Exp}(-q_{ii})$.

Putting these together with the known expansion of $P(h)$ near zero gives

$$\tilde{P}^t_{ij} = \lim_{h \to 0+} \frac{q_{ij}h + o(h)}{-q_{ii}h + o(h)} = -\frac{q_{ij}}{q_{ii}}.$$

Since $\tilde{P}^t_{ij}$ is independent of t, we obtain that Y_m, S_m are independent, and that $\tilde{P}_{ij} = \tilde{P}^t_{ij} = -q_{ij}/q_{ii}$. $\qquad\square$

Putting these results together shows that if we are given Q, we can calculate the holding time distributions and $\tilde{P}$, and, conversely, if we are given the holding time distributions and $\tilde{P}$, we can recover Q.

Example 4.22. Consider the birth-death chain from Example 4.9. The transition probabilities for the embedded chain are

$$\tilde{P} = \begin{array}{c} \\ 0 \\ 1 \\ 2 \\ 3 \\ \vdots \end{array} \begin{array}{c} \quad 0 \quad\quad 1 \quad\quad 2 \quad\quad 3 \\ \left(\begin{array}{ccccc} 0 & 1 & 0 & 0 & \cdots \\ \frac{\mu}{\mu+\lambda} & 0 & \frac{\lambda}{\mu+\lambda} & 0 & \cdot \\ 0 & \frac{\mu}{\mu+\lambda} & 0 & \frac{\lambda}{\mu+\lambda} & \cdots \\ 0 & 0 & \frac{\mu}{\mu+\lambda} & 0 & \cdots \\ \vdots & \vdots & \vdots & \vdots & \ddots \end{array}\right). \end{array}$$

From the jump chain and holding time distributions we obtain a method to simulate exact realizations of X.

GILLESPIE ALGORITHM. Also known as the *stochastic simulation algorithm* (SSA), or the *kinetic Monte Carlo algorithm* (KMC). Suppose $X_t = i$. Update the process as follows.

- Generate a random variable τ from an exponential distribution with parameter $-q_{ii}$ (i.e., with mean $-1/q_{ii}$);
- Choose a state j to jump to from the probability distribution given by the ith row of $\tilde{P}$;
- Jump to j at time $t + \tau$, i.e., set $X_s = i$ for $t \le s < t + \tau$, and set $X_{t+\tau} = j$.
- Repeat, starting at state j at time $t + \tau$.

This algorithm is used to simulate a wide range of problems, such as crystal growth, evolution of genetic mutations, virus spreading in a population, molecular motors moving along a microtubule, RNA folding, chemical reactions with a small number of molecules such an in the interior of a cell, and many more.

4.4. Forward and backward equations

We defined the generator Q from the full set of time-dependent transition probabilities, $(P(t))_{t \geq 0}$. Can we recover these transition probabilities from Q? We can, and will show this by deriving an evolution equation for $P(t)$. Compute the derivative of $P(t)$ as

$$(4.11) \qquad \frac{d}{dt} P(t) = \lim_{h \to 0^+} \frac{P(t+h) - P(t)}{h}.$$

We can factor $P(t + h) = P(t)P(h)$ using the Chapman–Kolmogorov equations, then interchange the limit and the sum involved in the matrix multiplication, since $|S| < \infty$, to find

$$\frac{d}{dt} P(t) = \lim_{h \to 0^+} \frac{P(t)P(h) - P(t)I}{h} = P(t)\left(\lim_{h \to 0^+} \frac{P(h) - I}{h}\right) = P(t)Q.$$

This gives a system of ODEs to solve for $P(t)$, subject to the initial condition $P(0) = I$.

We may also consider the evolution of a probability distribution $\mu(t)$, which is a row vector with components

$$(4.12) \qquad \mu_i(t) = P(X_t = i).$$

Since $\mu(t) = \mu(0)P(t)$ and therefore $\mu'(t) = \mu(0)P'(t)$, we can multiply the above equation on the left by $\mu(0)$ to obtain an evolution equation for $\mu(t)$. We obtain two versions of the forward equation.

THEOREM 4.23 (Forward Kolmogorov equation). *Given a time-homogeneous ctMC with generator Q, the transition probabilities $P(t)$ evolve as*

$$(4.13) \qquad \frac{dP}{dt} = PQ, \qquad P(0) = I.$$

Given initial probability distribution $\mu^{(0)}$, the probability distribution $\mu(t)$ defined in (4.12) evolves as

$$(4.14) \qquad \frac{d\mu}{dt} = \mu Q, \qquad \mu(0) = \mu^{(0)}.$$

Now we look for the backward equation. Returning to (4.11), we can factor out $P(t)$ on the right instead to get

$$\frac{d}{dt} P(t) = \lim_{h \to 0^+} \frac{P(h)P(t) - IP(t)}{h} = \left(\lim_{h \to 0^+} \frac{P(h) - I}{h}\right)P(t) = QP(t).$$

From this equation we may consider expectations of functions of the Markov chain. Let $f : S \to \mathcal{R}$ be a function and let $u(t)$ be a column vector with components

$$(4.15) \qquad u_k(t) = \mathbb{E}^k f(X_t) = \mathbb{E}[f(X_t)|X_0 = k].$$

Write $\underline{f} = (f(1), f(2), \ldots, f(N))^T$ so that $u(0) = \underline{f}$. Then $u(t) = P(t)\underline{f}$, and $u'(t) = P'(t)\underline{f}$, so multiplying the equation above by $\underline{f}$ on the right gives an evolution equation for $u(t)$. We obtain two versions of the backward equation.

THEOREM 4.24 (Backward Kolmogorov equation). *Given a time-homogeneous ctMC with generator Q, the transition probabilities evolve as*

$$(4.16) \qquad \frac{dP}{dt} = QP, \qquad P(0) = I,$$

and the statistic $u(t)$ defined in (4.15) evolves as

$$(4.17) \qquad \frac{du}{dt} = Qu, \qquad u(0) = \underline{f}.$$

From the forward and backward equations we may make several observations. First, putting (4.13) and (4.16) together shows that

$$QP(t) = P(t)Q,$$

i.e., the transition probability commutes with the generator. We can also solve explicitly for $P(t)$ to obtain

$$P(t) = e^{Qt}P(0) = e^{Qt},$$

where $e^{Qt} \equiv \sum_{n=0}^{\infty} \frac{1}{n!}Q^n t^n$ for any square matrix Q.[4]

Example 4.25 (Poisson process). Let us calculate the probability distribution of the Poisson process as a function of time. Let $\mu_j(t) = P(N_t = j)$, $j = 0, 1, 2, \ldots$. We solve for $\mu_j(t)$ using the forward Kolmogorov equations (4.14), recalling that $\mu(0) = (1, 0, \ldots)$. When $j = 0$ we have

$$\frac{d\mu_0}{dt} = -\lambda\mu_0, \qquad \mu_0(0) = 1.$$

The solution is $\mu_0(t) = e^{-\lambda t}$. The next equation is

$$\frac{d\mu_1}{dt} = \lambda\mu_0 - \lambda\mu_1, \qquad \mu_1(0) = 0.$$

Substituting for $\mu_0(t)$ and solving gives $\mu_1(t) = \lambda t e^{-\lambda t}$. In general, we have

$$\frac{d\mu_j}{dt} = -\lambda\mu_j + \lambda\mu_{j-1}, \qquad \mu_j(0) = 0 \quad (j > 0).$$

We can solve these by induction to find that

$$\mu_j(t) = \frac{\lambda^j t^j}{j!}e^{-\lambda t}.$$

Therefore, at fixed time t, N_t is a Poisson random variable with parameter λt.

4.5. Long-time behavior

The long-time behavior of a continuous-time Markov chain is similar to the discrete case.

DEFINITION 4.26. A probability distribution λ is a *limiting distribution* of a continuous-time Markov chain if, for all i, j, $\lim_{t\to\infty} P_{ij}(t) = \lambda_j$.

DEFINITION 4.27. A probability distribution π is a *stationary distribution* of a continuous-time Markov chain if

$$(4.18) \qquad \pi = \pi P(t) \qquad \text{for } t \geq 0.$$

---

[4]That this power series converges for an $N \times N$ generator Q is shown in (**Norris, 1998**, Section 2.10).

As in the discrete-time case, a *stationary distribution* is a probability distribution such that if the Markov chain starts with this distribution, then the distribution never changes. Also as in discrete time, a limiting distribution is a stationary distribution, but the converse is not true in general.

We can find a stationary distribution directly from the generator.

THEOREM 4.28. *A probability distribution π is a stationary distribution for a Markov chain with generator Q, if and only if*

(4.19)
$$\pi Q = 0.$$

Therefore, π is a left eigenvector of Q corresponding to eigenvalue 0, so we can find it by linear algebra.

PROOF. Take d/dt of (4.18) to get $\pi P'(t) = 0$. From the forward equation (4.13), this implies $\pi P(t)Q = 0$. But $\pi P(t) = \pi$, so the result follows. □

There is a formal link to the formula for a stationary distribution of a discrete-time Markov chain. Recall that if Y_n is a discrete-time Markov chain with transition matrix $\bar{P}$, then the stationary distribution solves $\pi(\bar{P} - I) = 0$. But $(\bar{P} - I)$ is like a forward-difference approximation to $\frac{dP}{dt}\big|_{t=0}$ using a time step $\Delta t = 1$.

Detailed balance is also similar to the discrete-time case.

DEFINITION 4.29. A ctMC with generator Q and stationary distribution π satisfies *detailed balance with respect to π* if it satisfies the *detailed balance equations*

(4.20)
$$\pi_i q_{ij} = \pi_j q_{ji}.$$

***Exercise* 4.3.** Show that if a ctMC satisfies detailed balance with respect to a probability distribution π, then π is a stationary distribution. Furthermore, show that Q is similar to a symmetric matrix, hence, argue it is diagonalizable with real eigenvalues.

When will a stationary distribution be a limiting distribution? Recall the following definition, which is only slightly modified from the discrete-time case.

DEFINITION 4.30. A continuous-time Markov chain is *irreducible* if, for all i, j, there exists $t > 0$ s.t. $P_{ij}(t) > 0$.

THEOREM 4.31. *The following are equivalent: for all $i, j \in S$,*

(i) $P_{ij}(t) > 0$ *for some $t > 0$ (the chain is irreducible);*
(ii) $P_{ij}(t) > 0$ *for all $t > 0$;*
(iii) *There exists a $n > 0$ s.t. $(\bar{P}^n)_{ij} > 0$ (the embedded chain is irreducible).*

This theorem implies there is no notion of periodicity for a continuous-time chain: if it can travel from i to j in some time t, it can travel from i to j in any time t.

In words, the reason this is true is as follows: if $P_{ij}(t) > 0$ for some t, then there exists a path in state space from $i \to j$, so the embedded chain is irreducible. Furthermore, there is a positive probability density of performing each step of the path in any positive time, and therefore there is a positive probability density of traveling from i to j in any amount of time s.

PROOF ((**Norris, 1998**), THEOREM 3.2.1, P. 111). Clearly (ii)$\Rightarrow$(i). For (i)$\Rightarrow$(iii), notice that if a ctMC is irreducible, then for each i, j there are states $i_0, i_1, \ldots i_n$ with $i_0 = i$, $i_n = j$, and $\tilde{P}_{i_0 i_1} \tilde{P}_{i_1 i_2} \ldots \tilde{P}_{i_{n-1} i_n} > 0$, where $\tilde{P}$ is the transition matrix for the embedded chain. For (iii)$\Rightarrow$(ii), further observe that $\tilde{P}_{i_0 i_1} \tilde{P}_{i_1 i_2} \ldots \tilde{P}_{i_{n-1} i_n} > 0$ implies $q_{i_0 i_1} q_{i_1 i_2} \ldots q_{i_{n-1} i_n} > 0$. If $q_{i' j'} > 0$ then (writing $\lambda_i = -q_{ii}$)

$$\begin{aligned}
P_{i' j'}(t) &= P(J_1 \leq t, Y_1 = j', J_2 > t) \\
&\geq P(J_1 \leq t, Y_1 = j', S_2 > t) \\
&= (1 - e^{-\lambda_{i'} t}) \tilde{P}_{i' j'} e^{-\lambda_{i'} t} > 0
\end{aligned}$$

for all t. Therefore, since one way to travel from i to j in some time t is by jumping at intervals of t/n,

$$P_{ij}(t) \geq P_{i_0 i_1}(t/n) \ldots P_{i_{n-1} i_n}(t/n) > 0$$

for all $t > 0$. □

THEOREM 4.32. *Let X be an irreducible continuous-time Markov chain with transition function $P(t)$ which is continuous at $t = 0$. Then*

(a) *if there exists a stationary distribution π then it is unique and it is a limiting distribution: $P_{ij}(t) \to \pi_j$ as $t \to \infty$, for all i and j;*
(b) *if there is no stationary distribution then $P_{ij}(t) \to 0$ as $t \to \infty$, for all i and j.*

This theorem holds when $|S| = \infty$ with no other conditions. For a sketch of a proof, see (**Grimmett and Stirzaker, 2001**, Theorem (21), Section 6.9, p. 261). Clearly, condition (b) can only hold if $|S| = \infty$, leading to a corollary when $|S| < \infty$.

COROLLARY 4.33. *A finite irreducible continuous-time Markov chain has a unique stationary distribution, and it is the limiting distribution.*

Example 4.34. A Poisson process is an example of a ctMC with no stationary distribution. It is not even irreducible, since the process can only increase.

4.6. Mean first-passage time

Recall that given a set $A \subset S$, the first-passage time to A is the random variable T_A defined by

$$T_A = \inf\{t \geq 0 : X_t \in A\},$$

The mean first-passage time (mfpt) to A, starting at $i \in S$, is $\tau_i = \mathbb{E}[T_A | X_0 = i]$. We can solve for the mfpt by solving a system of linear equations.

THEOREM 4.35 (Mean first-passage time). *The mean first-passage time for a continuous-time Markov chain solves the system of equations*

(4.21)
$$\begin{cases} \tau_i = 0 & j \in A \\ 1 + \sum_j Q_{ij} \tau_j = 0 & i \notin A. \end{cases}$$

System (4.21) is sometimes written (heuristically) as

$$Q' \tau = -1, \qquad \tau(A) = 0$$

where Q' is the matrix formed from Q by removing the rows and columns corresponding to states in A. Therefore the mfpt solves the nonhomogeneous backward equation with a Dirichlet boundary condition.

REMARK 4.36. Recall that for the discrete-time case, we had $(\bar{P} - I)\tau = -1$, $\tau(A) = 0$. Again, $(\bar{P} - I)$ is like a forward-difference approximation to $\frac{d\bar{P}}{dt}|_t = 0$ using a time step of $\Delta t = 1$.

The proof is slightly less straightforward than in the discrete case, since we need to account for the time spent in each state, not just where it transitions to next. It will use the notation of *conditional expectation*. Given two random variables A, B, we define the conditional expectation by

$$\mathbb{E}[A|B = b] = \begin{cases} \sum_a aP(A = a|B = b) & \text{if } A, B \text{ are discrete,} \\ \int_a aP(A = a|B = b)da & \text{if } A \text{ is continuous, } B \text{ is discrete.} \end{cases}$$

PROOF. Clearly, $\tau_i = 0$ for $i \in A$. Suppose $X_0 = i \notin A$. Recall that J_1 is the time of the next jump, and Y_1 is the state it next jumps to. We calculate the mfpt by conditioning on the first jump and then shifting by the time of the first jump, as

$$\tau_i = \mathbb{E}[T_A|X_0=i] = \mathbb{E}[J_1|X_0=i] + \mathbb{E}[T_A - J_1|X_0=i]$$
$$= \mathbb{E}[J_1|X_0=i] + \sum_{j \neq i} \mathbb{E}[T_A - J_1|Y_1=j, X_0=i]P(Y_1=j|X_0=i).$$

Now, we will use three short calculations:
- $\mathbb{E}[T_A - J_1|Y_1=j, X_0=i] = \mathbb{E}[T_A|X_0=j]$, by the strong Markov property (Theorem 4.15).
- $P(Y_1=j|X_0=i) = \tilde{P}_{ij} = \frac{q_{ij}}{-q_{ii}}$.
- $\mathbb{E}[J_1|X_0=i] = -1/q_{ii}$, since this is the mean of an exponential random variable with parameter $-q_{ii}$.

Substituting these calculations gives

$$\tau_i = \frac{1}{-q_{ii}} + \sum_{j \neq i} \tau_j \frac{q_{ij}}{-q_{ii}}.$$

Rearranging gives the desired equations.   □

4.7. Additional exercises

Exercise 4.4. Let X be a continuous-time Markov chain that hops between two states $\{1, 2\}$ with rates $\lambda, \mu > 0$, so its generator is

$$Q = \begin{pmatrix} -\mu & \mu \\ \lambda & -\lambda \end{pmatrix}.$$

(i) Calculate the transition probability matrix $P(t)$ at every time t.
(ii) Solve $\pi Q = 0$ for the stationary distribution and verify that $P_{ij}(t) \to \pi_j$ as $t \to \infty$.
(iii) Compute $\mathbb{E}[X^2(t)|X(0) = 1]$, $\mathbb{E}[X^2(t)|X(0) = 2]$. Show that these both approach the same quantity as $t \to \infty$ and explain where this quantity comes from.
(iv) Calculate the mean first-passage times to each state, starting from the other state.

Exercise 4.5. Show that not every discrete-time Markov chain can be embedded in a continuous-time chain. Let

$$P_1 = \begin{pmatrix} \alpha & 1-\alpha \\ 1-\alpha & \alpha \end{pmatrix}$$

for $0 < \alpha < 1$ be the transition matrix for a discrete-time Markov chain. Show that there exists a ctMC with transition probabilities $P(t)$ such that $P(1) = P_1$ if and only if $\frac{1}{2} < \alpha < 1$.

Exercise 4.6. Customers arrive in the lineup at Trader Joe's with rate λ and they are served with rate μ. Let $X(t)$ be the number of customers in line at time t and suppose $X(0) = 0$. Write down the generator of this Markov chain. Show that a stationary distribution exists if and only if $\lambda < \mu$, and find it. Does the process satisfy detailed balance?

Exercise 4.7. Repeat the question above assuming there are $c > 1$ checkout counters open and each serves customers with rate μ.

Exercise 4.8. Let π be the stationary for a continuous-time Markov chain with generator Q and let $\tilde{\pi}$ be the stationary distribution for the embedded chain. Show that $\pi_i = \tilde{\pi}_i/|q_{ii}|$.

Exercise 4.9. Let $X = (X_t)_{t \geq 0}$ be a Poisson process.
  (i) Suppose X has exactly one jump in the interval $[0, t]$. Show that the time at which that jump occurs is uniformly distributed on $[0, t]$.
      (Hint: calculate the cumulative distribution function of J_1, given $X_t = 1$. You can use known properties of the increments of a Poisson process.)
  (ii) Suppose $X_t = n$. Show the jump times $J_1, \ldots, J_n$ have the same distribution as an ordered sample of size n from the uniform distribution on $[0, t]$, i.e., they have joint density $f(t_1, \ldots, t_n) = n! \, t^{-n} 1_{0 \leq t_1 \leq \cdots \leq t_n \leq t}$.

Exercise 4.10. Let $X = \{X(t) : t \geq 0\}$ be a Markov chain having stationary distribution π. Suppose we sample X at the times of a Poisson process; let N be a Poisson process with intensity λ, independent of X, and define $Y_n = X(T_n+)$, the value taken by X immediately after the time T_n of the nth arrival of N. It can be shown that $Y = \{Y_n : n \geq 0, \; n \in \mathbb{Z}\}$ is a discrete-time Markov chain.[5] Show that Y has the same stationary distribution as X.

This is sometimes called the *Pasta property* (Poisson Arrivals See Time Averages). It holds for many suitable ergodic stochastic processes, not just Markov chains.

Exercise 4.11. Suppose you have a continuous-time Markov chain X on state space S with generator Q, and let $A, B \subset S$ be disjoint subsets of S. Recall the *committor function* (Exercise 2.16) is $q_i = P(X$ hits B before $A|X_0 = i)$. Show that q solves the following

---

[5]This follows immediately from the strong Markov property. It can also be shown directly from the regular Markov property. You can show this if you wish.

linear system of equations:

$$q_i = \sum_{j \neq i} q_j \frac{Q_{ij}}{-Q_{ii}} \quad (i \notin A \cup B), \qquad q_i = 0 \ (i \in A), \quad q_i = 1 \ (i \in B).$$

Exercise 4.12 (*Computation required*). Emails arrive in your inbox at a rate of 1.5 emails per minute. If there are less than 5 emails, you read each one carefully and delete them at a rate of 1 email per minute. If there are 5 or more emails, you scan them quickly and delete them at a rate of 2 emails per minute.

Let X_t be the number of emails in your inbox after t minutes of the day have elapsed. Assume that X_t is a continuous-time Markov chain.

   (i) Write down the generator for X_t.
  (ii) Write a code to simulate realizations of X_t, using the kinetic Monte Carlo method. Use this code to estimate:
      (a) The average time it takes you to clear your inbox (have no emails in it), given you start the day with 10 emails.
      (b) The probability that you clear your inbox without ever reaching 20 emails in your inbox.
 (iii) Now solve for quantities (a), (b) above using linear algebra. (You can do this on a computer.) If you make any approximations, clearly state what they are. Compare your answers to the ones in part (ii).

CHAPTER 5

Gaussian Processes and Stationary Processes

We turn now to study stochastic processes that are not necessarily Markov processes. This chapter will introduce two classes of stochastic processes that are commonly used as models: Gaussian processes and stationary processes.

5.1. Setup

We turn to introducing two key ideas required to describe more general classes of stochastic processes: finite-dimensional distributions and covariance functions.

5.1.1. Finite dimensional distributions. Recall that for a stochastic process $X = (X_t)_{t \in T}$ and a finite number of times $(t_1, t_2, \ldots, t_k) \in T^k$, called a *time slice*, we may form a random vector $(X_{t_1}, X_{t_2}, \ldots X_{t_k})$. Let the joint distribution of its components be $P_{t_1, t_2, \ldots, t_k}$, so that for Borel sets $F_i \subset \mathbb{R}$,

$$P_{t_1, t_2, \ldots, t_k}(F_1 \times F_2 \times \cdots \times F_k) = P(X_{t_1} \in F_1, X_{t_2} \in F_2, \ldots X_{t_k} \in F_k).$$

DEFINITION 5.1. The *finite-dimensional distributions* (fdds) of a stochastic process $(X_t)_{t \in T}$ is the collection of distributions at all finite time slices,

$$\{P_{t_1, t_2, \ldots, t_k}\}_{k \in \mathbb{N}, (t_1, \ldots, t_k) \in T^k}.$$

Examples 5.2. Here are some examples of processes and their fdds.

(1) A sequence of i.i.d. random variables with probability measure P. The parameter set is $T = \mathbb{Z}^+$, and the fdds are $P_{t_1, \ldots, t_k}(F_1 \times \cdots \times F_k) = \prod_{i=1}^k P(F_i)$.

(2) Markov chains. Let X_t be a continuous-time Markov chain with generator Q and initial probability distribution μ_0, and let $0 = t_0 < t_1 < \cdots < t_k$. Then the fdds are

$$P(X_{t_0} \in F_0, X_{t_1} \in F_1, \ldots, X_{t_k} \in F_k)$$
$$= \sum_{i_0 \in F_0} \mu_0(i_0) \sum_{i_1 \in F_1} P_{i_0 i_1}(t_1 - t_0) \cdots \sum_{i_k \in F_k} P_{i_{k-1} i_k}(t_k - t_{k-1}).$$

(3) Poisson process. For any $0 \le t_1 \le \ldots \le t_k$, let $\eta_1, \eta_2, \ldots, \eta_k$ be independent Poisson random variables with rates $\lambda t_1, \lambda(t_2 - t_1), \ldots, \lambda(t_k - t_{k-1})$. Then $P_{t_1, \ldots, t_k}$ is the joint distribution of $(\eta_1, \eta_1 + \eta_2, \ldots, \eta_1 + \eta_2 + \cdots + \eta_k)$.

The set of finite-dimensional distributions characterizes the pointwise statistics of a process. Starting from a set of fdds, one can construct a corresponding stochastic process, provided the fdds satisfy some basic consistency criteria (that they are invariant under permutations, and that their marginal distributions are consistent). This result is known as the *Kolmogorov Extension Theorem* ((**Koralov and Sinai, 2007**, p. 174) or

(**Grimmett and Stirzaker, 2001**, Section 8.7, p. 372)); there is a nice construction of it given in (**Tao, October 2010**).

However, knowing only the fdds of a stochastic process does not let us ask many questions that we may be interested in, such as whether the process is continuous or differentiable or bounded, what is the first-passage time to a given set, what is the running maximum at time t, etc. To decide such questions we need the values of the process at an uncountable number of points.

Here is an example to illustrate some of the difficulties.

Example 5.3. Let $U \sim \text{Uniform}([0, 1])$ be a random variable. Define two processes $X = (X_t)_{0 \le t \le 1}$ and $Y = (Y_t)_{0 \le t \le 1}$ by

$$X_t = 0 \quad \text{for all } t, \qquad Y_t = \begin{cases} 1 & \text{if } U = t, \\ 0 & \text{otherwise.} \end{cases}$$

Then X and Y have the same fdds, since $P(U = t) = 0$ for all t. But X, Y are different processes. Some differences include: X is continuous whereas Y is not; $\sup_t X = 0$ whereas $\sup_t Y = 1$; $P(X_t=0 \text{ for all } t) = 1$ whereas $P(Y_t=0 \text{ for all } t) = 0$.

This example may seem trivial, but one can often construct less trivial examples of different processes with the same fdds. Such processes are called *versions* of each other. Any theory which studies properties of sample paths must take care to specify which version of a process is being studied. Typically one considers processes which are right-continuous and have limits from the left (so-called "càdlàg" processes, an abbreviation of the French phrase "continue à droite, limites à gauche.") Conditions under which which a stochastic process has a càdlàg version have been characterized ((**Grimmett and Stirzaker, 2001**, Theorem 8.7.6, p. 373); (**Breiman, 1992**, p. 300)). In this course we will always assume we are working with a càdlàg process.

At the same time, fdds also give us *more* information about a stochastic process than we often need—certainly more information than we are able to measure in practice. Therefore, we turn to other ways to characterize stochastic processes.

5.1.2. Covariance functions. The most widely used way to characterize properties of a stochastic process is by its mean and covariance function, which are related to be the one- and two-point fdds.

DEFINITION 5.4. The *mean* of a stochastic process is $m(t) = \mathbb{E}X_t$ for $t \in T$.

Recall that if we have a random vector $X = (X_1, \dots, X_n)^T$, its covariance matrix is

$$\Sigma = \text{Cov}(X, X) = \mathbb{E}XX^T - (\mathbb{E}X)(\mathbb{E}X)^T.$$

The i, jth element is the covariance of X_i, X_j, i.e., $\Sigma_{ij} = \text{Cov}(X_i, X_j) = \mathbb{E}X_iX_j - (\mathbb{E}X_i)(\mathbb{E}X_j)$. This concept generalizes to random functions.

DEFINITION 5.5. The *covariance function* of a real-valued stochastic process $(X_t)_{t \in T}$ is

(5.1) $\qquad B(s, t) \equiv \mathbb{E}\left[(X_s - \mathbb{E}X_s)(X_t - \mathbb{E}X_t)\right] = \mathbb{E}X_sX_t - m(s)m(t), \qquad s, t \in T.$

Notice that $B(t, t) = \mathbb{E}X_t^2 - (\mathbb{E}X_t)^2$ gives the variance of the process at a single point t.

One can show that a covariance *matrix* is positive semidefinite, i.e., $x^T \Sigma x \geq 0$ for all $x \in \mathbb{R}^n$.[1] A similar statement is true for covariance *functions*.

DEFINITION 5.6. A function $B(s,t)$ is *positive (semi)definite* if the matrix $(B(t_i, t_j))_{i,j=1}^k$ is positive (semi)definite for all finite time slices $\{t_i\}_{i=1}^k$.

LEMMA 5.7. *The covariance function $B(s,t)$ of a stochastic process is positive semi-definite.*

Exercise 5.1. Prove Lemma 5.7.

REMARK 5.8. An equivalent definition of positive semidefinite comes from defining an operator $\mathcal{K}$ on $L^2(\mathbb{R})$ by

$$(5.2) \qquad \mathcal{K}f = \int B(s,t)f(t)dt.$$

One can verify this operator is symmetric with respect to the L^2 inner product. Then B is positive semidefinite if the operator $\mathcal{K}$ is positive semidefinite with respect to the L^2 inner product—that is, if $\langle \mathcal{K}f, f \rangle = \int B(s,t)f(t)f(s)dtds \geq 0$ for all $f \in L^2(\mathbb{R})$.

Example 5.9. Let us calculate the covariance function of a Poisson process $(N_t)_{t \geq 0}$ with parameter λ. Recall (Examples 4.10 and 4.25) that $\mathbb{E}N_t = \lambda t$, $\mathrm{Var}(N_t) = \lambda t$, and $N_t - N_s$, N_s are independent when $t > s$. Therefore, for $t \geq s$,

$$\begin{aligned}
B(s,t) &= \mathbb{E}N_t N_s - (\mathbb{E}N_t)(\mathbb{E}N_s) \\
&= \mathbb{E}(N_t - N_s)N_s + \mathbb{E}N_s^2 - \lambda^2 ts \\
&= \lambda^2(t-s)s + \lambda s + \lambda^2 s^2 - \lambda^2 ts \\
&= \lambda s.
\end{aligned}$$

Repeating the calculation with $s > t$ gives that $B(s,t) = \lambda \min(s,t)$.

It will be useful later to work in complex space, so we also define these concepts for complex-valued processes.

DEFINITION 5.10. A *complex-valued stochastic process* is one whose real and imaginary parts are real-valued stochastic processes, i.e., it has the form $X_t = Y_t + iZ_t$ where $(Y_t)_{t \in T}$, $(Z_t)_{t \in T}$ are real-valued stochastic processes.

The mean of a complex-valued stochastic process is defined as before, $m(t) = \mathbb{E}X_t = \mathbb{E}Y_t + i\mathbb{E}Z_t$.

DEFINITION 5.11. The *covariance function* of a complex-valued stochastic process is

$$B(s,t) = \mathbb{E}[(X_s - \mathbb{E}X_s)\overline{(X_t - \mathbb{E}X_t)}] = \mathbb{E}X_s \overline{X_t} - (\mathbb{E}X_s)(\overline{\mathbb{E}X_t}).$$

You can check that the covariance function is Hermitian: $B(s,t) = \overline{B(t,s)}$. It is also positive semidefinite, where now we use the complex definition: B is positive semi-definite if $\sum_{i,j} B(t_i, t_j) z_i \overline{z_j} \geq 0$ for all finite time slices $\{t_i\}_{i=1}^k$ and all complex-valued vectors $z = (z_1, \ldots, z_k)^T$.

---

[1] Briefly, assuming $\mathbb{E}X = 0$: $v^T \Sigma v = \mathbb{E}v^T X X^T v = \mathbb{E}|X^T v|^2 \geq 0$.

5.2. Gaussian processes

Gaussian processes are used in a number of applications because they are easy to simulate and because their fdds can be completely characterized. They are a reasonable starting point for a model because the central limit theorem suggests that a superposition of uncorrelated processes should lead to Gaussian statistics.

DEFINITION 5.12. A random vector $X = (X_1, \dots, X_n)$ is a *multivariate Gaussian* if its probability density function has the form

$$(5.3) \qquad f(x_1, \dots, x_n) = \frac{1}{\sqrt{(2\pi)^n |\Sigma|}} e^{-\frac{1}{2}(x-\mu)^T \Sigma^{-1}(x-\mu)},$$

where $\mu \in \mathbb{R}^n$ and $\Sigma \in \mathbb{R}^{n \times n}$ is a positive definite symmetric matrix. Write $X \sim N(\mu, \Sigma)$.

Recall that $\mu = \mathbb{E}X$ and $\Sigma = \text{Cov}(X, X)$. A few other useful facts about multivariate Gaussians are listed in Appendix A.A.3.

DEFINITION 5.13. $X = (X_t)_{t \in T}$ is a *Gaussian process* if all its fdds are Gaussian, i.e., if $(X_{t_1}, \dots, X_{t_k})$ is a multivariate Gaussian for any $(t_1, \dots, t_k) \in T^k$.

To construct a Gaussian process we must provide two things: its mean $m(t)$, and its covariance function, a positive semidefinite function $B(s, t)$. These two objects completely determine the finite-dimensional distributions of the process, and by the Kolmogorov extension theorem, there exists a process with such fdds. This is a powerful statement, since means and covariances are readily measurable.

DEFINITION 5.14. A *Brownian motion* or *Wiener process* is a continuous Gaussian process $W = (W_t)_{t \geq 0}$ with mean $m(t) = 0$ and covariance $B(s, t) = \min(s, t)$ for $s, t \geq 0$, and such that $W_0 = 0$.

Some realizations of a Brownian motion are shown in Figure 6.1. We will see another definition of Brownian motion in Chapter 6.

Notice that a Brownian motion $W = (W_t)_{t \geq 0}$ has the same covariance function as a Poisson process with $\lambda = 1$. If we define a process $Y = (Y_t)_{t \geq 0}$ by $Y_t = N_t - t$, where N_t is a Poisson process with rate $\lambda = 1$, then Y, W both have mean $m(t) = 0$ and covariance function $B(s, t) = \min(s, t)$. However, these processes are clearly not the same; some differences from W include that Y is piecewise linear, does not have Gaussian fdds, and is not continuous.

Exercise 5.2. Show, from Definition 5.14, that the Wiener process has stationary independent increments. That is, show that
  (a) the distribution of $W_t - W_s$ depends only on $t - s$;
  (b) the variables $W_{t_j} - W_{s_j}$, $1 \leq j \leq n$ are independent whenever the intervals $(s_j, t_j]$ are disjoint.

ALGORITHM TO SIMULATE A GAUSSIAN PROCESS. Here is one algorithm to simulate a Gaussian process with mean $m(t)$ and positive definite covariance $B(s, t)$. Suppose we want to generate realizations evaluated at a discrete set of points $t_1, t_2, \dots, t_n$ to obtain a random vector $X = (X_{t_1}, \dots, X_{t_n})$.
  • Form the $n \times n$ covariance matrix $\Sigma = (B(t_i, t_j))_{i,j=1}^n$.

- Find a matrix A that is a square root of Σ: $\Sigma = AA^T$.

  For example, A could be the lower triangular matrix in the Cholesky decomposition of Σ, which exists because Σ is positive definite. Or we could construct it from the singular value decomposition $\Sigma = UDV^{-1}$ as $A = U\sqrt{D}V^{-1}$.
- Choose an i.i.d. sequence of random variables $\xi_i \sim N(0, 1)$ for $i = 1, \ldots, n$, and let $\xi = (\xi_1, \xi_2, \ldots, \xi_n)^T$. Let

$$X = A\xi + \vec{m}, \qquad \vec{m} = (m(t_1), \ldots, m(t_n))^T.$$

To show that X has the desired distribution, notice that X is a multivariate Gaussian, since it is a linear transformation of the multivariate Gaussian ξ. It remains to show that X has the correct mean and covariance matrix:

$$\mathbb{E}X = A\mathbb{E}\xi + \vec{m} = \vec{m}, \qquad \mathbb{E}(X - \vec{m})(X - \vec{m})^T = \mathbb{E}A\xi\xi^T A^T = AIA^T = \Sigma.$$

While this algorithm works in theory, it is not always numerically stable in practice, since the covariance matrix Σ can be ill-conditioned, so algorithms to compute its square root perform poorly. In Section 5.5.5 we will learn another method based on the spectral decomposition of the process that is numerically more stable.

5.3. Stationary processes

Another important class of processes are those for which the distribution is invariant with time. For example, one might assume this is the case for
- waves in the ocean,
- fluctuations in annual mean temperature (prior to 1800...),
- the bond angles in a polymer that is in thermodynamic equilibrium,
- a Markov chain that has been run for a long time,
- turbulent velocities in the atmosphere,
- the Earth's background magnetic field,

and many more systems. It would not be the case for a process that still retains memory of its initial condition, such as a protein shortly after we observe it in a particular configuration; or a process that can wander far away without bound, such as a random walk on an infinite lattice.

5.3.1. Strongly stationary and weakly stationary processes.

DEFINITION 5.15. A stochastic process is *strongly stationary* if the fdds are invariant with shifts in time, i.e.,

$$P_{t_1+h,t_2+h,\ldots,t_k+h} = P_{t_1,\ldots,t_k} \qquad \text{for all } h > 0,$$

for all $k \in \mathbb{N}$, $(t_1, \ldots, t_k) \in T^k$.

In words, the statistics of the process do not change with shifts of time.

While this is a natural definition of stationarity, it is usually too hard to work with in practice: it is impossible to verify empirically (how can one test an infinite collection of higher-order statistics?), and furthermore, it may be too strong in many cases when the information we are interested in depends only on the one-point and two-point statistics via the mean and covariance function. A weaker but more commonly used notion of stationarity comes from considering these statistics only.

Consider what happens to the mean and covariance function of a strongly stationary process when we shift the process in time.

- Mean: $\mathbb{E}X_t = \mathbb{E}X_{t+h}$, so $m(t) = m(t+h)$ for all h, so the mean must be constant.
- Covariance: $\mathbb{E}X_{s+h}\overline{X_{t+h}} = \mathbb{E}X_s\overline{X_t}$, so $B(s+h, t+h) = B(s, t)$ for all h. Therefore $B(s, t) = f(s - t)$ for some function f.

This motivates a weaker definition of stationarity.

DEFINITION 5.16. A stochastic process is *weakly stationary* if

$$m(t) = m(0), \qquad B(s, t) = C(s - t).$$

The function $C(t) = \mathbb{E}(X_{s+t} - m(0))\overline{(X_s - m(0))}$ is called the *covariance function* (this is a slight abuse of terminology).

The covariance function for a stationary process has a few nice properties. Without loss of generality, they are presented here for a process with $m(t) = 0$.

(i) $C(0) = \mathbb{E}|X_t|^2$ is the variance of the process.
(ii) $|C(t)| \leq C(0)$ for all $t \in \mathbb{R}$. To see why, calculate:

$$|C(t)| = \underbrace{|\mathbb{E}X_{t+s}\overline{X_s}| \leq (\mathbb{E}|X_{t+s}|^2\mathbb{E}|X_s|^2)^{1/2}}_{\text{Cauchy–Schwartz}} = C(0).$$

(iii) If C is real-valued, then $C(t) = C(-t)$; if C is complex-valued, then $C(t) = \overline{C(-t)}$. This follows by definition.
(iv) $C(t)$ is a *positive semidefinite function*: the matrix $(C(t_j - t_i))_{i,j=1}^k$ is positive semidefinite for all finite slices $\{t_i\}_{i=1}^k$. You can show this yourself as an exercise, or see (**Pavliotis, 2014**, p. 7).

REMARK 5.17. As for nonstationary processes, an equivalent definition of positive semidefiniteness comes from considering the operator $\mathcal{K}$ on $L^2(\mathbb{R})$ defined by $\mathcal{K}f = \int C(s - t)f(t)dt$ (recall (5.2)). Then C is positive semidefinite if $\mathcal{K}$ is positive semidefinite with respect to the L^2 inner product.

A weakly stationary process is *not* strongly stationary in general. However, if the process is Gaussian, then the two notions are equivalent.

LEMMA 5.18. *If $(X_t)_{t \geq 0}$ is Gaussian and it is weakly stationary, then it is strongly stationary.*

PROOF. This follows because the mean and covariance completely characterize the fdds of a Gaussian process. $\square$

Example 5.19 (Independent sequences). Let $X = X_0, X_1, \ldots$ be a sequence of i.i.d. random variables with mean 0 and variance σ^2. Then X is strongly stationary with covariance function $C(n) = \sigma^2$ if $n = 0$, $C(n) = 0$ otherwise.

Example 5.20 (Identical sequences). Let Y be a random variable with mean 0 and variance σ^2, and let $X = X_0, X_1, \ldots$ be defined by $X_n = Y$ for all n. Then X is strongly stationary and its covariance function is $C(n) = \sigma^2$ for all n.

Example 5.21 (Markov chains). Let X be a Markov chain (discrete or continuous) and let $X_0 \sim \pi$, where π is the stationary distribution. Then X is strongly stationary. (Exercise: check this by checking the fdds.) Let us calculate the covariance function of $f(X)$ for some function f, supposing X is a discrete-time chain with N states and assuming further that detailed balance holds, so we may assume a full set of real eigenvalues λ_k and right and left eigenvectors $\phi^{(k)}, \psi^{(k)}$ of the transition matrix.

$$
\begin{aligned}
C_f(t) &= \mathbb{E}f(X_0)f(X_t) - (\mathbb{E}f(X_0))^2 \\
&= \sum_{i,j=1}^{N} f(i)f(j)P(X_t = j | X_0 = i)P(X_0 = i) - \left(\sum_{i=1}^{N} f(i)\pi_i\right)^2 \\
&= \sum_{i,j=1}^{N} f(i)f(j)\left(\sum_k \lambda_k^t \phi_i^{(k)}\psi_j^{(k)}\right)\pi_i - \left(\sum_{i=1}^{N} f(i)\pi_i\right)^2 \\
&= \sum_{k=1}^{N} \lambda_k^t \left(\sum_{i=1}^{N} f(i)\phi_i^{(k)}\pi_i\right)^2 - \left(\sum_{i=1}^{N} f(i)\pi_i\right)^2
\end{aligned}
$$

since $\phi_j^{(k)} = \psi_j^{(k)}\pi_j$. Now, recall that $\lambda_1 = 1$ and $\phi^{(1)} = (1, \ldots, 1)^T$. Therefore, the last term above equals the first term in the sum, so we may relabel the sum to start at $k = 2$. Therefore, defining the weighted inner product $\langle f, g \rangle_\pi = \sum_{i=1}^{N} f(i)g(i)\pi_i$, we have

$$
C_f(t) = \sum_{k=2}^{N} \lambda_k^t \left(\sum_{i=1}^{N} f(i)\phi_i^{(k)}\pi_i\right)^2 = \sum_{k=2}^{N} e^{t\log\lambda_k}\langle f, \phi^{(k)}\rangle_\pi^2.
$$

If there is only one eigenvalue equal to 1, then the covariance function is composed of a sum of decaying exponentials. At long times, $C_f(t) \to 0$, and the long-time rate of decay is controlled by the logarithm of the second-largest eigenvalue. Since all terms above are real-valued, the covariance function can never drop below zero. This is a special property that arises when the Markov chain satisfies detailed balance; in general, a covariance function can oscillate about zero.

Example 5.22. Let A, B be uncorrelated (not necessarily independent), real-valued random variables with mean 0 and common variance σ^2. Let $\lambda \in [0, 2\pi]$ and define a process $X = (X_t)_{t\in\mathbb{R}}$ by

$$
(5.4) \qquad\qquad X_t = A\cos(\lambda t) + B\sin(\lambda t).
$$

Then $\mathbb{E}X_t = 0$ and X has covariance function

$$
\begin{aligned}
C(s, s+t) &= \mathbb{E}\left[(A\cos(\lambda s) + B\sin(\lambda s)))(A\cos(\lambda(s+t)) + B\sin(\lambda(s+t))\right] \\
&= \mathbb{E}\left[A^2\cos(\lambda s)\cos(\lambda(s+t)) + B^2\sin(\lambda s)\sin(\lambda(s+t))\right] \\
&= \sigma^2\cos(\lambda t).
\end{aligned}
$$

The mean is constant and the covariance function depends only on the separation t, so X is weakly stationary. In general, X is not strongly stationary unless there are extra conditions on the joint distribution of A, B (**Grimmett and Stirzaker, 2001**, p. 362).

Notice this process and its covariance function can also be written as

$$
X_t = \text{Re}\{(A - iB)e^{i\lambda t}\} = \frac{1}{2}((A - iB)e^{i\lambda t} + (A + iB)e^{-i\lambda t}), \qquad C(s, t) = \frac{\sigma^2}{2}(e^{i\lambda t} + e^{-i\lambda t}).
$$

This representation as a sum of complex exponentials is not an accident; we will use it in a simulation algorithm in Section 5.5.5.

***Exercise* 5.3.** Show that if $(X_t)_{t\in\mathbb{R}}$ is strongly stationary, and $Y_t = f(X_t)$, for some function f, then $(Y_t)_{t\in\mathbb{R}}$ is also strongly stationary. Can you make up an example to show the same statement does not hold in general if strongly stationary is replaced by weakly stationary?

5.3.2. Separation of variables for a weakly stationary process. Recall that Example 5.22 showed the process $X_t = \text{Re}\{(A - iB)e^{i\lambda t}\}$ is weakly stationary when A, B are uncorrelated. This suggests that stationary processes could have a representation as a sum of complex exponentials. Let us ask what such a representation must look like.

Example 5.23. Consider a process of the form

$$X_t = \xi h(t),$$

where $h(t)$ is a deterministic complex-valued function of time, and ξ is a complex-valued random variable. What conditions on $\xi, h(t)$ make X_t weakly stationary?

The mean is $m(t) = (\mathbb{E}\xi)h(t)$. This is only constant when either $h(t)$ is constant or $\mathbb{E}\xi = 0$. Let us suppose $h(t)$ is not constant, so $\mathbb{E}\xi = 0$.

The covariance function is $B(s, t) = (\mathbb{E}\xi\bar{\xi})h(s)\overline{h(t)}$. We need $h(s)\overline{h(t)} = f(s-t)$ for some function f. Setting $s = t$ shows we need $|h(t)|^2 = f(0) = cst$. Therefore $h(t)$ has the form

$$h(t) = Ae^{i\phi(t)}$$

for some real number $A \neq 0$ and some real-valued function $\phi(t)$. The covariance function is now

$$B(s + t, s) = \mathbb{E}X_{s+t}\overline{X_s} = A^2\mathbb{E}|\xi|^2 e^{i(\phi(s+t)-\phi(s))}.$$

To determine ϕ we require $\frac{dB(s+t,s)}{ds} = 0$ or, equivalently, $\frac{d\log B(s+t,s)}{ds} = 0$, which implies

$$\frac{d\phi(s)}{ds} = \frac{d\phi(s + t)}{ds}.$$

Since this holds for all t we must have $\phi'(s) = cst$, so $\phi(t) = \alpha t + \beta$ for some real-valued numbers α, β. Reorganizing constants and absorbing some into the definition of ξ shows that

$$X_t = \xi e^{i\lambda t},$$

where $\lambda \in \mathbb{R}$ and ξ is a complex-valued random variable with $\mathbb{E}\xi = 0$.

The example above can be seen as a form of separation of variables. A stochastic process depends on two variables, time t and the element ω in a probability space Ω. The representation above as $X(t, \omega) = \xi(\omega)h(t)$ is like a particular solution that one would look for using separation of variables. Therefore, if we want to generalize the example, we could consider a sum of functions that are separated in this way.

Example 5.24. Consider a sum of two exponentials, as

$$X_t = \xi_1 e^{i\lambda_1 t} + \xi_2 e^{i\lambda_2 t},$$

where ξ_1, ξ_2 are complex random variables, $\lambda_1 \neq \lambda_2$, and $\lambda_1, \lambda_2 \neq 0$. When is X_t weakly stationary? The mean is

$$\mathbb{E}X_t = \mathbb{E}\xi_1 e^{i\lambda_1 t} + \mathbb{E}\xi_2 e^{i\lambda_2 t},$$

which is independent of t only if $\mathbb{E}\xi_1 = \mathbb{E}\xi_2 = 0$, since the functions $e^{i\lambda_1 t}$, $e^{i\lambda_2 t}$ are linearly independent. The covariance is

$$B(s,t) = (\mathbb{E}|\xi_1|^2)e^{i\lambda_1(s-t)} + (\mathbb{E}|\xi_2|^2)e^{i\lambda_2(s-t)} + (\mathbb{E}\xi_1\overline{\xi_2})e^{i(\lambda_1 s - \lambda_2 t)} + (\mathbb{E}\overline{\xi_1}\xi_2)e^{i(\lambda_2 s - \lambda_1 t)}.$$

For this to be a function of only $s - t$, we require $\mathbb{E}\xi_1\overline{\xi_2} = 0$, so that each of ξ_1, ξ_2 are mean-zero, uncorrelated random variables. In this case the covariance function is

$$C(t) = b_1 e^{i\lambda_1 t} + b_2 e^{i\lambda_2 t}, \qquad b_j = \mathbb{E}|\xi_j|^2.$$

If we further ask that the covariance function be real-valued, then we need $\lambda_2 = -\lambda_1$, and $b_2 = \overline{b_1}$. We may construct such an example with real-valued random variables A, B as

$$\xi_1 = \overline{\xi_2} = A - iB \qquad \text{with} \quad \mathbb{E}A^2 = \mathbb{E}B^2, \quad \mathbb{E}AB = 0.$$

That is, the variance of the real and imaginary parts of ξ_1 are equal, and ξ_2 is the complex conjugate of ξ_1. In this case X_t and $C(t)$ can be expressed as

$$X_t = 2A\cos(\lambda t) + 2B\sin(\lambda t), \qquad C(t) = 4\mathbb{E}A^2\cos(\lambda t).$$

Exercise 5.4. Generalize Example 5.24: consider a process formed from a superposition of many frequencies, as

$$(5.5) \qquad X_t = \sum_{j=1}^{\infty} \xi_j e^{i\lambda_j t}.$$

Derive conditions on the ξ_j and the λ_j for $X = (X_t)_{t \in \mathbb{R}}$ to be a weakly stationary process. Derive further conditions to ensure that X is real-valued.

In Section 5.5.5 we will use the representation (5.5) to generate realizations of a stationary Gaussian process.

5.4. Spectral representation of a covariance function of a weakly stationary process

A powerful representation of a covariance function comes from looking at it in spectral space.

THEOREM 5.25 (Bochner's theorem). *A continuous function $C(t)$, $t \in \mathbb{R}$ is positive semidefinite if and only if there exists a nondecreasing, right continuous, bounded real function $F(\lambda)$, such that*

$$(5.6) \qquad C(t) = \int_{-\infty}^{\infty} e^{i\lambda t}\,dF(\lambda).$$

DEFINITION 5.26. The function $F(x)$ in Theorem 5.25 is called the *spectral distribution function*.

The integral in (5.6) is a Riemann–Stieltjes integral, which is a convenient way to express integrals and sums that share the same stochastic interpretation, using a single formula. The two most important special cases of the Riemann–Stieltjes integral are (5.8), (5.9), explained momentarily. In general, the Riemann–Stieltjes integral of a function f with respect to a function g over an interval $[a, b]$ is defined by

$$(5.7) \qquad \int_a^b f(x)dg(x) = \lim_{\max_i |x_{i+1}-x_i| \to 0} \sum_{i=0}^n f(x_i^*)[g(x_{i+1}) - g(x_i)],$$

where $a = x_0 < x_1 < \cdots < x_n = b$ is a partition of $[a, b]$, and $x_i^* \in [x_i, x_{i+1}]$. A sufficient condition for this limit to exist is that f be continuous and g be of bounded variation (**Rudin, 1976**).

REMARK 5.27. Theorem 5.25 was discovered independently by Khinchin slightly after its publication by Bochner, so it is sometimes called the *Bochner–Khinchin theorem*. It is usually stated for characteristic functions of a real-valued random variable X, defined by $\phi(t) = \mathbb{E}e^{itX} = \int e^{itx} dG(x)$, where $G(x)$ is the cumulative distribution function of X. We can arbitrarily choose $G(-\infty) = 0$, so the only difference between F above and a cdf G is that $F(\infty) = const$, while $G(\infty) = 1$.

REMARK 5.28. The link to random variables leads to another interpretation of (5.6), due to (**Grimmett and Stirzaker, 2001**, p. 382). If Λ is a random variable with cdf $F(\lambda)$, then $g_\Lambda(t) = e^{it\Lambda}$ is a pure oscillation with a random frequency, and $C(t) = \mathbb{E}g_\Lambda(t)$ is the average value of this pure oscillation (up to a normalizing constant).

We will provide a partial proof of Theorem 5.25 momentarily, but first we look at two special cases that encapsulate much of what we encounter in practice.

(1) $F(\lambda)$ is absolutely continuous with respect to the Lebesgue measure. Then there is a function $f(\lambda)$ such that

$$dF(\lambda) = f(\lambda)d\lambda \qquad \Leftrightarrow \qquad f(\lambda) = F'(\lambda) \quad \text{almost everywhere.}$$

The function $f(\lambda)$ is called the *spectral density function*. Since $F(\lambda)$ is non-decreasing, we must have $f(\lambda) \geq 0$. Then, Bochner's theorem says that a positive semidefinite function $C(t)$ has the representation

$$(5.8) \qquad C(t) = \int_{-\infty}^\infty f(\lambda)e^{i\lambda t}d\lambda, \qquad \text{so that} \quad f(\lambda) = \frac{1}{2\pi}\int_{-\infty}^\infty C(t)e^{-i\lambda t}dt.$$

That is, the Fourier transform[2] of $C(t)$ satisfies $f(\lambda) \geq 0$. This is an important result—*the Fourier transform of a covariance function* (when it exists) *is a nonnegative function*. Conversely, *given a nonnegative function, its inverse Fourier transform is a positive semidefinite function*, hence it can be the covariance function for a weakly stationary process.

The above representation will hold when $C \in L^1(\mathbb{R})$ (**Lindgren, 2013**, Theorem 3.4, p. 80).

(2) $F(x)$ is piecewise constant, with jumps of size $\{b_i\}_{i=1}^\infty$ at a countable set of points $\{\lambda_i\}_{i=1}^\infty$. Then

$$F(\lambda) = \sum_{j:\lambda_j \leq \lambda} b_j \qquad \Leftrightarrow \qquad F'(\lambda) = \sum_j b_j \delta(\lambda - \lambda_j).$$

---

[2]Note that this differs from the conventional definition of the Fourier transform, which puts the factor of 2π elsewhere. This is something to be aware of when comparing analytical calculations or when using built-in numerical algorithms to compute the Fourier transform.

Because $F(x)$ is nondecreasing, we must have $b_i > 0$. The covariance function has the form

(5.9)
$$C(t) = \sum_{j=1}^{\infty} b_j e^{i\lambda_j t}.$$

We obtain a representation of $C(t)$ that looks like a discrete inverse Fourier transform, although the frequencies λ_i are not restricted to be equally spaced. Thus, although $C \notin L^1(\mathbb{R})$ since $C(t)$ oscillates forever, and it may not be periodic over any interval, we still obtain a representation of $C(t)$ in spectral space.

PARTIAL PROOF OF BOCHNER'S THEOREM. For the "if" part, assume $C(t)$ has representation (5.6). We show it is positive semidefinite. Let $\{t_i\}_{i=1}^k$ be a finite time slice and let $\{z_i\}_{i=1}^k$ be a collection of complex numbers. We have

$$\sum_{j,k} z_j \overline{z_k} C(t_j - t_k) = \sum_{j,k} z_j \overline{z_k} \int_{-\infty}^{\infty} e^{i\lambda t_j} e^{-i\lambda t_k} dF(\lambda)$$

$$= \int_{-\infty}^{\infty} \sum_{j,k} z_j e^{i\lambda t_j} \overline{z_k e^{i\lambda t_k}} dF(\lambda)$$

$$= \int_{-\infty}^{\infty} \left| \sum_j z_j e^{i\lambda t_j} \right|^2 dF(\lambda) \geq 0.$$

The "only if" part is more work. See (**Lindgren, 2013**, pp. 75–78) or (**Grimmett and Stirzaker, 2001**, pp. 381 & 182) for a proof based on similar results for characteristic functions.   □

REMARK 5.29. The partial proof above shows why the Fourier transform of a positive semidefinite function must be nonnegative—if there are frequencies λ where $f(\lambda)$ is negative and hence $F(\lambda)$ decreases, then by considering a function z whose Fourier transform has support only near these frequencies, we obtain an inner product above that is negative.

The spectral distribution function tells us which frequencies are represented in the covariance function, and hence also in the process X_t.

DEFINITION 5.30. The *spectrum* of a process is the set of real numbers λ for which the spectral distribution function satisfies $F(\lambda + \epsilon) - F(\lambda - \epsilon) > 0$ for all $\epsilon > 0$.

For the two special cases we have:
  (1) If $F(\lambda)$ is absolutely continuous, then by (5.8) the spectrum is $\{\lambda : f(\lambda) > 0\}$, the support of the spectral density function $f(\lambda)$.
  (2) If $F(\lambda)$ is piecewise constant, then by (5.9) its spectrum is the set $\{\lambda_i\}_{i=1}^{\infty}$.

A process's spectrum could also have a mixture of discrete and continuous components. (It could also have "singular" components, which typically do not arise in applications).

Example 5.31. Consider a process with covariance function

$$C(t) = A e^{-\frac{t^2}{2\sigma^2}},$$

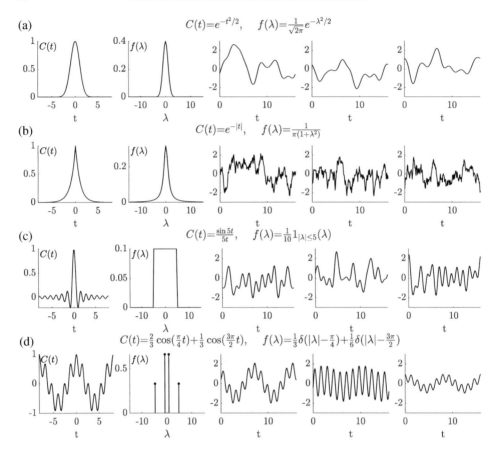

FIGURE 5.1. Examples of covariance functions, their spectral densities, and three independent realizations of stationary Gaussian processes with each corresponding covariance function.

with parameters $A, \sigma > 0$. Its Fourier transform is

$$f(\lambda) = \frac{A\sigma}{\sqrt{2\pi}} e^{-\frac{\lambda^2 \sigma^2}{2}}.$$

Since $f(\lambda) > 0$ for all λ, we know from Bochner's theorem that $C(t)$ must be positive definite. Furthermore, the spectrum of the process is $\{\lambda : \lambda \in \mathbb{R}\}$. Figure 5.1(a) shows realizations of this process.

Example 5.32. Consider a process with covariance function

$$C(t) = Ae^{-\alpha|t|},$$

with parameters $A, \alpha > 0$. Its Fourier transform is

$$f(\lambda) = \frac{1}{2\pi} \int_{-\infty}^{\infty} C(t)e^{-i\lambda t}dt = \frac{A}{\pi} \frac{\alpha}{\lambda^2 + \alpha^2}.$$

Again, the spectrum of the process is $\{\lambda : \lambda \in \mathbb{R}\}$. A Gaussian process with this co-variance function is called a *stationary Ornstein-Uhlenbeck process*. This is the only example of a stationary, Gaussian, Markov process, and it is used extremely frequently in modelling. Figure 5.1(b) shows realizations of this process; notice it is less smooth than the process in Example 5.31. The smoothness of the process is related to the smoothness of $C(t)$ at $t = 0$.

Example 5.33. Consider a process with spectral density function

$$f(\lambda) = \frac{1}{10} 1_{|\lambda| \leq 5}(\lambda).$$

The spectrum of the corresponding process is $\{\lambda : -5 < \lambda < 5\}$. Since $f(\lambda) \geq 0$, Bochner's Theorem tells us its inverse Fourier Transform is a covariance function:

$$C(t) = \int_{-\infty}^{\infty} f(\lambda) e^{i\lambda t} d\lambda = \frac{\sin 5t}{5t}.$$

Figure 5.1(c) shows realizations of this process. Notice that frequencies near the cutoff $\lambda = 5$ are visually apparent in both the covariance function and the realizations.

Example 5.34. Consider a process with

$$f(\lambda) = \frac{1}{3}\delta\left(\lambda - \frac{\pi}{4}\right) + \frac{1}{3}\delta\left(\lambda + \frac{\pi}{4}\right) + \frac{1}{6}\delta\left(\lambda - \frac{3\pi}{2}\right) + \frac{1}{6}\delta\left(\lambda + \frac{3\pi}{2}\right).$$

This process has a discrete spectrum, $\{\pm\frac{\pi}{4}, \pm\frac{3\pi}{2}\}$. The corresponding covariance function is

$$C(t) = \frac{2}{3}\cos\frac{\pi}{4}t + \frac{1}{3}\cos\frac{3\pi}{2}t.$$

Figure 5.1(d) shows realizations of this process.

Notice that all of these examples had a real-valued covariance function, $C(t) \in \mathbb{R}$, and hence the corresponding realizations were also real-valued. A necessary condition for a real-valued covariance function and hence a real-valued process, is that the spectral density be symmetric about zero, $f(\lambda) = f(-\lambda)$.

Example 5.35. Turbulent fluids are frequently characterized by their energy spectrum, which may be obtained as the Fourier transform of the covariance function of one component of the velocity field. Different conditions such as the aspect ratio of the fluid, the presence or absence of rotation, etc., are predicted to give rise to different universal forms for the energy spectrum. For example, Figure 5.2 (left) shows measurements of the streamwise (parallel to mean flow) velocity in a wind tunnel. The velocity qualitatively resembles a stochastic process. Computing the covariance function of this process over long times and taking the Fourier transform gives the energy spectrum $E(\lambda)$, shown in Figure 5.2 (right). The spectrum is close to a power law $E(\lambda) \propto \lambda^{-5/3}$ over several decades of frequencies λ, a form that has been observed to hold for a variety of turbulent systems at high Reynolds number and was given a theoretical explanation by Kolmogorov (**Frisch, 1995**, Chapter 5).

5.5. Simulating stationary Gaussian processes

Stationary processes have a representation in spectral space, which leads to an efficient, stable method to simulate realizations of them. Recall from Example 5.24 and its

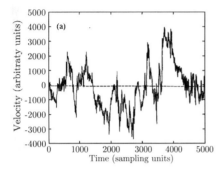 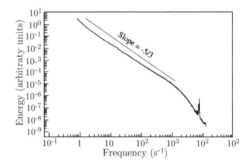

FIGURE 5.2. Left: measurements of the streamwise velocity in a wind tunnel over a period of 1 second with the mean flow subtracted. Measurements were obtained by a hot wire protruding into the tunnel. Right: energy spectrum computed from similar measurements in the wind tunnel, with Reynolds number 2720. (Graphs from Turbulence: The Legacy of A. N. Kolmogorov, Cambridge University Press, 1995. Reproduced with permission of the Licensor through PLSclear.)

generalization in Exercise 5.4 that given a collection of complex-valued random variables $\{\xi_i\}_{i=1}^\infty$ satisfying $\mathbb{E}\xi_i = 0$ and $\mathbb{E}\xi_i\overline{\xi_j} = 0$ for all $j \neq k$, we can construct a real or complex-valued stationary process $X = (X_t)_{t\in\mathbb{R}}$ and its covariance function $C(t)$ as

$$(5.10) \qquad X_t = \sum_{j=1}^\infty \xi_j e^{i\lambda_j t}, \qquad C(t) = \sum_{j=1}^\infty b(\lambda_j) e^{i\lambda_j t} \quad \text{where} \quad b(\lambda_j) = \mathbb{E}|\xi_j|^2.$$

In fact, Bochner's theorem for a process with a discrete spectrum—(5.9)—tells us there is no other way to represent the covariance function. Interestingly, this representation of X shows that a stationary stochastic process can be thought of as one whose Fourier coefficients are random variables.

We can generate realizations of a stationary process with a discrete spectrum by following the recipe in (5.10), provided we deal with a few additional considerations: how to choose the distribution of ξ_i, how to approximate a process with a continuous spectrum as one with a discrete spectrum, and how to generate a real-valued process.

Clearly, the choice of distribution for the ξ_i lead to different types of processes. X will be Gaussian, if and only if the ξ_i are Gaussian. In this case, if the ξ_i are uncorrelated, they must also be independent.

A process with a continuous spectrum can be efficiently turned into one with a discrete spectrum by considering the process on a long but finite interval at a set of equally-spaced grid points and with periodic boundary conditions. That is, consider generating realizations of the process at a set of N equally spaced points $\{t_j\}_{j=0}^{N-1}$ on an interval of length L. The grid spacing is $\Delta t = \frac{L}{N}$ and the corresponding grid spacing in spectral space is determined from the discrete Fourier transform to be $\Delta k = \frac{2\pi}{L}$. It is convenient to choose the time and spectral grid points as[3]

$$(5.11) \quad t_j = j\Delta t - L/2, \quad j = 0, 1, \ldots, N-1; \qquad k_n = n\Delta k - \Delta k \frac{N}{2}, \quad n = 0, 1, \ldots, N-1.$$

A real-valued process can be obtained from a complex-valued process by taking real or imaginary parts. If $X = X^{(1)} + iX^{(2)}$ is a stationary complex-valued Gaussian process with real covariance function $C(t)$, then $X^{(1)}, X^{(2)}$ are independent, real-valued Gaussian processes with identical covariance functions $C(t)/2$ (**Hida and Hitsuda, 1993**). Therefore, to generate a real-valued process, we may generate a complex-valued process with covariance function $2C(t)$ then take its real and imaginary parts, giving two independent realizations.

Putting this all together, we obtain the following algorithm.

ALGORITHM TO SIMULATE A STATIONARY GAUSSIAN PROCESS. Here is how to generate a stationary complex-valued Gaussian process X with mean zero and covariance function $C(t)$, on the set of grid points (5.11). Evaluate the covariance function at the time grid points to obtain $\{C(t_j)\}_{j=0}^{N-1}$, and then compute the discrete Fourier transform of this sequence[4] to obtain $\{\hat{C}(k_n)\}_{n=0}^{N-1}$, which is associated with the spectral grid points. These sequences are related as

$$(5.12) \qquad \hat{C}(k_n) = \frac{\Delta t}{2\pi} \sum_{j=0}^{N-1} C(t_j) e^{-it_j k_n}, \qquad C(t_j) = \Delta k \sum_{n=0}^{N-1} \hat{C}(k_n) e^{it_j k_n}.$$

Construct X as

$$(5.13) \qquad X(t_j) = \sum_{n=0}^{N-1} \xi_n e^{it_j k_n}, \qquad \text{where} \quad \xi_n = \sqrt{\frac{1}{2}\hat{C}(k_n)\Delta k} \, (A_n + iB_n),$$

and $A_n, B_n \sim N(0, 1)$ are independent standard normals.

Two independent real-valued Gaussian processes Y, Z are obtained by choosing $\xi_n = \sqrt{\hat{C}(k_n)\Delta k} \, (A_n + iB_n)$, constructing X as above, and setting $Y = \text{Re}\{X\}$, $Z = \text{Imag}\{X\}$.

This algorithm is numerically stable; and it is efficient, particularly if using the fast Fourier transform to evaluate (5.13). It should be preferred to the Cholesky decomposition method from Section 5.5.2.

You might have noticed that the scaling of the random Fourier coefficients in (5.13) is unusual—their magnitude scales with spectral spacing as $\xi_i \sim \sqrt{\Delta k}$. One might expect that $\xi_i \sim \Delta k$, so the sum in (5.13) approaches an integral as the grid spacing $\Delta k \to 0$. In fact, because the ξ_i are uncorrelated mean-zero random variables, they must be scaled differently in order to obtain a finite, nonzero function in this limit. We will return to this point in Chapter 7 when we construct stochastic integrals.

Exercise 5.5. Verify that the process X constructed in (5.13) above has the correct covariance at the grid points $\{t_j\}$.

---

[3]We shift space by $L/2$ to avoid numerical problems when $C(t)$ is not periodic on the chosen interval. Similarly we shift frequencies by $\Delta k \frac{N}{2}$, because then it is easier to make up functions $\hat{C}(k)$ which are symmetric in k, as is required if $C(t) \in \mathbb{R}$.

[4]The convention for where to put the factor of 2π differs here from the usual definition of the discrete Fourier transform.

Exercise **5.6.** Show that a real-valued field may alternatively be generated by choosing the Fourier coefficients as

$$\xi(k_n) = \sqrt{\frac{L\hat{C}(k_n)}{2}}(A_n + iB_n) \quad (0 < k_n < N/2),$$

$$\xi(k_n) = \sqrt{L\hat{C}(k_n)}A_n \quad (k_n = 0, N/2)$$

$$\xi(k_n) = \bar{\xi}(-k_n) \quad (k_n < 0).$$

Here A_n, B_n are independent $N(0, 1)$ random variables.

REMARK 5.36. We have introduced this method for stationary Gaussian processes, but it can be extended to nonstationary Gaussian processes by replacing the complex exponential $e^{i\lambda_j t}$ by functions $e_j(t)$ which are eigenfunctions of the operator $\mathcal{K}$ defined in (5.2). In fact, you can check that complex exponentials are the eigenfunctions of the operator $\mathcal{C}f := \int C(t - s)f(s)ds$, which is why they appear in our representations.

REMARK 5.37. Our algorithm to simulate a Gaussian process is related to a deeper representation of such processes in spectral space. In fact, one can show the following spectral theorem (**Grimmett and Stirzaker, 2001**; **Yaglom, 1962**): given a mean-square continuous (see Exercise 5.9), stationary stochastic process $(X_t)_{t\in\mathbb{R}}$ with mean zero and spectral distribution function $F(\lambda)$, there exists a complex-valued stochastic process $(Z(\lambda))_{\lambda\in\mathbb{R}}$ such that

(5.14) $$X_t = \int_{-\infty}^{\infty} e^{i\lambda t} dZ(\lambda).$$

$Z(\lambda)$ has the following properties:
  (i) Orthogonal increments: if the intervals $[\lambda_1, \lambda_2], [\lambda_3, \lambda_4]$ are disjoint, then
$$\mathbb{E}(Z(\lambda_2) - Z(\lambda_1))\overline{(Z(\lambda_4) - Z(\lambda_3))} = 0.$$
  (ii) Spectral weight: if $\lambda_1 \le \lambda_2$, then
$$\mathbb{E}|Z(\lambda_2) - Z(\lambda_1)|^2 = F(\lambda_2) - F(\lambda_1).$$

An efficient way to summarize the properties of Z is (**Lindgren, 2013**, p. 87)

$$\mathbb{E}dZ(\lambda)dZ(\mu) = \begin{cases} dF(\lambda) & \text{if } \lambda - \mu \\ 0 & \text{if } \lambda \ne \mu. \end{cases}$$

This spectral representation gives a way to determine relationships between a process and its derivatives, its integrals, its convolution with various functions, and linear functionals of the process in general. For example, once we know the spectral representation of X_t, we can calculate the spectral representation of X_t', and hence of its covariance function, by differentiating under the integral in (5.14).

5.6. Ergodic properties of weakly stationary processes

If a process is stationary, then we may hope to extract all the statistical information we need from a single trajectory of the process. This would be useful when we have access to only one trajectory, such as measurements of the daily temperature in New York City, measurements of the velocity field at a single location in the ocean, or a single run of a molecular dynamics or Monte Carlo simulation, where it can be hard to obtain several independent realizations because of a long burn-in time before one can start collecting statistics. However, it is not obvious that the time average of a function of of a single trajectory should equal the average over an ensemble of trajectories, and in fact this is only true when the covariance function decays quickly enough.

Ergodic theorems in general relate time averages to ensemble averages. We will look at one version of the ergodic theorem for stationary processes, which gives conditions under which the time average of a stationary process converges in *mean-square* to its mean value. Recall that a sequence of random variables $\{X_n\}_{n \in \mathbb{N}}$ converges in mean-square to another random variable Y, written $X_n \xrightarrow{m.s.} Y$, if $\lim_{n \to \infty} \mathbb{E}|X_n - Y|^2 = 0$.

THEOREM 5.38 (Ergodic theorem for stationary processes (**Pavliotis, 2014**)). *Let $(X_t)_{t \geq 0}$ be a weakly stationary process with mean μ and covariance $C(t)$, and suppose that $C(t) \in L^1(\mathbb{R})$. Then*

$$(5.15) \qquad \lim_{T \to \infty} \mathbb{E}\left| \frac{1}{T} \int_0^T X_s \, ds - \mu \right|^2 = 0.$$

In other words, $\frac{1}{T} \int_0^T X_t \, dt \xrightarrow{m.s.} \mu$. This theorem generalizes trivially to weakly stationary sequences $X_1, X_2, \ldots$.

The ergodic theorem shows that if the correlation function decays quickly enough, then we may compute an expectation of a random variable by time-averaging a *single* trajectory. So, the following are equivalent: either we can simulate or observe a system for a very long time and compute the average along that trajectory, or we can average over many short independent simulations or observations.

REMARK 5.39. There are both stronger and weaker ergodic theorems. If X_t is strongly stationary then the convergence in the ergodic theorem is almost surely (**Grimmett and Stirzaker, 2001**, Section 9.5). A weaker version of the theorem (**Grimmett and Stirzaker, 2001**, Section 9.5) says that, with no restrictions on the covariance function, there exists a random variable Y such that $\frac{1}{T} \int_0^T X_t \, dt \xrightarrow{m.s.} Y$.

PROOF OF ERGODIC THEOREM. Calculate:

$$\mathbb{E}\left| \frac{1}{T} \int_0^T X_s \, ds - \mu \right|^2 = \frac{1}{T^2} \mathbb{E}\left| \int_0^T (X_s - \mu) \, ds \right|^2$$

$$= \frac{1}{T^2} \int_0^T \int_0^T \mathbb{E}(X_t - \mu)(X_s - \mu) dt ds$$

$$= \frac{1}{T^2} \int_0^T \int_0^T C(t - s) dt ds.$$

The second step uses Fubini's theorem to interchange the expectation and the integral. Now we change variables to $u = t - s$, $v = t + s$. The domain of integration in (u, v) is

$[-T, T] \times [|u|, 2T - |u|]$, and the Jacobian is $\frac{\partial(t,s)}{\partial(u,v)} = \frac{1}{2}$. The integral becomes

$$\int_0^T \int_0^T C(t - s)\, dt\, ds = \int_{-T}^T \int_{|u|}^{2T-|u|} \frac{1}{2} C(u)\, dv\, du$$

$$= \int_{-T}^T (T - |u|) C(u)\, du$$

$$= 2 \int_0^T (T - u) C(u)\, du,$$

where the last step follows because $C(u)$ is symmetric. Substituting into the above calculations gives

$$\mathbb{E} \left| \frac{1}{T} \int_0^T X_s\, ds - \mu \right|^2 = \frac{2}{T^2} \int_0^T (T - u) C(u)\, du$$

$$\leq \frac{2}{T} \int_0^T \left| \left(1 - \frac{u}{T}\right) C(u) \right|\, du$$

$$\leq \frac{2}{T} \int_0^\infty C(u)\, du$$

by the dominated convergence theorem. This quantity goes to 0 as $T \to \infty$, since $C \in L^1(\mathbb{R})$. $\square$

REMARK 5.40. The proof makes it clear we can weaken the condition that $C \in L^1(\mathbb{R})$—it is enough to know that $\lim_{T\to\infty} \frac{1}{T} \int_0^T C(u)(1 - \frac{u}{T})\, du = 0$.

Exercise 5.7. Let Y be a random variable and let $X_t = Y$ for all t. Show the statement of the ergodic theorem fails to hold, and identify the condition in the statement of the ergodic theorem that is not satisfied by this process.

Example 5.41 (Ergodic theorem for Markov chains). Let $X = (X_n)_{n\in\mathbb{N}}$ be a regular Markov chain with finite state space S, and suppose $X_0 \sim \pi$, where π is the unique stationary distribution of the chain. Suppose you have a realization of the chain and want to empirically determine π_k for some state k. You can do this as follows: define a collection of indicator functions $I = \{I_n : n \geq 0\}$ by

$$I_n = \begin{cases} 1 & \text{if } X_n = k \\ 0 & \text{otherwise.} \end{cases}$$

Then the partial sum $S_n = \sum_{j=0}^{n-1} I_j$ is the number of visits to state k before the nth jump.

You can show that X is strongly stationary.[5] From this, it follows that the process $(I_n)_{n \in \mathbb{N}}$ is strongly stationary (Exercise 5.3). The mean of $(I_n)_{n \in \mathbb{N}}$ is $\mathbb{E} I_0 = \pi_k$ and the covariance is $C(n) = \mathbb{E} I_0 I_n - \pi_k^2 = \pi_k P_{kk}^n - \pi_k^2$.

To use the ergodic theorem above, we must check that $C(n) \in L^1$. We use the fact that $|P_{ij}^n - \pi_j| \le C_0 e^{-\beta n}$ for some $C_0 > 0$ and n large enough, where $\beta = -\log|\lambda_2| > 0$ and λ_2 is the eigenvalue of P with the second largest norm. Therefore,

$$\sum_{m=0}^{\infty} |C(m)| = \pi_k \sum_{m=0}^{\infty} \|\!|P_{kk}^n - \pi_k^2\| \le \pi_k \sum_{m=0}^{\infty} C_0 e^{-\beta m} = \frac{C_0 \pi_k}{1 - e^{-\beta}}.$$

Therefore by the Eegodic theorem,

$$\frac{1}{n} S_n = \frac{1}{n} \sum_{j=0}^{n-1} I_j \xrightarrow{m.s.} \pi_k.$$

Example 5.42 (Taylor diffusion[6] (**Taylor, 1921**)). Consider a particle in a turbulent velocity field with position $x(t)$ and Lagrangian velocity $u_L(t) = \frac{dx(t)}{dt}$. For simplicity we focus on one coordinate, so $x(t), u_L(t) \in \mathbb{R}$. If the velocity field is random then the particle is pushed and pulled in many different directions, and over long enough times it should look like a Brownian motion, whose mean-square displacement is proportional to t. Therefore, we can define a particle's "effective" diffusion coefficient by considering its mean-square displacement over long times,

$$(5.16) \qquad D \equiv \lim_{t \to \infty} \frac{1}{2} \frac{d}{dt} \mathbb{E}(x(t))^2 = \lim_{t \to \infty} \frac{1}{2} \frac{d}{dt} \mathbb{E} \left(\int_0^t u_L(t) dt \right)^2.$$

Suppose the Lagrangian velocity is a stationary stochastic process with mean zero and covariance function $C(t) \in L^1$. Then, following the calculations in the proof of the ergodic theorem,

$$\mathbb{E} \left(\int_0^t u_L(t) dt \right)^2 = \dots = 2t \int_0^t \left(1 - \frac{u}{t} \right) C(u) du \qquad \text{see calcs in proof}$$

$$\approx 2t \int_0^t C(u) du \qquad \text{for } t \text{ large}$$

$$\approx 2t \int_0^{\infty} C(u) du.$$

This gives

$$(5.17) \qquad D = \int_0^{\infty} C(u) du.$$

---

[5] Let us check:

$$P(X_{t_1+h} = x_1, \cdots, X_{t_n+h} = x_n)$$
$$= P(X_{t_1+h} = x_1) P(X_{t_2+h} = x_2 | X_{t_1+h} = x_1) \cdots P(X_{t_n+h} = x_n | X_{t_{n-1}+h} = x_{n-1})$$
$$= P(X_{t_1} = x_1) P(X_{t_2} = x_2 | X_{t_1} = x_1) \cdots P(X_{t_n} = x_n | X_{t_{n-1}} = x_{n-1})$$
$$= P(X_{t_1} = x_1, \cdots, X_{t_n} = x_n).$$

[6] Note that "Taylor diffusion" or "Taylor dispersion" also refers to the enhanced axial diffusion of a tracer in a shear flow, an effect also analyzed by G. I. Taylor.

In other words, the diffusion coefficient is the integral of the covariance function of the Lagrangian velocity. Therefore, a more slowly decaying covariance function leads to a higher diffusion coefficient; physically, this is because the effective step size of the random walk is larger. This formula can be used in a wide variety of contexts; for example, one can use it to calculate the effective diffusivity due to interacting waves in the ocean (**Holmes-Cerfon et al., 2011**), or to calculate diffusion coefficients of a large particle in a sea of smaller particles, such as a grain of dust in a water bath.

5.7. Additional exercises

Exercise 5.8. Show that if the covariance function $C(t)$ of a weakly stationary stochastic process X_t is continuous at $t = 0$, then $C(t)$ is uniformly continuous for all $t \in \mathbb{R}$.

Hint: apply Cauchy–Schwartz to $|C(t+h) - C(t)|^2 = \mathbb{E}|(X_{t+h} - X_t)X_0|^2$. You may assume $\mathbb{E}X_t = 0$.

Exercise 5.9. A stochastic process X_t is *mean-square continuous* if $\lim_{h\to 0} \mathbb{E}|X_{t+h} - X_t|^2 = 0$. Show that $C(t)$ is continuous at 0 if and only if X_t is mean-square continuous.

Exercise 5.10. Let $X_t = N_{t+\alpha} - N_t$, where $(N_t)_{t\geq 0}$ is a Poisson process and $\alpha > 0$ is a fixed number. Show that X_t is strongly stationary.

Exercise 5.11. Let $\{\xi_n : n = 0, \pm 1, \pm 2, \ldots\}$ be uncorrelated random variables with $\mathbb{E}\xi_n = \mu$, $\mathbb{E}(\xi_n - \mu)^2 = \sigma^2$. Let $a_1, a_2, \ldots a_m$ be arbitrary real numbers and consider the stochastic process

$$X_n = a_1\xi_n + a_2\xi_{n-1} + \ldots + a_m\xi_{n-m+1}.$$

(i) Calculate the mean, variance, and covariance function of $(X_n)_{n\in\mathbb{Z}}$. Show that it is a weakly stationary process.
(ii) Set $a_k = 1/\sqrt{m}$ for $k = 1, \ldots, m$ and calculate the covariance function. Describe (or sketch) the covariance function for the case $m = 1$, and explain what happens in the limit $m \to \infty$.

Exercise 5.12. Suppose you run a Markov chain in the stationary distribution to get $X_0, X_1, X_2, \ldots \sim \pi$. (For example, you could be implementing an MCMC method.) You wish to estimate $\mathbb{E}_\pi f(X_i)$ for some function f. You estimate the average after n steps of the chain as

$$\hat{f}_n = \frac{1}{n}\sum_{i=1}^{n} f(X_i).$$

Show that if n is large, then the variance of your estimator is

$$\text{Var}(\hat{f}_n) \approx \frac{1}{n}\sum_{i=-\infty}^{\infty} C_Y(i),$$

where $C_Y(i)$ is the covariance function for the process Y given by $Y_i = f(X_i)$. Specifically, show that $n\,\text{Var}(\hat{f}_n) \to \sum_{i=-\infty}^{\infty} C_Y(i)$ as $n \to \infty$.

You may assume that $Y_0, Y_1, \ldots$ is weakly stationary, and that $C_Y \in L^1$.

Hint: First show that $\text{Var}(\hat{f}_n) = \frac{1}{n}\sum_{i=-(n-1)}^{n-1} \frac{n-|i|}{n}C_Y(i)$.

***Exercise* 5.13** (*Computation required*)**.** Simulate realizations of a stationary Gaussian process[7] with the following covariance functions:

$$C(t) = e^{-|t|}, \qquad C(t) = \frac{1}{\sqrt{2\pi}} e^{-\frac{t^2}{2}},$$

and one more of your choosing on an interval $[-L/2, L/2)$ using N points, following these instructions.

    (i) Explain why the additional covariance function you chose is positive semi-definite.

   (ii) For each set of realizations, plot about 5 trajectories (you can plot them on the same plot), for $L \approx 10 - 20$.

  (iii) For each covariance function, verify that the process you simulate has the correct covariance function.[8]

  (iv) Simulate each covariance function using both methods: Cholesky decomposition of the covariance matrix, and the spectral decomposition. Do this for varying L and varying N, and comment on which method fails first as L or N get large. Explain briefly why it fails.

   (v) Comment on which covariance function produced the smoothest realizations, and which produced the least smooth. Which property of the covariance function do you think this is related to?

---

[7] I would recommend implementing the sums in (5.12) and (5.13) directly if you are not worried about efficiency. Many high-level programming languages (Matlab, Python, etc.) have built-in functions to compute the fast Fourier transform, which will be more efficient; however, they may cause a lot of headaches in figuring out how to convert between their Fourier transform conventions and the one used in this book. If, however, you are worried about efficiency, it is worth suffering through these headaches.

[8] Many languages have functions to compute the autocovariance.

CHAPTER 6

Brownian Motion

Brownian motion is perhaps the most important stochastic process we will see in this course. It is named after Scottish botanist Robert Brown, who in 1827 noticed that pollen grains suspended in water move about at random even when the water is still. Some people thought this motion was because grains come from living matter and are moving about of their own accord. To rule out this explanation, Brown showed that inanimate objects like dust particles move in the same erratic fashion. Brown was not the first person to notice this peculiar motion—for example, it was described by a Roman, Lucretius, in a poem in 60 BC, and pointed out by Dutch scientist Jan Ingenhousz in 1785—but he was the first to investigate it systematically.

Brown's work inspired physicists to investigate the origin of this random motion. It was finally understood by Einstein in 1905 (**Einstein, 1905**), who showed how the random motion could arise if water were made of many discrete components rather than forming a continuum. He argued that this indirectly confirmed that matter was made of atoms. Smoluchowski constructed a related model in 1906 which was experimentally verifiied by Jean Baptiste Perrin in 1908, who received the Nobel prize for his work.

Meanwhile, mathematicians realized that a function describing a particle moving according to Brownian motion would have some bizarre properties and could not be constructed as a function using classical mathematical techniques. Several mathematicians tried to invent new mathematics to construct a Brownian motion (e.g., Theile in 1880, Bachelier in 1900), and a rigorous construction was finally given by Wiener in 1923. For this reason, in mathematics, Brownian motion is often called a *Wiener process*.

We will start by asking how to construct a stochastic process that could model the erratic motion of a dust particle or other processes that are "very random." We would like the process to be "as random as possible," because if there were any deterministic or predictable parts of the process, then we could model that part in a more conventional way. Therefore, we will ask for a continuous process whose derivative is independent at each point in time—the idea being that if the derivative has some correlations, then we could predict the value of the process at least some of the time into the future, and then the process would not be as random as possible. It turns out that the best approximation for such a process is a Brownian motion.

We will first study the path properties of Brownian motion and then we will look at what we can say about its statistics. Brownian motion is our first example of a diffusion process, a type of process we will study a lot in the coming chapters, so we will also use this chapter to introduce some of the tools to think about more general Markov processes.

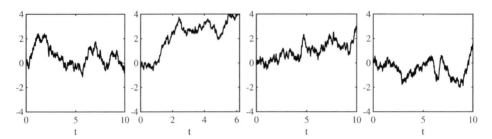

FIGURE 6.1. Realizations of Brownian motion over 10 time units.

6.1. Definition and transition densities

DEFINITION 6.1. A *Brownian motion* or *Wiener process* $W = (W_t)_{t \geq 0}$ is a real-valued stochastic process that satisfies the following properties:
  (i) $W_0 = 0$;
  (ii) Independent increments: the random variables $W_v - W_u$, $W_t - W_s$ are independent whenever $u \leq v \leq s \leq t$, so the intervals (u, v), (s, t) are disjoint;
  (iii) Normal increments:[1] $W_t - W_s \sim N(0, t - s)$ for all $0 \leq s < t$;
  (iv) Continuous sample paths: with probability 1, the function $t \to W_t$ is continuous.

Some realizations are shown in Figure 6.1.

That such a process exists—and that its probability law is uniquely determined by the above properties—is a result shown in many probability texts (e.g., (**Durrett, 2019**, p. 373), (**Karatzas and Shreve, 1991**), and (**Breiman, 1992**)). The major difficulty is in showing property (iv): that there exists a version of Brownian motion that is continuous everywhere, almost surely.

The properties of Brownian motion are a lot like those of the Poisson process. Property (iii) implies the increments are stationary, so a Brownian motion has stationary independent increments, just like the Poisson process. The differences from the Poisson process are that the increments of Brownian motion have a normal distribution, not a Poisson distribution, and that it is a continuous process.

With these properties we can say a lot about the trajectories and statistics of the process. One thing they allow us to do is calculate all the finite-dimensional distributions.

---

[1] Somewhat remarkably, it is possible to replace this condition with the condition that the increments $W_{s+t} - W_t$ do not depend on t, plus a continuity condition $\lim_{s \to 0} \frac{P(|W_{s+t} - W_t| \geq \delta)}{s} = 0$ for all $\delta > 0$. That this implies the increments are normal comes from the central limit theorem by breaking up an increment over a finite interval into a sum of increments over smaller intervals. See (**Breiman, 1992**, Chapter 12, p. 248).

Example 6.2. Let us calculate the two-point distributions $P(W_s \in A, W_t \in B)$ with $A, B \subset \mathbb{R}$ and $s < t$. We have

$$P(W_s \in A, W_t \in B) = P(W_t - W_s + W_s \in B, W_s \in A)$$

$$= \int_{x \in A} P(W_t - W_s \in B - x, W_s \in [x, x + dx))$$

$$= \int_{x \in A} P(W_t - W_s \in B - x) P(W_s \in [x, x + dx))$$

$$= \int_{x \in A} \int_{y \in B} \frac{1}{\sqrt{2\pi(t - s)}} e^{-\frac{(y-x)^2}{2(t-s)}} \frac{1}{\sqrt{2\pi s}} e^{-\frac{x^2}{2s}} \, dy dx.$$

The third step follows from the independent increments property, (ii), and the last step follows from the normal increments property, (iii). This calculation shows the joint density for (W_s, W_t) is

$$(6.1) \qquad p_{s,t}(x, y) = \frac{1}{\sqrt{2\pi(t - s)}} e^{-\frac{(y-x)^2}{2(t-s)}} \frac{1}{\sqrt{2\pi s}} e^{-\frac{x^2}{2s}} \, .$$

This density is Gaussian, so (W_s, W_t) is a two-dimensional Gaussian vector.

DEFINITION 6.3. The two-point transition density is the probability density for $W_t = y$, given $W_s = x$:

$$(6.2) \qquad p(y, t | x, s) dy = P(W_t \in [y, y + dy] | W_s = x) = \frac{1}{\sqrt{2\pi(t - s)}} e^{-\frac{(y-x)^2}{2(t-s)}} \, dy.$$

Notice that we can write the the two-point density (6.1) in terms of the two-point transition density as

$$p_{s,t}(x, y) = p(y, t | x, s) p(x, s | 0, 0).$$

Example 6.4. Let us calculate the n-point fdds. Let $t_1 < \cdots < t_n$, and let

$$p_{t_1, t_2, \ldots, t_n}(x_1, x_2, \ldots, x_n)$$

be the joint density of $(W_{t_1}, \cdots, W_{t_n})$. Similar calculations to Example 6.2 show that

$$p_{t_1, t_2, \ldots, t_n}(x_1, x_2, \ldots, x_n) = p(x_1, t_1 | 0, 0) \, p(x_2, t_2 | x_1, t_1) \cdots p(x_n, t_n | x_{n-1}, t_{n-1}).$$

That is, the joint density at n different timepoints is obtained by multiplying the two-point transition densities together. Since each of these are Gaussian the whole product is Gaussian, and we find the n-point fdd is a multivariate Gaussian.

Recall that earlier, in Definition 5.14, we defined Brownian motion as a Gaussian process with mean 0 and covariance $B(s, t) = \min(s, t)$.

PROPOSITION 6.5. *Definitions* 6.1 *and* 5.14 *are equivalent.*

Therefore, you can work with whichever one is more convenient for the problem at hand.

PROOF. (**Durrett, 2019**, p. 373) Let us show that Definition 6.1 $\Rightarrow$ Definition 5.14; the reverse implication is left as an exercise. Given a Brownian motion satisfying Definition 6.1, we need to show that it is Gaussian with the right mean and covariance. That it is Gaussian follows from our calculation of the n-point fdds in Example 6.4.

Since $W_t \sim N(0, t)$ by property (iii) of Definition 6.1, we have $\mathbb{E}W_t = 0$. Let us compute its covariance. For $s < t$,

$$
\begin{aligned}
B(s, t) &= \mathbb{E}W_s W_t - (\mathbb{E}W_s)(\mathbb{E}W_t) \\
&= \mathbb{E}W_s (W_t - W_s + W_s) \\
&= (\mathbb{E}W_s)\mathbb{E}(W_t - W_s) + \mathbb{E}W_s^2 \\
&= s.
\end{aligned}
$$

The penultimate step follows since $W_t - W_s$ is independent of W_s (property (ii)), and the third by the distribution of the increments (property (iii)). We have shown the covariance is $\min(s, t)$. □

Exercise 6.1. Show that Definition 5.14 $\Rightarrow$ Definition 6.1.

6.2. Brownian motion as a limit of random walks

One way to construct a Brownian motion is by scaling random walks. Let $X_1, X_2, \ldots$ be i.i.d. random variables with mean 0 and variance 1. For the sake of illustration let us suppose $X_i = \pm 1$; the argument below will hold for more general step distributions. Construct stochastic processes $S = S_0, S_1, S_2, \ldots$ as

$$
(6.3) \qquad\qquad\qquad\qquad S_n = \sum_{i=1}^{n} X_i.
$$

Then S is a simple symmetric random walk on the integers. Consider the properties of S:

(i) $\mathbb{E}S_n = 0$.

(ii) $\mathrm{Var}(S_n) = n$.

(iii) S has stationary increments.

   To see why, note that, for $n > m$,

$$
S_n - S_m = X_{m+1} + \cdots X_n, \qquad S_{n-m} = X_1 + \cdots + X_{n-m}.
$$

   Each of $S_n - S_m, S_{n-m}$ is a sum of $n - m$ i.i.d random variables, so $S_n - S_m \sim S_{n-m}$.

(iv) S has independent increments.

   To see why, let $0 < q < r \leq m < n$, and write

$$
S_n - S_m = X_{m+1} + \cdots + X_n, \qquad S_r - S_q = X_{q+1} + \cdots + X_r.
$$

   Each of $S_n - S_m, S_r - S_q$ is a sum of distinct, independent random variables, so they are independent.

(v) For n large, $S_n \approx N(0, n)$. This follows from the central limit theorem.

Therefore, S has many of the properties of a Brownian motion. In fact, it approaches a Brownian motion if we scale it in a particular way. Suppose we scale spatial steps by Δx, and time steps by Δt. The rescaled process at time $t = n\Delta t$ with $n = 0, 1, \ldots$, is

$$
(6.4) \qquad\qquad\qquad S_t^{\Delta t, \Delta x} = \Delta x \, S_{t/\Delta t} = \Delta x \left(X_1 + \cdots + X_{t/\Delta t}\right).
$$

We want to consider the limit of the process $S_t^{\Delta t, \Delta x}$ as $\Delta t, \Delta x \to 0$. How should these parameters be related? If the limit is to approach a Brownian motion, then at the very least the variance should match that of a Brownian motion. Since

$$\text{Var}(S_t^{\Delta t, \Delta x}) = \frac{(\Delta x)^2}{\Delta t}t,$$

we should choose

$$\frac{(\Delta x)^2}{\Delta t} = 1.$$

This is an important point—*for a Brownian motion, space scales as the square root of time*. We will call this *diffusive scaling*. It will come up again and again throughout the book.

To go further, write $\Delta t = 1/n$, $\Delta x = 1/\sqrt{n}$, and define a sequence of processes in terms of parameter n. It is convenient to make a continuous-time process by linearly interpolating between the discrete values of t. The interpolated rescaled process is

(6.5)
$$S_t^{(n)} = \underbrace{\frac{S_{[nt]}}{\sqrt{n}}}_{\substack{\text{rescaled} \\ \text{random walk}}} + \underbrace{\frac{(nt - [nt])(S_{[nt]+1} - S_{[nt]})}{\sqrt{n}}}_{\text{needed for interpolation}},$$

where $[nt]$ means the largest integer less than or equal to nt. We would like to show $S^{(n)} = (S_t^{(n)})_{t \geq 0}$ converges in some way to a Brownian motion as $n \to \infty$. (See Section 6.6.7 for more details on how to precisely define the manner of convergence.)

First, consider the one-point distributions of $S^{(n)}$. Given a fixed time t, the random variable $S_{[nt]}$ in (6.5) is a sum of $[nt]$ i.i.d. random variables with mean 0 and variance 1. Therefore, the central limit theorem applies and says that

$$\frac{S_{[nt]}}{\sqrt{n}} \Rightarrow N(0, t) \sim W_t \qquad \text{as } n \to \infty,$$

where $\Rightarrow$ means convergence in distribution: the cumulative distribution functions of $S_{[nt]}/\sqrt{n}$ converge to the cumulative distribution function of $N(0, t)$ at all points of continuity of the latter (in this case, everywhere). One can show the interpolation term in (6.5) converges to 0 in probability (**Durrett, 1996**, Section 8.5), and that this implies $S_t^{(n)} \Rightarrow W_t$: at a single time point the distribution of the scaled random walk converges to the distribution of Brownian motion at that time point.

Now, consider the k-point distributions. Given $0 < t_1 < \cdots < t_k \leq 1$,

$$\left(\frac{S_{[nt_1]}}{\sqrt{n}}, \frac{S_{[nt_2]}}{\sqrt{n}} - \frac{S_{[nt_1]}}{\sqrt{n}}, \ldots, \frac{S_{[nt_k]}}{\sqrt{n}} - \frac{S_{[nt_{k-1}]}}{\sqrt{n}}\right) \Rightarrow (W_{t_1}, W_{t_2} - W_{t_1}, \cdots W_{t_k} - W_{t_{k-1}})$$

as $n \to \infty$, also by the central limit theorem—applied separately to each component—where now weak convergence is of the random vectors' joint distributions. This is true because each component of the vector on the left is a sum of different i.i.d random variables, hence, the components are independent, so we may apply the central limit theorem separately to each component and obtain a vector of independent Gaussian random variables in the limit, equal in distribution to the vector on the right. Again, taking a little care with the interpolation term, this implies weak convergence of the finite dimensional distributions of $S^{(n)}$ to those of W.

To go further—and to talk about the convergence of the entire path at once—requires more than the central limit theorem. *Donsker's theorem* or *Donsker's invariance principle* says that $S^{(n)} \Rightarrow W$ on $[0, 1]$, where the weak convergence is in the metric space $(\mathcal{C}([0, 1]), \|\cdot\|_\infty)$ (defined in Section 6.6.7, Example 6.19). This theorem is proved in (**Durrett, 1996**, Section 8.5), (**Durrett, 2019**, Section 7.6), or (**Karatzas and Shreve, 1991**, p. 70).

The most useful consequence of Donsker's theorem is that it allows us to approximate a functional of a random walk with the same functional applied to Brownian motion, for which it is sometimes easier to obtain an analytic understanding (or vice versa). One can show from Donsker's theorem that, given a functional $\psi : \mathcal{C}([0,1]) \to \mathbb{R}$ that is continuous with probability 1 (with respect to the measure of W),

$$\psi(S^{(n)}) \Rightarrow \psi(W) \qquad \text{as } n \to \infty.$$

That is, the distribution of the random variables $\psi(S^{(n)})$ converges to the distribution of the random variable $\psi(W)$ (**Durrett, 1996**, Section 8.5, Theorem 5.8). Let us apply this result to a few specific examples.

Example 6.6. Let $\psi(f) = f(t)$. That is, we wish to study the value of a process at a single point: its one-point distribution. Then ψ is continuous since $|\psi(f) - \psi(g)| = |f(t) - g(t)| \le \|f - g\|_\infty$, so Donsker's theorem implies that $S_t^{(n)} \Rightarrow W_t$. This is what we argued above—that the one-point distributions converge.

Example 6.7. Let $\psi(f) = \max\{f(t) : t \in [0,1]\}$. Again ψ is continuous, since $|\psi(f) - \psi(g)| \le \|f - g\|_\infty$, and we have that

$$\max_{t \in [0,1]} S_t^{(n)} \Rightarrow M_1 \equiv \max_{t \in [0,1]} W_t.$$

That is, the maximum of the scaled random walk, over the interval $[0,1]$, converges in distribution to the maximum of Brownian motion over the same interval. Therefore, if you know the distribution of the maximum of a Brownian motion, you can use it to approximate the distribution of the maximum of a random walk, and vice versa. You will be asked to do this in Exercise 6.6.

Example 6.8. Let $\psi(f) = \int_0^1 f^k(t)dt$ for some integer $k > 0$. Then ψ is continuous, and Donsker's theorem implies $\int_0^1 (S_t^{(n)})^k dt \Rightarrow \int_0^1 B_t^k dt$. (**Durrett, 1996**, p. 292) shows that $\int_0^1 (S_t^{(n)})^k dt - n^{-1-(k/2)} \sum_{m=1}^n S_m^k \to 0$ in probability, and that this implies

$$\frac{1}{n^{1+k/2}} \sum_{m=1}^n S_m^k \Rightarrow \int_0^1 B_t^k dt.$$

We obtain a statement about sums of k-powers of random walks, which, remarkably, does not require $\mathbb{E}|X_i^k| < \infty$ for $k > 2$.

6.3. Properties of Brownian motion

Brownian motion has a number of useful and sometimes surprising properties, surveyed in this section.

PROPOSITION 6.9 (Scaling properties of Brownian motion). *A Brownian motion* $(W_t)_{t \ge 0}$ *satisfies the following:*

    (i) $(-W_t)_{t \ge 0}$ *is a Brownian motion (symmetry);*
    (ii) $(W_{t+s} - W_s)_{t \ge 0}$ *for fixed s is a Brownian motion (translation property);*
    (iii) $\frac{1}{\sqrt{c}} W_{ct}$, *with $c > 0$ is a fixed constant is a Brownian motion (scaling);*
    (iv) $(t W_{1/t})_{t \ge 0}$ *is a Brownian motion (time-inversion).*

Property (iii) shows that Brownian motion is like a fractal: it looks statistically "the same" at all scales no matter how much you zoom in, provided that space and time are scaled in the right way. Again, we see the diffusive scaling space $\propto \sqrt{\text{time}}$. Properties (i)–(iii) follow naturally from the construction of Brownian motion as a limit of random walks.

PROOF. (i), (ii), and (iii) follow straightforwardly from Definition 6.1 by checking the required conditions are satisfied. For example, for (iii): let $X_t = c^{-1/2} W_{ct}$. Then

(i) $X_0 = c^{-1/2} W_0 = 0$;

(ii) X_t has independent increments—this is straightforward to check;

(iii) Normal increments: for $t \geq s$, $X_t - X_s = c^{-1/2}(W_{ct} - W_{cs}) \sim c^{-1/2} N(0, c(t-s)) \sim N(0, t-s)$;

(iv) Continuity—this follows from continuity of W_t.

To check (iv), we use Definition 5.14 of Brownian motion as a Gaussian process. We have that $t W_{1/t}$ is Gaussian with mean 0. It has covariance function $\mathbb{E} st W_{1/s} W_{1/t} = st\left(\frac{1}{s} \wedge \frac{1}{t}\right) = s \wedge t$. It is continuous for $t > 0$. It remains to check that it is continuous at 0. But $\lim_{t \to 0} t W_{1/t} = \lim_{s \to \infty} \frac{W_s}{s} \to 0$ almost surely, by Proposition 6.10(i). $\square$

PROPOSITION 6.10 (Behavior of Brownian motion as $t \to \infty$).

(i) $\lim_{t \to \infty} \frac{W_t}{t} = 0$ a.s.

(ii) $\limsup_{t \to \infty} \frac{W_t}{\sqrt{t}} = \infty$ a.s., $\quad \liminf_{t \to \infty} \frac{W_t}{\sqrt{t}} = -\infty$ a.s.

(iii) (Law of the iterated logarithm)

$$\limsup_{t \to \infty} \frac{W_t}{\sqrt{2t \log \log t}} = 1 \quad a.s., \qquad \limsup_{t \to 0+} \frac{W_t}{\sqrt{2t \log \log 1/t}} = 1 \quad a.s..$$

If lim sup is replaced by lim inf in either of the above, the limits are -1.

In the above, a.s. stands for almost surely, which means the event happens with probability 1.

PROOF.

(i) (From (**Breiman, 1992**, p. 265).) This follows from the strong law of large numbers (SLLN). For $n \in \mathbb{N}$ we can write $W_n = (W_1 - W_0) + (W_2 - W_1) + \ldots + (W_n - W_{n-1})$, which is a sum of i.i.d. random variables. By the SLLN, $W_n/n \to 0$ a.s. To obtain behavior at noninteger t, let

$$Z_k = \max_{0 \leq t \leq 1} |W_{k+t} - W_k|.$$

Notice that Z_k are i.i.d. random variables. For $t \in [k, k+1]$,

$$\left| \frac{W_t}{t} - \frac{W_k}{k} \right| \leq \frac{1}{k(k+1)} |W_k| + \frac{1}{k} Z_k.$$

The first term on the RHS $\to 0$ a.s. as we just showed, and Z_k has the same distribution as $\max_{0 \leq t \leq 1} |W_t|$. It can be shown that $\mathbb{E} Z_k < \infty$ (Exercise 6.5), and that this implies $Z_k/k \to 0$ a.s. (**Breiman, 1992**, Chapter 3, Problem 10).

(ii) This follows from the law of the iterated logarithm.

(iii) See, e.g., (**Durrett, 2019**, Section 7.9, p. 431) or (**Breiman, 1992**, p. 263) or (**Karatzas and Shreve, 1991**, p. 112). One only needs to show one of these limits, since they are related to each other by the time inversion property, Proposition 6.9(iv). $\square$

THEOREM 6.11 (Differentiability of Brownian motion). *With probability one, sample paths of a Brownian motion are not differentiable at any point.*

A proof may be found in any graduate probability textbook, e.g., (**Breiman, 1992**, Theorem 12.25) or (**Karatzas and Shreve, 1991**, Theorem 9.18). Here is a heuristic explanation for why the derivative does not exist. Suppose we try to compute the derivative at t:

$$(6.6) \qquad \xi_t = \frac{dW_t}{dt} = \lim_{h \to 0} \frac{W_{t+h} - W_t}{h}.$$

But $W_{t+h} - W_t \sim N(0, h)$ so $\frac{W_{t+h} - W_t}{h} \sim N(0, \frac{1}{h})$. This is a Gaussian random variable with a variance that blows up to infinity, so it cannot converge to anything as $h \to 0$.

Another argument comes from observing that $X_h = W_{t+h} - W_t$ is a Brownian motion (by the translation property), and then that $Y_s = sX_{1/s}$ for $s = 1/h$ is a Brownian motion (by the time-inversion property). So then $\frac{dW_t}{dt} = \lim_{s \to \infty} Y_s$, which does not exist.

These arguments show the derivative does not exist at a particular point t. Theorem 6.11 makes a much stronger argument, which is that the derivative does not exist *anywhere* with probability 1. That is, for any given path, there is not even a single point at which a sample path of Brownian motion is differentiable!

6.4. White noise

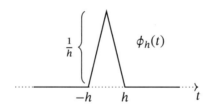

FIGURE 6.2. A sketch of $\phi_h(t) = \phi_h(s, s + t)$, the covariance function of $\{(W_{t+h} - W_t)/h\}_{t \geq 0}$.

Although Brownian motion is not differentiable, in the physics literature it is common to speak of the derivative of Brownian motion, where it is called *white noise*. It turns out that even though white noise does not exist in a classical sense, it does exist as a "generalized" process, similar to how $\delta(t)$ is not a function but a generalized function. We will not pursue this analogy further (though see (**Koralov and Sinai, 2007**, Chapter 17) for details on generalized processes), but instead will turn to studying the properties of white noise that we will return to when constructing the stochastic integral in Chapter 7.

Let us pretend for a moment that the derivative of Brownian motion exists, and see what we can learn about it by calculating its mean and covariance function (**Evans, 2013**, p. 41). For the mean, from (6.6),

$$\mathbb{E}\xi_t = \mathbb{E} \lim_{h \to 0} \frac{W_{t+h} - W_t}{h} = \lim_{h \to 0} \frac{\mathbb{E}W_{t+h} - \mathbb{E}W_t}{h} = 0,$$

and for the covariance,

$$\text{Cov}(\xi_s, \xi_t) = \lim_{h \to 0} \mathbb{E}\left(\frac{W_{t+h} - W_t}{h}\right)\left(\frac{W_{s+h} - W_s}{h}\right) = \lim_{h \to 0} \phi_h(s, t),$$

where

$$\phi_h(s, t) = \frac{1}{h^2}\left[(t+h) \wedge (s+h) - (t+h) \wedge s - t \wedge (s+h) + s \wedge t\right]$$

(6.7)
$$= \begin{cases} 0 & \text{if } |s - t| > h \\ \frac{1}{h^2}(h - |s - t|) & \text{if } |s - t| \le h. \end{cases}$$

The function $\phi_h(s, t)$ is only a function of $s - t$, so we can also write it (with an abuse of notation) as $\phi_h(t) = \phi_h(s, s + t)$ (Figure 6.2). As $h \to 0$, $\phi_h(t)$ becomes narrower and taller, but the area under the function remains constant, $\int \phi_h(t)dt = 1$. Therefore, we expect $\phi_h(t) \to \delta(t)$ as $h \to 0$. So, formally at least, we should have

(6.8)
$$\text{Cov}(\xi_s, \xi_t) = \mathbb{E}\xi_s\xi_t = \delta(s - t).$$

Therefore, white noise ξ_t is a weakly stationary stochastic process with mean zero and covariance function $C(t) = \delta(t)$.

Why is ξ_t called "white noise"? This term describes its spectrum. The spectral density of the covariance function is

$$f(\lambda) = \frac{1}{2\pi}\int_{-\infty}^{\infty} e^{-i\lambda t}\delta(t)\,dt \quad = \frac{1}{2\pi} \quad \text{for all } \lambda \in \mathbb{R}.$$

The spectral density is flat: all frequencies contribute equally. Just as white light is a superposition of light from all wavelengths equally, white noise is a superposition of random oscillations of all frequencies equally.

6.5. Quadratic variation

The concept of quadratic variation will be critical to constructing the stochastic integral, a task we will undertake in Chapter 7. First, recall some concepts from analysis.

DEFINITION 6.12. The *total variation* of a function $f : [a, b] \to \mathbb{R}$ over an interval $[a, b]$ is defined by

(6.9)
$$V(f) = \sup_{\sigma} \sum_{i=0}^{n-1} |f(t_{i+1}) - f(t_i)|,$$

where the supremum is over all partitions $\sigma = \{t_0, t_1, \ldots, t_n\}$ of $[a, b]$, i.e., such that $a = t_0 < t_1 < \cdots < t_n = b$. If $V(f) < \infty$ then f is said to be of *bounded variation*, and if $V(f) = \infty$ then f is said to be of *infinite variation*.

Functions f of bounded variation are used to define the Riemann–Stieltjes integral $\int_a^b g(x)df(x)$, which we saw in Section 5.5.4. This integral is well defined when f is of bounded variation and g is continuous (**Rudin, 1976**).

Recall from analysis that if a function is of bounded variation on $[a, b]$, then it has a derivative almost everywhere on $[a, b]$ (i.e., except for a set of measure zero) (**Rudin, 1976**). Conversely, if a function is nowhere differentiable, then it must have infinite variation on any interval. Since Brownian motion is nowhere differentiable with probability 1 (Theorem 6.11), its total variation must be ∞ with probability 1. Nevertheless, there is another measure of variation which is finite for Brownian motion—the quadratic variation.

DEFINITION 6.13. The *quadratic variation* of a function f on $[0, t]$ with respect to a partition $\sigma = \{t_0, t_1, \ldots, t_n\}$ of $[0, t]$ is

(6.10)
$$Q_t^\sigma(f) = \sum_{i=0}^{n-1} |f(t_{i+1}) - f(t_i)|^2.$$

We would like to define the quadratic variation of a Brownian motion W on $[0, t]$ as $\sup_\sigma Q_t^\sigma(W)$. However, for a stochastic process we need to be careful with how the supremum over partitions is calculated, since not all types of stochastic convergence will give a finite result. We use the following notion of convergence.

DEFINITION 6.14. A sequence of random variables $X_1, X_2, \ldots$ *converges in mean-square* to another random variable X, written $X_n \xrightarrow{m.s.} X$ or m. s. $\lim_{n \to \infty} X_n = X$, if $\mathbb{E}|X_n - X|^2 \to 0$ as $n \to \infty$.

There are various other notions of convergence, reviewed in Section A.A.1.4.

PROPOSITION 6.15. *Let* $\sigma = \{t_0, t_1, \ldots, t_n\}$ *be a partition of* $[0, t]$, *and let* $|\sigma| = \max_{0 \leq i \leq n-1} |t_{i+1} - t_i|$. *The quadratic variation of Brownian motion converges in mean-square to* t *as* $|\sigma| \to 0$:

$$Q_t^\sigma(W) = \sum_{i=0}^{n-1} |W_{t_{i+1}} - W_{t_i}|^2 \xrightarrow{m.s.} t.$$

Formally, over some time interval Δt we expect the change in W—call it ΔW—to behave as $(\Delta W)^2 = \Delta t$. We see the diffusive scaling yet again.

PROOF. (From (**Koralov and Sinai, 2007**, p. 269).) Write $\Delta W_i = W_{t_{i+1}} - W_{t_i}$, and $\Delta t_i = t_{i+1} - t_i$. Then

$$\mathbb{E}\left(Q_t^\sigma(W) - t\right)^2 = \mathbb{E}\left(\sum_{i=0}^{n-1} \Delta W_i^2 - \Delta t_i\right)^2$$

$$= \sum_{i=0}^{n-1} \mathbb{E}(\Delta W_i^2 - \Delta t_i)^2 + \sum_{i,j=0, i \neq j}^{n-1} \mathbb{E}(\Delta W_i^2 - \Delta t_i)(\Delta W_j^2 - \Delta t_j).$$

Now, we have

$$\mathbb{E}(\Delta W_i^2 - \Delta t_i)(\Delta W_j^2 - \Delta t_j) = \Delta t_i \Delta t_j - \Delta t_i \Delta t_j - \Delta t_i \Delta t_j + \Delta t_i \Delta t_j = 0,$$

since $\Delta W_i, \Delta W_j$ are independent for $i \neq j$. Therefore,

$$
\mathbb{E}\left(Q_t^\sigma(W) - t\right)^2 = \sum_{i=0}^{n-1} \mathbb{E}(\Delta W_i^2 - \Delta t_i)^2
$$

$$
\leq \sum_{i=0}^{n-1} \mathbb{E}\Delta W_i^4 + \Delta t_i^2 \qquad \text{since } (a-b)^2 \leq a^2 + b^2 \text{ for } a, b \geq 0
$$

$$
= 4 \sum_{i=0}^{n-1} \Delta t_i^2 \qquad \text{since } \mathbb{E}(W_t - W_s)^4 = 3|t - s|^2
$$

$$
\leq 4 \max_{0 \leq i \leq n-1}(t_{i+1} - t_i) \sum_{i=0}^{n-1}(t_{i+1} - t_i)
$$

$$
= 4t|\sigma| \; \to 0 \text{ as } |\sigma| \to 0. \qquad \square
$$

REMARK 6.16. Almost sure convergence of the quadratic variation of Brownian motion requires additional assumptions on the sequence of partitions (**Fernandez de la Vega, 1974**; **Levental and Erickson, 2003**).

DEFINITION 6.17. The quadratic variation of a stochastic process[2] X over $[0, t]$, if it exists as a limit in probability, is denoted as $[X]_t$, and is thought of as a function of t.

Since mean-square convergence implies convergence in probability, Proposition 6.15 showed that $[W]_t = t$.

We can use the finiteness of $[W]_t$ to show the total variation of Brownian motion is infinite with probability 1. Given a partition σ of $[0, t]$, the quadratic variation is bounded by the total variation for a partition $V^\sigma(W)$ as

$$
\sum_{i=0}^{n-1} |W_{i+1} - W_i|^2 \leq \max_{0 \leq i \leq n-1} |W_{i+1} - W_i| \sum_{i=0}^{n-1} |W_{i+1} - W_i|
$$

$$
= \max_{0 \leq i \leq n-1} |W_{i+1} - W_i| V^\sigma(W).
$$

Since W is continuous on the compact set $[0, t]$ and it is uniformly continuous on this set (and hence for each $\epsilon > 0$), there is a $\delta > 0$ such that $\max_{0 \leq i \leq n-1} |W_{i+1} - W_i| < \epsilon$ for all $|\sigma| < \delta$. Since the left-hand side converges to t in mean-square as $|\sigma| \to 0$, and since $\max_{0 \leq i \leq n-1} |W_{i+1} - W_i| \to 0$ as $|\sigma| \to 0$, we must have that $V^\sigma(W) \to \infty$ in mean-square and, hence, in probability.

Exercise **6.2.** Show the quadratic variation of Brownian motion over an interval $[s, t]$ with $0 \leq s < t$ is $t - s$. Argue that the total variation of Brownian motion over any interval is infinite with probability 1.

Exercise **6.3.** Let $f : \mathbb{R} \to \mathbb{R}$ be a function of finite total variation. Show that $[f]_t = 0$.

6.6. Brownian motion as a Markov process

Suppose we know the value of Brownian motion for all times up to some time s. What can we say about W_t for $t > s$? Since $W_t = W_s + (W_t - W_s)$, and the increment

---

[2]Technically of a continuous local martingale.

$W_t - W_s$ is independent of all observations up to time s, the distribution of W_t only depends on W_s, and not any earlier observations. In other words,

$$(6.11) \qquad P(W_t \in F | W_{t_{n-1}} = x_{n-1}, \ldots, W_{t_0} = x_0) = P(W_{t_n} \in F | W_{t_{n-1}} = x_{n-1}),$$

where $t_0 < t_1 < \cdots < t_n$, and the conditional probability is defined as $P(W_t \in F | W_s = y) = \lim_{\epsilon \searrow 0} P(W_t \in F | W_s \in [y, y + \epsilon))/\epsilon$, and similarly for conditioning on multiple points. Therefore, Brownian motion is a Markov process.

Let us survey how some of the ideas we developed for Markov chains extend to Brownian motion (we will encounter these ideas again when we study general diffusion processes in Chapter 8 and beyond). To describe the transition probabilities for a Markov process with a discrete state space, we have a transition matrix $P(t)$ or $P(s, t)$. For a process with a continuous state space, we need a transition density $p(y, t | x, s)$, which is the function such that

$$P(W_t \in A | W_s = x) = \int_{y \in A} p(y, t | x, s) dy.$$

We calculated the transition density $p(y, t | x, s)$ for Brownian motion in Example 6.2; see (6.2). This function satisfies a few nice properties. It is *time-homogeneous*:

$$p(y, t | x, s) = p(y, t - s | x, 0)$$

for all t, s. Additionally, it satisfies two partial differential equations in each of its pairs of arguments. The *forward Kolmogorov equation* is

$$(6.12) \qquad \partial_t p = \frac{1}{2} \partial_{yy} p \quad (t > s), \qquad p(y, s | x, s) = \delta(y - x).$$

The *backward Kolmogorov equation* is

$$(6.13) \qquad \partial_s p = -\frac{1}{2} \partial_{xx} p \quad (s < t), \qquad p(y, t | x, t) = \delta(x - y).$$

You can verify all of these results by direct calculation from (6.2).

Now, suppose we shift the Brownian motion so it starts with some nonzero initial condition, which could be random, but we subsequently let it evolve as a Brownian motion. That is, we construct a stochastic process X_t with initial distribution $X_0 \sim \rho_0$ for some density ρ_0, but with the same transition density as Brownian motion. How does the density $\rho(y, t)$ of X_t evolve in time?

Since $\rho(y, t) = \int p(y, t | x, s) \rho_0(x) dx$, we may apply $\partial_t, \partial_{yy}$ to this expression and use (6.12) to get

$$(6.14) \qquad \partial_t \rho = \frac{1}{2} \partial_{yy} \rho \quad (t > 0), \qquad \rho(y, 0) = \rho_0(y).$$

This is another version of the forward Kolmogorov equation, which says the probability density evolves in time according to the heat equation.

Suppose instead we wish to evaluate a statistic of our process, $u(x, t) = \mathbb{E}_x f(X_t) = \mathbb{E}[f(X_t) | X_0 = x]$, where $f : \mathbb{R} \to \mathbb{R}$ is a bounded function. The statistic may be computed from the transition density as $u(x, t) = \int f(y) p(y, t | x, s) dy$. To relate the evolution of p in x to its evolution in t, we use the fact that p is time-homogeneous, so that

$$\partial_s p(y, t | x, s) = \partial_s p(y, t - s | x, 0) = -\partial_t p(y, t - s | x, 0) = -\partial_t p(y, t | x, s).$$

Therefore, applying $\partial_t = -\partial_s$ and ∂_{xx} to this expression and using (6.13), the initial condition gives

$$(6.15) \qquad \partial_t u = \frac{1}{2}\partial_{xx}u \quad (t > 0), \qquad u(x,0) = f(x).$$

This is another version of the backward Kolmogorov equation, which, for a Brownian motion is again the heat equation.

Recall that the fundamental quantity that characterized a continuous-time Markov chain was its generator (Definition 4.6), which we used to obtain the forward and backward equations. Continuous Markov processes are also characterized by generators, which are defined in a similar way (recall Exercise 4.2): the generator is the operator $\mathcal{L}$ such that

$$(6.16) \qquad (\mathcal{L}f)(x) = \lim_{t \to 0} \frac{\mathbb{E}_x f(X_t) - f(x)}{t}$$

for all $x \in \mathbb{R}$ and all bounded functions $f : \mathbb{R} \to \mathbb{R}$.

Let us calculate the generator $\mathcal{L}$ of Brownian motion (**Varadhan, 2007**). We have

$$\mathbb{E}_x f(X_t) = \int_{-\infty}^{\infty} f(y) \frac{1}{\sqrt{2\pi t}} e^{-\frac{(y-x)^2}{2t}} dy = \int_{-\infty}^{\infty} f(x + z\sqrt{t}) \frac{1}{\sqrt{2\pi}} e^{-\frac{z^2}{2}} dz,$$

so the infinitesimal generator is

$$(6.17) \qquad (\mathcal{L}f)(x) = \lim_{t \to 0} \int_{-\infty}^{\infty} \frac{f(x + z\sqrt{t}) - f(x)}{t} \frac{1}{\sqrt{2\pi}} e^{-\frac{z^2}{2}} dz.$$

Suppose f is bounded and has three bounded derivatives,[3] so we can expand it using Taylor's formula as

$$f(x + z\sqrt{t}) - f(x) = z\sqrt{t}f'(x) + \frac{tz^2}{2}f''(x) + \frac{t^{3/2}z^3}{6}f'''(\xi)$$

for some $\xi \in [x, x + z\sqrt{t}]$. By the boundedness of f''', the final term is bounded by $t^{3/2}C|z|^3$ for some constant C. Substituting this expansion into (6.17) and calculating the integral directly shows that

$$(6.18) \qquad \mathcal{L}f = \frac{1}{2}\partial_{xx}f.$$

The generator of Brownian motion is the Laplacian operator. It is not an accident that the backward equation is related to the generator as $\partial_t u = \mathcal{L}u$—we will see why in Chapter 10. We will also see that there is a relationship with the forward equation, which is more subtle to describe.

6.7. Additional Information on weak convergence

DEFINITION 6.18. A metric space (S, ρ) is a set S, combined with a metric ρ: a function satisfying for all $x, y, z \in S$, (i) $\rho(x, x) = 0$, (ii) $\rho(x, y) = \rho(y, x)$, and (iii) $\rho(x, y) + \rho(y, z) \geq \rho(x, z)$ (the triangle inequality).

Recall that a metric may be derived from a norm $\| \cdot \|$ as $\rho(x, y) = \|x - y\|$.

---

[3]This assumption is not necessary for the result to hold, but makes its derivation easier.

Example 6.19. Examples of metric spaces with metrics derived from norms include
   (i) $(\mathbb{R}^d, |\cdot|_p)$ where $|\cdot|_p$ is the l_p-norm on d-dimensional vectors, so the metric
       is $\rho(x, y) = |x - y|_p = (\sum_{i=1}^{d}(x_i - y_i)^p)^{1/p}$.
  (ii) $(\mathcal{C}([0, 1]), \|\cdot\|_\infty)$, where $\mathcal{C}([0, 1])$ is the space of continuous functions on $[0, 1]$,
       and $\|\cdot\|_\infty$ is the sup-norm, so the metric is $\rho(f, g) = \|f - g\|_\infty = \sup\{|f(t) - g(t)| : t \in [0, 1]\}$.

DEFINITION 6.20. Consider a sequence of random variables $X_1, X_2, \ldots$ defined on a sequence of probability spaces $\{(\Omega_n, \mathcal{F}_n, P_n)\}_{n=1}^{\infty}$ and taking values in some metric space (S, ρ). Let $(\Omega, \mathcal{F}, P)$ be another probability space on which another random variable X is defined, which also takes values in (S, ρ). Then $\{X_n\}_{n=1}^{\infty}$ *converges in distribution* or *converges weakly* to X, written $X_n \Rightarrow X$, if $\mathbb{E}_n f(X_n) \to \mathbb{E} f(X)$ for all bounded, continuous, real-valued functions f, where $\mathbb{E}_n, \mathbb{E}$ denote expectations with respect to the measures associated with X_n, X (**Durrett, 1996**, Chapter 8).

If $X_n, X \in \mathbb{R}^d$ or if $X_n, X \in \mathbb{R}^\infty$ (the space of sequences $(x_1, x_2, \ldots)$), then weak convergence is equivalent to convergence of all the finite-dimensional distributions (**Durrett, 1996**, Chapter 8, Theorem 2.7).

6.8. Additional exercises

Exercise 6.4. A d-dimensional Brownian motion is a vector $\underline{W}_t = (W_t^1, W_t^2, \ldots W_t^d)^T$ such that each component is an independent Brownian motion.[4] Let Q be a $d \times d$ orthonormal matrix, i.e., the columns (and rows) form an orthonormal basis of $\mathbb{R}^d$. For example, Q could represent a rotation or a reflection. Show that $\underline{Y}_t = (Y_t^1, \ldots, Y_t^d) = Q\underline{W}_t$ is also a d-dimensional Brownian motion.

Exercise 6.5. Let $M_t = \max_{0 \le s \le t} B_s$ be the maximum of Brownian motion over the interval $[0, t]$. Let us show that, for $a > 0$, the probability of M_t satisfies

$$(6.19) \qquad P(M_t \ge a) = \int_a^\infty \sqrt{\frac{2}{\pi t}} e^{-x^2/2t} \, dx.$$

This shows that M_t has the same distribution as $|W_t|$.
   (i) Show that, for $a > 0$, $P(M_t \ge a) = P(B_t > a) + P(M_t \ge a, B_t \le a)$.
  (ii) Argue that $P(M_t \ge a, B_t \le a) = P(M_t \ge a, B_t \ge a)$.
       To do this, you will need to use the *strong Markov property* of Brownian motion, which says that if T is a stopping time, then $(B_{T+t} - B_T)_{t \ge 0}$ is a Brownian motion. Consider applying this property to T_a, the first-passage time to level a. Also remember that $\{T_a \le t\} = \{M_t \le a\}$.
 (iii) Finish the proof to obtain (6.19).

Exercise 6.6. Suppose we are playing a game where we win or lose \$1 with equal probability each time you play. Let S_n be the net amount of money you have won after n games, and let $G_n = \max_{0 \le k \le n} S_k$ be the maximum amount of money you have

---

[4]"Independent" means that any collection of random variables $\{W_{t_k}^i\}_{k=1}^n$ is independent of any other collection of random variables $\{W_{s_k}^j\}_{k=1}^m$ for $i \ne j$, and similarly for collections from more than two processes. Because these are Gaussian, you can determine whether or not they are independent from the covariance $\text{Cov}(W_s^i, W_t^j)$.

ever won over the course of n games. Use your results from the previous question and Donsker's theorem to estimate the mean and standard deviation of G_n when n is large.

Exercise 6.7. Compute the following quadratic variations. You can use the fact that if $X_n \xrightarrow{m.s.} X$ and $Y_n \xrightarrow{m.s.} Y$, then $X_n + Y_n \xrightarrow{m.s.} X + Y$.
(i) $[aW]_t$;
(ii) $[aW + b]_t$;
(iii) $[t]_t$ (the quadratic variation of the function $f(t) = t$);
(iv) $[W^{(1)} + W^{(2)}]_t$ where $W^{(1)}, W^{(2)}$ are independent Brownian motions.

Exercise 6.8. Show that the 4th variation of Brownian motion with respect to a partition σ converges to 0 in mean-square as $|\sigma| \to 0$.

The 4th variation of a function f on $[a, b]$ with respect to a partition

$$\sigma = \{t_0, t_1, \ldots, t_n\}$$

$(a = t_0 < t_1 < \cdots < t_n = b)$ is

(6.20) $$V^4(f; \sigma) = \sum_{i=0}^{n-1} |f(t_{i+1}) - f(t_i)|^4.$$

Exercise 6.9. Consider a *deterministic* process X_t which solves an ODE:

$$\frac{dX_t}{dt} = a(X_t), \qquad X_0 = x,$$

where the function $a(x)$ is bounded. Let $\mathcal{L}$ be the infinitesimal generator of X_t. Calculate $\mathcal{L}f$, where f is assumed to be a bounded function with two bounded continuous derivatives.

Note: In physics, the operator $\mathcal{L}$ for this kind of equation is called the *Liouville operator*.

CHAPTER 7

Stochastic Integration

A great many phenomena that evolve stochastically can be modeled as ODEs with forcing terms that are stochastic processes. This chapter considers a natural way to set up such models and shows how to modify the definition of an integral in order to solve them.

7.1. How to write down differential equations with noise

Let us first take a look at some situations we might wish to model.

(1) A particle moving in a fluid. Its position $x(t)$ at time t evolves in a velocity field $u(x, t)$ as

$$\frac{dx}{dt} = u(x, t) + \eta(t),$$

where $\eta(t)$ is a stochastic process, representing for example diffusion, or unresolved components of the velocity field.

(2) Population growth. Let $N(t)$ be the population size at time t. It could evolve with a randomly perturbed growth rate as

$$\frac{dN}{dt} = (\underbrace{a(t)}_{\substack{\text{growth} \\ \text{rate}}} + \underbrace{\eta(t)}_{\text{noise}})N(t).$$

(3) Polymer dynamics. Given angles $\phi(t) \in \mathbb{R}^m$ of a polymer (Figure 7.1) and a potential energy $U(\phi)$, the angles might evolve as

$$\frac{d\phi}{dt} = -\nabla U(\phi) + \eta(t),$$

where $\eta(t)$ is again a stochastic forcing, representing the random collisions the solvent molecules make with the polymer.

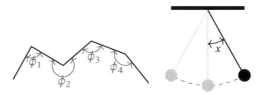

FIGURE 7.1. Schematics of a polymer (left) and a pendulum (right).

(4) Stochastically forced harmonic oscillator. Let $x(t)$ be the angle of a pendulum undergoing small displacements (Figure 7.1). It could evolve as

$$\underbrace{m\frac{d^2x}{dt^2}}_{\text{acceleration}} + \underbrace{\gamma\frac{dx}{dt}}_{\text{damping}} + \underbrace{kx}_{\substack{\text{restoring} \\ \text{force, eg spring}}} = \underbrace{\eta(t)}_{\substack{\text{stochastic} \\ \text{forcing}}}.$$

The general form of these equations is

(7.1)
$$\frac{dX_t}{dt} = b(X_t, t) + \sigma(X_t, t)\eta(t),$$

where $X = (X_t)_{t \geq 0}$ is a stochastic process, b is a deterministic forcing, $\eta(t)$ is a stochastic process representing the "noise" or uncertainty in our model, and σ modulates the amplitude of the noise.

What is a good model for the noise? We want it to be "as random as possible," because any deterministic parts could be modeled separately in b, σ, or by introducing additional variables to capture time-correlations. This suggests we should choose the noise to be stationary, with
   (i) Mean $\mathbb{E}\eta(t) = 0$;
   (ii) Covariance function $C_\eta(t) = \delta(t)$, so that $\eta(t_1), \eta(t_2)$ are uncorrelated if $t_1 \neq t_2$.
Therefore, $\eta(t)$ should be a white noise, which was introduced in Section 6.6.4 as the derivative of a Brownian motion, $\eta(t) = \frac{dW_t}{dt}$.

Although white noise derivative does not exist in a classical sense, we can make sense of (7.1) in an integrated sense. Suppose we integrate (7.1) from 0 to t and suppose we can replace $\eta(s)ds = \frac{dW_s}{ds}ds$ with dW_s:

$$X_t = X_0 + \int_0^t b(X_s, s)ds + \int_0^t \sigma(X_s, s)dW_s.$$

If we can make sense of each of the two integrals on the RHS, then we can make sense of the solution to (7.1).

The first integral has the form

$$\int_0^t g(s, \omega)ds \qquad \text{where} \quad g(s, \omega) = b(X_s(\omega), s),$$

and ω is an element of the sample space associated with the Brownian motion. Provided $g(s, \omega)$ is integrable for each ω with probability 1, this integral exists as a regular Riemann integral with probability 1, and produces a random variable as its output.

The second integral has the form

$$\int_0^t f(s, \omega)dW_s \qquad \text{where} \quad f(s, \omega) = \sigma(X_s(\omega), s).$$

This is a new form of integral. In general, it does not exist as a Riemann or Riemann–Stieltjes integral (see Section 5.5.4), since W has infinite variation. We will spend the rest of the chapter studying this integral, defining it properly, and studying some of its properties.

7.2. What is the Itô integral and why do we need it?

Here is an example to illustrate some of the problems that arise with defining this integral.

Example 7.1. Let $f(s, \omega) = W_s(\omega)$ and consider the integral

$$I = \int_0^t W_s \, dW_s.$$

Let us see what goes wrong if we try to calculate I as a Riemann–Stieltjes integral. Suppose we partition the interval $[0, t]$ into equally spaced points $\{0, \Delta t, 2\Delta t, \ldots, n\Delta t\}$, and approximate the integrand using different points within each grid box. We will compare approximations by calculating their expectations.

(1) Approximate the integrand at the left-hand endpoint.

$$I_{LH}^{(n)} = \sum_{k=0}^{n-1} W_{k\Delta t} \left(W_{(k+1)\Delta t} - W_{k\Delta t} \right), \qquad \mathbb{E}I_{LH}^{(n)} = \sum_{k=0}^{n-1} k\Delta t - k\Delta t = 0.$$

(2) Approximate the integrand at the right-hand endpoint.

$$I_{RH}^{(n)} = \sum_{k=0}^{n-1} W_{(k+1)\Delta t} \left(W_{(k+1)\Delta t} - W_{k\Delta t} \right), \qquad \mathbb{E}I_{RH}^{(n)} = \sum_{k=0}^{n-1} (k+1)\Delta t - k\Delta t = t.$$

(3) Approximate the integrand at the midpoint.

$$I_M^{(n)} = \sum_{k=0}^{n-1} W_{(k+\frac{1}{2})\Delta t} \left(W_{(k+1)\Delta t} - W_{k\Delta t} \right), \qquad \mathbb{E}I_M^{(n)} = \sum_{k=0}^{n-1} (k+\tfrac{1}{2})\Delta t - k\Delta t = \frac{t}{2}.$$

Depending on which point is used to approximate the integrand, the expectations differ by an $O(1)$ amount. Hence, as $\Delta t \to 0$, each approximation will produce a different random variable. This is one consequence of the fact that the Riemann–Stieltjes integral of the expression defining I does not exist.

To get around this problem, we must decide ahead of time which point to use to approximate the integrand. Each choice gives rise to a different integral. The two most common ones are defined below; we will see shortly how to construct these more rigorously.

DEFINITION 7.2. The *Itô integral* is the mean-square limit of the Riemann sums using the LH endpoint to evaluate the integrand. For a sequence of partitions $\sigma = \{t_0, t_1, \ldots, t_n\}$ of $[0, t]$, writing $\Delta W_j = W_{t_{j+1}} - W_{t_j}$, the Itô integral is

$$\int_0^t f(s, \omega) \, dW_s = \text{m. s.} \lim_{|\sigma| \to 0} \sum_{j=0}^{n-1} f(t_j, \omega) \Delta W_j.$$

Recall that mean-square convergence was defined in Definition 6.14.

DEFINITION 7.3. The *Stratonovich integral* is the mean-square limit of the Riemann sums using the trapezoidal rule to evaluate the integrand. For a sequence of partitions $\sigma = \{t_0, t_1, \ldots, t_n\}$ of $[0, t]$, the Stratonovich integral is

$$\int_0^t f(s, \omega) \circ dW_s = \text{m. s.} \lim_{\max_j |\Delta t_j| \to 0} \sum_{j=0}^{n-1} \frac{f(t_j, \omega) + f(t_{j+1}, \omega)}{2} \Delta W_j.$$

The Stratonovich integral may alternatively be defined as the mean-square limit of the Riemann sums using the midpoint rule evaluate the integrand:

$$\int_0^t f(s, \omega) \circ dW_s = \underset{\max_j |\Delta t_j| \to 0}{\text{m. s. lim}} \sum_{j=0}^{n-1} f(t_{j+\frac{1}{2}}, \omega) \Delta W_j.$$

One can show that the trapezoidal rule and the midpoint rule give the same limit in mean-square, and hence, you can use either to compute the Stratonovich integral. In practice, calculations with the trapezoidal rule are usually easier (see Exercise 7.5).

Most of stochastic calculus is developed around the Itô itegral, though in physical problems the Stratonovich integral is occasionally easier to use as we will discuss in Chapter 8. It does not really matter which integral you work with, as you can always convert from one to the other.

Example 7.4. Evaluate $I = \int_0^t W_s dW_s$.

SOLUTION. Start with a partition $\sigma = \{t_0, t_1, \ldots, t_n\}$ of $[0, t]$, let $|\sigma| = \max_j \Delta t_j$ and write the approximation using this partition as

$$I_t^\sigma = \sum_{j=0}^{n-1} W_j \Delta W_j$$

$$= \frac{1}{2} \sum_{j=0}^{n-1} (W_{j+1}^2 - W_j^2) - \frac{1}{2} \sum_{j=0}^{n-1} (W_{j+1} - W_j)^2 \quad \text{since } 2W_j \Delta W_j = \Delta(W_j^2) - (\Delta W_j)^2$$

$$= \frac{1}{2}(W_t^2 - W_0^2) - \frac{1}{2} Q_t^\sigma(W),$$

where $Q_t^\sigma(W)$ is the quadratic variation of the Brownian motion $W = (W_t)_{t \geq 0}$ with respect to the partition. We showed in Chapter 6 that $Q_t^\sigma(W) \xrightarrow{m.s.} t$ as $|\sigma| \to 0$, so

$$I_t^\sigma \xrightarrow{m.s.} I = \frac{1}{2} W_t^2 - \frac{1}{2} t \qquad \text{as } |\sigma| \to 0.$$

⋈

Notice that if we had treated the integral $\int_0^t W_s dW_s$ as a Riemann Stieltjes integral, we would have written

$$\text{(Warning! Incorrect calculations)} \qquad d\left(\frac{1}{2} W_t^2\right) = W_t dW_t,$$

and obtained the incorrect result $\int_0^t d\left(\frac{1}{2} W_s^2\right) = \frac{1}{2} W_t^2$. This shows we do not expect the chain rule to hold in Itô calculus; there is something fundamentally new about the Itô integral.

Exercise 7.1. Show that $\int_0^t W_s \circ dW_s = \frac{1}{2} W_t^2$.

These exercises show that, as our calculations in Example 7.1 suggested, the Itô and Stratonovich integrals give different results. Notice that the chain rule (via the incorrect calculations above) does give the correct result for the Stratonovich integral. This is not an accident.

7.3. Rigorous construction of the Itô integral

Definition 7.2 of the Itô integral is only heuristic because we do not yet know whether this definition actually exists—is there a mean-square limit of the approximations as we refine the partition? And is this limit independent of the sequence of partitions? In this section we give an overview of how to rigorously construct the Itô integral, outlining the major steps, and filling in details when these are helpful for future calculations. The remaining details can be found in the references, e.g., (**Durrett, 1996**; **Karatzas and Shreve, 1991**; **Grimmett and Stirzaker, 2001**).

We start by specifying the set of functions for which the Itô integral is well defined. In the following, W is a Brownian motion defined on a sample space Ω with probability measure P.

DEFINITION 7.5. A stochastic process $f(t, \omega) : [0, \infty) \times \Omega \to \mathbb{R}$ is *adapted to W* or simply *adapted* if, for all $t \geq 0$, $f(t, \omega)$ is a function only on the values of $W_s(\omega)$ for $s \leq t$ (and/or of time), and not on any values in the future nor on any other stochastic processes.[1] In other words, we can decide the value of $f(t, \omega)$ knowing the history of W up to time t. A random variable X is adapted to $(W_s)_{0 \leq s \leq t}$ if its value can be decided from $(W_s)_{0 \leq s \leq t}$.

Examples 7.6. Which of the following stochastic processes are adapted to W?
  (i) $X_t = W_{t/2}$
  (ii) $X_t = W_{2t}$
  (iii) $X_t = \int_0^t W_s ds$.
  (iv) $X_t = W_t V_t$ where V is a Brownian motion independent of W.
  (v) $X_t = W_t + \xi$ where ξ is a Bernoulli random variable independent of W.
  (vi) $X_t = \sin(t^2 + 5) + e^{-t}$.

SOLUTION. (i), (iii), (vi) are adapted. (ii), (iv), (v) are not adapted. ⋈

Note that when there are additional sources of randomness, as in (iv) and (v), one can modify the definition of adapted to allow X_t to depend on values in an enlarged probability space, as long as W_t remains a Brownian motion in the enlarged probability space (e.g., (**Øksendal, 2003**, Section 3.3)). We will frequently assume such a modification, e.g., when we work with multiple independent Brownian motions as in (iv), or when we consider a random initial condition for a stochastic process, as in (v).

DEFINITION 7.7. Let $\mathcal{V}$ be the class of stochastic processes $f : [0, \infty) \times \Omega \to \mathbb{R}$ such that f is adapted (to W or to an enhanced probability space), and such that $\|f\|_{\mathcal{V}} < \infty$, where the norm $\| \cdot \|_{\mathcal{V}}$ is defined by[2]

$$(7.2) \qquad \|f\|_{\mathcal{V}}^2 := \mathbb{E}\left(\int_0^\infty f^2(t, \omega) dt \right).$$

---

[1] The rigorous definition of adapted is that the random variable $\omega \to f(t, \omega)$ is $\mathcal{F}_t$-measurable, where $\mathcal{F}_t$ is the σ-algebra generated by the random variables $\{W_s\}_{s \leq t}$, and which includes all the null events $\mathcal{N} = \{A \in \mathcal{F} : P(A) = 0\}$, where $\mathcal{F}$ is the σ-algebra associated with $(W_t)_{t \geq 0}$. That is, $\mathcal{F}_t$ is the smallest σ-algebra containing sets of the form $\{\omega : W_{t_1}(\omega) \in F_1, W_{t_2}(\omega) \in F_2, \ldots, W_{t_k} \in F_k\}$, where $t_1, \ldots, t_k \leq t$, and $F_j \subset \mathbb{R}$ are Borel sets augmented by the null sets. See (**Grimmett and Stirzaker, 2001**, Section 13.8).

[2] We are ignoring questions of measurability here. See (**Durrett, 1996**) for more details.

We refer to $\mathcal{V}$ as the *class of adapted functions*. It can be shown that $\mathcal{V}$ is a Hilbert space with norm[3] $\| \cdot \|_\mathcal{V}$ ((**Grimmett and Stirzaker, 2001**, p. 540) and references therein).

We will define the Itô integral for $f \in \mathcal{V}$ over an infinite interval, written

$$(7.3) \qquad\qquad I(f) = \int_0^\infty f(s, \omega) dW_s.$$

The integral over a finite interval is included by multiplying by an indicator function: $\int_0^t f dW_s = \int_0^\infty f(s, \omega) 1_{s \le t}(s) dW_s$.

The Itô integral $I(f)$ is a random variable defined on the probability space Ω. A useful way to compare integrals is via the $L^2(\Omega)$-norm $\| \cdot \|_2$, defined for random variables $X : \Omega \to \mathbb{R}$ as $\|X\|_2^2 = \mathbb{E}X^2$, so that

$$(7.4) \qquad\qquad \|I(f)\|_2^2 = \mathbb{E}\left(\int_0^\infty f(t, \omega) dW_t \right)^2 .$$

Here is the strategy for constructing the Itô integral in (7.3).

  (1) Define it for a class of "simple" functions $\Phi \subset \mathcal{V}$.
  (2) Show that $f \in \mathcal{V}$ can be approximated by a sequence of simple functions $\{\phi_n\}_{n=1}^\infty \subset \Phi$, such that $\|\phi_n - f\|_\mathcal{V} \to 0$ as $n \to \infty$.
  (3) Define $I(f) = \text{m. s.} \lim_{n \to \infty} I(\phi_n)$ and show this limit is well defined.

STEP 1.

DEFINITION 7.8. Let $0 = t_0 < t_1 < \cdots < t_n = T$, for some $T > 0$. A function $\phi \in \mathcal{V}$ is an *adapted step function* or a *simple function* if[4]

$$\phi(t, \omega) = e_0(\omega) 1_{\{0\}}(t) + \sum_{j=0}^{n-1} e_j(\omega) 1_{(t_j, t_{j+1}]}(t),$$

where random variable e_j is adapted to $(W_s)_{s \le t_j}$ and has $\mathbb{E}e_j^2 < \infty$.

Such a function ϕ is piecewise constant, with constants that are random variables depending on values of the particular Brownian path only up to the beginning of the current time interval (Figure 7.2). The Itô integral for adapted step functions is defined as

$$(7.5) \qquad\qquad I(\phi) = \int_0^\infty \phi \, dW_t = \sum_{j=0}^{n-1} e_j(\omega)(W_{t_{j+1}}(\omega) - W_{t_j}(\omega)).$$

This integral has two important properties.

LEMMA 7.9 (Nonanticipating property for adapted step functions). *If ϕ is an adapted step function, then*

$$(7.6) \qquad\qquad \mathbb{E} \int_0^\infty \phi dW_t = 0.$$

---

[3]Technically, it is a norm on the set of equivalence classes obtained from the equivalence relation $\psi \sim \phi$ whenever $P(\psi = \phi) = 1$.

[4]The fact that the interval is $(t_j, t_{j+1}]$ and not $[t_j, t_{j+1})$ is not important for Brownian motion, but it does make a difference when integrating against other types of semimartingales.

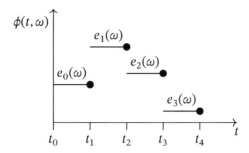

FIGURE 7.2. A realization of an adapted step function.

PROOF. Writing $\Delta W_j = W_{t_{j+1}} - W_{t_j}$, notice that $e_j, \Delta W_j$ are independent because e_j is adapted so it only depends on values of W_s for $s \leq t_j$, and ΔW_j only depends on values of W_s for $s \in (t_j, t_{j+1}]$. Therefore, $\mathbb{E}I(\phi) = \sum_j \mathbb{E}e_j \mathbb{E}\Delta W_j = 0$. □

LEMMA 7.10 (Itô isometry for adapted step functions). *If ϕ is an adapted step function, then*

(7.7)
$$\mathbb{E}\left(\int_0^\infty \phi \, dW_t\right)^2 = \mathbb{E}\int_0^\infty \phi^2 \, dt.$$

In other words, the norms (7.2) and (7.4) for Itô integrals are related by $\|I(\phi)\|_2 = \|\phi\|_V$. This relationship allows us to convert between the norm $\|\cdot\|_V$ defined on adapted functions, and the norm $\|\cdot\|_2$ defined on their Itô integrals—it allows us to say that if $\|\phi_1 - \phi_2\|_V$ is small, then $\|I(\phi_1) - I(\phi_2)\|_2$ is also small.

PROOF.

$$\mathbb{E}\left(\int_0^\infty \phi \, dW_t\right)^2 = \mathbb{E}\left(\sum_i e_i \Delta W_i\right)^2 = \mathbb{E}\left(\sum_j e_j^2 (\Delta W_j)^2 + 2\sum_{j<k} e_j e_k \Delta W_j \Delta W_k\right).$$

As before, $e_j, \Delta W_j$ are independent. We also have that if $j < k$, then ΔW_k is independent of $e_j, e_k, \Delta W_j$. Therefore, the above equals

$$\sum_j \mathbb{E}e_j^2 \Delta t_j + 2\sum_{j<k} \mathbb{E}(e_j e_k \Delta W_j)\underbrace{\mathbb{E}\Delta W_k}_{=0} = \mathbb{E}\sum_j e_j^2 \Delta t_j = \mathbb{E}\int_0^\infty \phi^2 \, dt. \qquad \square$$

STEP 2.

PROPOSITION 7.11. *Given $f \in \mathcal{V}$, there exists a sequence of adapted step functions $\phi = \{\phi_n\}_{n=1}^\infty$ such that $\|\phi_n - f\|_V \to 0$ as $n \to \infty$.*

PROOF. We prove this for f continuous, following (**Koralov and Sinai, 2007**, Section 20.3). (Showing one can approximate a noncontinuous process over an infinite interval is harder.) First, suppose f is supported on $t \in [0, M]$. Let $\Delta t = T/n$ and define a simple function

$$\phi_n(t, \omega) = f(0, \omega)1_{\{0\}}(t) + \sum_{j=0}^{n-1} f(j\Delta t, \omega)1_{(j\Delta t, (j+1)\Delta t]}(t).$$

The sequence $\{\phi_n\}$ converges to $f(t, \omega)$ almost surely uniformly in $t \in [0, M]$. If f is bounded on $[0, M] \times \Omega$ (meaning $|f(t, \omega)| \leq c$ for all $t \in [0, M]$, $\omega \in \Omega$), then $\lim_{n \to \infty} \|\phi_n - f\|_V \to 0$, by the dominated convergence theorem.

If f is not bounded, then define a sequence of adapted bounded processes to approximate f as

$$Y_n(t, \omega) = \begin{cases} -n & f(t, \omega) < -n \\ f(t, \omega) & -n \leq f(t, \omega) \leq n \\ n & f(t, \omega) > n \end{cases}$$

Then $\lim_{n \to \infty} \|Y_n - f\|_V = 0$. Each Y_n can be approximated by a sequence of simple processes, from which we can extract a sequence which converges to f.

If the support of f is $t \in [0, \infty)$, then, for each M, we may find a sequence of simple processes which converges to $Z_m(t, \omega) = f(t, \omega) 1_{[0, M]}(t)$. Since $\lim_{M \to \infty} \|Z_m - f\|_V = 0$, we may fnd a sequence of simple processes which converges to f. □

STEP 3. Given $f \in V$ and a sequence of adapted step functions $\phi = \{\phi_n\}_{n=1}^{\infty}$ such that $\|\phi_n - f\|_V \to 0$ as $n \to \infty$, the Itô integral is defined as

(7.8) $I(f) = \text{m. s. } \lim_{n \to \infty} I(\phi_n).$

To show that $I(f)$ is well defined, we need to show (i) that the limit exists, and (ii) that it is independent of the particular sequence of adapted step functions. For (i), notice that $\phi_m - \phi_n$ is an adapted step function, so

$\|I(\phi_m) - I(\phi_n)\|_2 = \|I(\phi_m - \phi_n)\|_2$	Itô integral is linear for step functions
$= \|\phi_m - \phi_m\|_V$	Itô isometry for step functions, (7.7)
$\leq \|\phi_m - f\|_V + \|\phi_n - f\|_V$	triangle inequality on norm $\| \cdot \|_V$
$\to 0 \quad \text{as } m, n \to \infty$	by construction of ϕ_n.

Therefore, the sequence $I(\phi_n)$ is a Cauchy sequence in $\| \cdot \|_2$, so from a theorem in probability theory,[5] there is a random variable $I(\phi)$ such that $I(\phi_n) \xrightarrow{m.s.} I(\phi)$ as $n \to \infty$.

To show (ii), suppose there is another sequence of adapted step functions $\rho = \{\rho_n\}_{n=1}^{\infty}$ such that $\|\rho_n - f\|_V \to 0$ as $n \to \infty$, and let $I(\rho)$ be the limit of the corresponding integrals. By the triangle inequality,

$$\|I(\phi) - I(\rho)\|_2 \leq \|I(\phi) - I(\phi_n)\|_2 + \|I(\phi_n) - I(\rho_n)\|_2 + \|I(\rho_n) - I(\rho)\|_2.$$

The first and third terms on the right-hand side go to zero as $n \to \infty$. The second term can be bounded using the Itô isometry and the triangle inequality as

$$\|I(\phi_n - \rho_n)\|_2 = \|\phi_n - \rho_n\|_V \leq \|\phi_n - f\|_V + \|\rho_n - f\|_V,$$

which also goes to zero as $n \to \infty$. Therefore, $\|I(\phi) - I(\rho)\|_2 = 0$, so $I(\phi) = I(\rho)$ with probability 1.

We obtain a construction of the Itô integral, from (7.8).

---

[5] The theorem says that if a sequence of random variables $\{X_n\}$ is a Cauchy sequence—meaning that $X_n - X_m \xrightarrow{\gamma} 0$ as $n, m \to \infty$, where γ is any of the stochastic modes of convergence—then there exists a random variable X such that $X_n \xrightarrow{\gamma} X$ (**Breiman, 1992**, Section 2.8).

7.4. Properties of the Itô integral

Given $f, g \in \mathcal{V}$, the Itô integral has the following properties.

(i) (Linearity) for $a, b \in \mathbb{R}$, $\int_0^\infty (af + bg)dW_t = a \int_0^\infty f dW_t + b \int_0^\infty g dW_t$.

(ii) (Nonanticipating property)

$$(7.9) \qquad \mathbb{E} \int_0^\infty f dW_t = 0.$$

(iii) (Itô isometry)

$$(7.10) \qquad \mathbb{E}\left(\int_0^\infty f dW_t \right)^2 = \mathbb{E} \int_0^\infty f^2 dt.$$

PROOF. We show property (iii) and leave the others as exercises. We already showed this property holds for adapted step functions (Lemma 7.10), so we must show it holds in the limit (7.8). Consider a sequence of adapted step functions $\phi = \{\phi_n\}_{n=1}^\infty$ such that $\|\phi_n - f\|_\mathcal{V} \to 0$ as $n \to \infty$. By the triangle inequality,

$$\left| \|f\|_\mathcal{V} - \|I(f)\|_2 \right| \leq \left| \|f\|_\mathcal{V} - \|\phi_n\|_\mathcal{V} \right| + \left| \|\phi_n\|_\mathcal{V} - \|I(\phi_n)\|_2 \right| + \left| \|I(\phi_n)\|_2 - \|I(f)\|_2 \right|.$$

The first term goes to 0 by a variant of the triangle inequality. The second term is identically 0. The third term goes to 0, since $\|I(\phi_n) - I(f)\|_2 \to 0$. Therefore, all terms on the RHS converge to 0 as $n \to \infty$, so $\|f\|_\mathcal{V} = \|I(f)\|_2$, which is what we need to show. $\qquad \square$

***Exercise* 7.2.** Show properties (i) and (ii) in the same way as above.

Example 7.12. Compute

(i) $\mathbb{E} \int_0^T W_t dW_t$; and

(ii) $\mathbb{E}\left(\int_0^T W_t dW_t \right)^2$.

SOLUTION. $\mathbb{E} \int_0^T W_t dW_t = 0$, by the nonanticipating property.
$\mathbb{E}\left(\int_0^T W_t dW_t \right)^2 = \int_0^T \mathbb{E} W_t^2$ by the Itô isometry. Hence, it equals

$$\int_0^T \mathbb{E} W_t^2 = \int_0^T t dt = T^2/2.$$

$\bowtie$

Another property is:

(iv) the integral $I_t = \int_0^t f(s, \omega)dW_s$ can be chosen to depend continuously on t almost surely.

For a proof, see (**Øksendal, 2003**, Section 3.2).

Finally, a generalization of the Itô isometry is:

(v) for $g, h \in \mathcal{V}$,

$$(7.11) \qquad \mathbb{E}\left(\int_0^t g(s, \omega)dW_s \int_0^t h(s, \omega)dW_s \right) = \int_0^t \mathbb{E}[g(s, \omega)h(s, \omega)]ds.$$

To prove this property, apply Itô's isometry with $f = h + g$.

There is a formal method to derive the Itô isometry (7.10) and its generalization (7.11), which can be helpful in evaluating related integrals. Write (7.11) as

$$\mathbb{E}\left[\left(\int_0^t g(u)dW_u\right)\left(\int_0^t h(v)dW_v\right)\right] = \int_0^t\int_0^t \mathbb{E}[g(u)h(v)dW_u dW_v].$$

Now, decompose the integrand on the RHS into different pieces, depending on the relationship between u, v. Since $1_{v<u}(u,v) + 1_{u<v}(u,v) + 1_{u=v}(u,v) = 1$, where $1_A(u,v)$ is the indicator function for set A; and since $g(u), h(v)$ are adapted so they are each independent of dW_u, dW_v, respectively, we can write

$$
\begin{aligned}
\mathbb{E}[g(u)h(v)dW_u dW_v] = {}& \mathbb{E}[g(u)h(v)1_{v<u}(u,v)dW_u dW_v] \\
& + \mathbb{E}[g(u)h(v)1_{u<v}(u,v)dW_u dW_v] \\
& + \mathbb{E}[g(u)h(v)1_{u=v}(u,v)dW_u dW_v].
\end{aligned}
$$

To evaluate the expectations of differentials, recall that in Chapter 6 we defined white noise as $\eta(t) = ``\frac{dW_t}{dt}"$, and showed it has mean zero and covariance function $\mathbb{E}\eta(t)\eta(s) = \mathbb{E}\frac{dW_s}{ds}\frac{dW_t}{dt} = \delta(t-s)$. Therefore, formally, we may substitute $\mathbb{E}dW_u = \mathbb{E}dW_v = 0$, $\mathbb{E}dW_u dW_v = \delta(u-v)dudv$, to obtain

$$
\begin{aligned}
\int_0^t\int_0^t \mathbb{E}[g(u)h(v)dW_u dW_v] = {}& \int_0^t\int_0^t \mathbb{E}[g(u)h(v)]\delta(u-v)dudv \\
& + \int_0^t\int_0^t \mathbb{E}[g(u)h(v)1_{u<v}dW_u]\mathbb{E}dW_v \\
& + \int_0^t\int_0^t \mathbb{E}[g(u)h(v)1_{v<u}dW_v]\mathbb{E}dW_u \\
= {}& \int_0^t \mathbb{E}[g(u)h(u)]du.
\end{aligned}
$$

7.5. Itô formula

We can finally begin to make sense of the "stochastic" ODE (7.1). Rewrite (7.1) as

(7.12) $dX_t = b(X_t,t)dt + \sigma(X_t,t)dW_t,$

to see that X_t should be the solution to the following integral equation:

(7.13) $X_t = X_0 + \int_0^t b(X_s,s)ds + \int_0^t \sigma(X_s,s)dW_s.$

The second integral is an Itô integral, which exists because $\sigma(X_s,s)$ only depends on $(W_u)_{0\le u<s}$, so it should be adapted (we will study the existence of solutions to (7.13) in more depth in Chapter 8). In practice, one usually writes (7.12) to mean (7.13). A solution to (7.13) is called a *diffusion process*. We may also consider the more general equation

(7.14) $X_t = X_0 + \int_0^t b(s,\omega)ds + \int_0^t \sigma(s,\omega)dW_s$

where $b, \sigma \in \mathcal{V}$. A solution to (7.14) is called an *Itô process*. Clearly, a diffusion process is a particular kind of Itô process.

Suppose we have an Itô process X_t, and suppose $Y_t = g(X_t, t)$. What equation does Y_t satisfy?

If the rules of classical calculus were satisfied, we would write $\frac{dY_t}{dt} = \frac{\partial g}{\partial t} + \frac{\partial g}{\partial x}\frac{dX_t}{dt}$ and so

(7.15)

$$\text{(Incorrect!)} \qquad dY_t = \frac{\partial g}{\partial t}(X_t, t)dt + \frac{\partial g}{\partial x}(X_t, t)b(t, \omega)dt + \frac{\partial g}{\partial x}(X_t, t)\sigma(t, \omega)dW_t.$$

We saw in Example 7.4 that this chain rule does not hold for Itô integrals. Therefore, we need to develop a new version of the chain rule that works for the Itô integral.

THEOREM 7.13 (Itô formula). *Let X_t be the solution to*

$$dX_t = b(t, \omega)dt + \sigma(t, \omega)dW_t,$$

where b, σ are adapted functions. Given $g \in C^2([0, \infty) \times \mathbb{R})$, the process $Y_t = g(X_t, t)$ solves the equation

(7.16)

$$dY_t = \frac{\partial g}{\partial t}(X_t, t)dt + \frac{\partial g}{\partial x}(X_t, t)dX_t + \frac{1}{2}\frac{\partial^2 g}{\partial x^2}(X_t, t)(dX_t)^2,$$

with probability 1, where $(dX_t)^2$ is computed according to the rules

$$dt \cdot dt = dt \cdot dW_t = dW_t \cdot dt = 0, \qquad dW_t \cdot dW_t = dt.$$

Specifically,
(7.17)

$$dY_t = \left(\frac{\partial g}{\partial t}(X_t, t) + \frac{\partial g}{\partial x}(X_t, t)b(t, \omega) + \frac{1}{2}\frac{\partial^2 g}{\partial x^2}(X_t, t)\sigma^2(t, \omega)\right)dt + \frac{\partial g}{\partial x}(X_t, t)\sigma(t, \omega)dW_t.$$

Compared to the chain rule from classical calculus (7.15), the Itô formula includes an extra drift term $\frac{1}{2}\sigma^2\frac{\partial g}{\partial x}dt$.

A heuristic explanation for the Itô formula comes from Taylor-expanding $g(X_t, t)$ near some point (x, t):

$$\Delta Y = \frac{\partial g}{\partial t}\Delta t + \frac{\partial g}{\partial x}\Delta X + \frac{1}{2}\frac{\partial^2 g}{\partial x^2}(\Delta X)^2 + \frac{1}{3!}\frac{\partial^3 g}{\partial x^3}(\Delta X)^3 + \dots.$$

To approximate ΔY to $O(\Delta t)$, one must account for the fact that $\Delta W \sim O(\Delta t^{1/2})$, and, therefore, we must go to second-order in the Taylor expansion to retain all the terms that are first-order in Δt. We keep terms involving $(\Delta W)^2 \sim O(\Delta t)$ but throw out terms containing Δt^2 or $\Delta t\Delta W \sim O(\Delta t^{3/2})$.

Example 7.14. Let $Y_t = \frac{1}{2}W_t^2$. What is dY_t?

SOLUTION. Let $X_t = W_t$, $g(x, t) = \frac{1}{2}x^2$, $Y_t = g(X_t, t) = \frac{1}{2}W_t^2$. We know that $dX_t = dW_t$. Then

$$dY_t = \frac{\partial g}{\partial x}dX_t + \frac{1}{2}\frac{\partial^2 g}{\partial x^2}(dX_t)^2 = X_t dX_t + \frac{1}{2}(dX_t)^2 = W_t dW_t + \frac{1}{2}dt.$$

Let us solve this equation to check its consistency.

$$Y_t = \int_0^t W_s dW_s + \int_0^t \frac{1}{2}ds = \frac{1}{2}W_t^2 - \frac{1}{2}t + \frac{1}{2}t = \frac{1}{2}W_t^2.$$

We obtain the correct formula for Y_t.   ⋈

Example 7.15. Let $Y_t = e^{W_t}$. What is dY_t?

SOLUTION. Here, $g(x, t) = e^x$, so Itô's formula yields

$$dY_t = \frac{\partial g}{\partial x} dW_t + \frac{1}{2} \frac{\partial^2 g}{\partial x^2} (dW_t)^2 = \frac{1}{2} e^{W_t} dt + e^{W_t} dW_t = \frac{1}{2} Y_t dt + Y_t dW_t.$$

Notice the extra drift term $\frac{1}{2} Y_t dt$ that arises in Itô calculus.   ⋈

We turn to a partial proof of Itô's formula, for which we use the following lemma.

LEMMA 7.16. *Let $f \in V$ be bounded (uniformly in ω), piecewise continuous for $t \in [0, T]$, and consider a sequence of partitions $\sigma = \{t_0, t_1, \ldots, t_n\}$ of $[0, T]$. Let $t_j^* \in [t_j, t_{j+1}]$ be an arbitrary point in each grid box. Then*

$$(7.18) \qquad \sum_{j=0}^{n-1} f(t_j^*, \omega)(W_{t_{j+1}} - W_{t_j})^2 \xrightarrow{p} \int_0^T f(t, \omega) dt \qquad \text{as } |\sigma| \to 0,$$

where $\xrightarrow{p}$ means convergence in probability.

PROOF. This is similar to our proof of the quadratic variation of W (Proposition 6.15). For a given partition, write $\Delta t_j = t_{j+1} - t_j$, $\Delta W_j = W_{t_{j+1}} - W_{t_j}$, $f_j = f(t_j) = f(t_j, \omega)$. Calculate

$$\mathbb{E} \left(\sum_j f_j (\Delta W_j)^2 - \sum_j f_j \Delta t_j \right)^2$$

$$= \mathbb{E} \left(\sum_{j,k} f_j f_k ((\Delta W_j)^2 - \Delta t_j)((\Delta W_k)^2 - \Delta t_k) \right)$$

$$= \sum_j \mathbb{E} f_j^2 \underbrace{\mathbb{E}((\Delta W_j)^2 - \Delta t_j)^2}_{=2(\Delta t_j)^2} + 2 \sum_{j>k} \mathbb{E} f_j f_k ((\Delta W_k)^2 - \Delta t_k) \underbrace{\mathbb{E}((\Delta W_j)^2 - \Delta t_j)}_{=0}$$

$$= \sum_j \mathbb{E} f_j^2 (\Delta t_j)^2 \to 0 \qquad \text{as } |\sigma| \to 0.$$

In the second step, we use the fourth moment of a standard normal to write $\mathbb{E}(\Delta W_j)^4 = 3(\Delta t_j)^2$, and we know that for $j > k$, ΔW_j is independent of $f_j, f_k, \Delta W_k$, since f is adapted. We have shown that

$$\sum_{j=0}^{n-1} f(t_j)(W_{t_{j+1}} - W_{t_j})^2 - \sum_j f(t_j) \Delta t_j \xrightarrow{m.s.} 0.$$

Since f is bounded, the dominated convergence theorem implies that

$$\sum_j f(t_j) \Delta t_j \xrightarrow{a.s.} \int_0^T f(t) dt,$$

where $\xrightarrow{a.s.}$ means almost sure convergence. If f is continuous, then apply Cauchy–Schwartz to obtain

$$\mathbb{E} \left| \sum_j (f(t_j^*) - f(t_j))(\Delta W_j)^2 \right| \leq \left(\mathbb{E} \sup_j |f(t_j^*) - f(t_j)|^2 \right)^{1/2} \left(\mathbb{E} (\sum_{j=1}^{n-1} (\Delta W_j)^2)^2 \right)^{1/2}.$$

The first term on the RHS goes to 0 since f is uniformly continuous on $[0, T]$ and bounded. The second term can be bounded using straightforward calculations by $3T^2$. Therefore, $\sum_j (f(t_j^*) - f(t_j))(\Delta W_j)^2 \to 0$ in $L^1(\Omega)$.

If f is only piecewise continuous, then notice that we can break up the sum on the LHS into partition boxes j with no discontinuity, and partition boxes j with a discontinuity. The sum over those with no discontinuity is bounded by a term that goes to zero in L^1 as above. The sum over those with a discontinuity also goes to zero, because $\sup_j |f(t_j^*) - f(t_j)|^2 < \infty$ since f is bounded and $\mathbb{E}(\sum_{j \text{ discts}} (\Delta W_j)^2)^2 \xrightarrow{m.s.} 0$ since there are only a finite number of discontinuities and the size of the grid boxes is going to 0.

Since mean-square convergence, almost-sure convergence, and $L^1(\Omega)$ convergence all imply convergence in probability, putting the results together gives (7.18). □

PARTIAL PROOF OF ITÔ'S FORMULA. This follows (**Koralov and Sinai, 2007**), (**E et al., 2019**), and (**Øksendal, 2003**). A complete proof can be found in (**Karatzas and Shreve, 1991**) and (**Durrett, 1996**). For simplicity, we consider Itô's formula on a time interval $[0, t]$ for $g = g(x)$; the proof for $g = g(x, t)$ is very similar and introduces no further difficulties. We further assume that g, g_x, g_{xx} are bounded on $\mathbb{R}$; this is the main assumption that is technical to remove. Finally, we assume that b, σ are bounded, adapted step functions. If they are not, we may consider a limit of adapted step functions.[6]

Our strategy is to find—for each $\omega \in \Omega$ in a set of probability 1—a sequence of partitions along which the approximate integrals converge to (7.17), since this implies (7.17) holds for each such ω and, hence, almost surely. Consider a sequence of partitions of $[0, t]$ each of the form $\delta = \{t_0, t_1, \ldots, t_n\}$. We will consider the limit of various approximate integrals as $|\delta| = \sup_j \Delta t_j \to 0$. We may choose each partition such that the discontinuities of b, σ lie on the grid points of the partition.

Write $Y_t = g(X_t) = \sum_{j=0}^{n-1} g(X_{t_{j+1}}) - g(X_{t_j})$ and then use Taylor's theorem to expand about $g(X_{t_j})$ to obtain

$$Y_t - Y_0 = \sum_j g(X_{t_{j+1}}) - g(X_{t_j}) = \sum_j g'(X_{t_j}) \Delta X_j + \sum_j \frac{1}{2} g''(\xi_j)(\Delta X_j)^2,$$

where $\Delta X_j = X_{t_{j+1}} - X_{t_j}$ and ξ_j lies between $X_{t_j}, X_{t_{j+1}}$. Since b, σ have discontinuities on the grid points, $\Delta X_j = b(t_j)\Delta t_j + \sigma(t_j)\Delta W_j$ holds exactly. Therefore, the first term is

$$\sum_j g'(X_{t_j})\Delta X_{t_j} = \sum_j g'(X_{t_j})b(t_j)\Delta t_j + \sum_j g'(t_j)\sigma(t_j)\Delta W_j.$$

But g', b are bounded, so by the dominated convergence theorem,

$$\sum_j g'(X_{t_j})b(t_j)\Delta t_j \xrightarrow{a.s.} \int_0^t g'(X_s)b(s)ds \qquad \text{as } |\delta| \to 0.$$

---

[6]To handle nonbounded g, g_x, g_{xx}, one would use a technique called "'localization": consider Itô's formula up to the stopping time $T_M = \inf\{t : |X_t| \geq M \text{ or } [X]_t \geq M\}$. On $[0, T_M]$ the functions $g(X_t), g_x(X_t), g_{xx}(X_t)$ are bounded, and may be assumed without loss of generality to have compact support, so the proof proceeds as in the text; at the end takes $M \to \infty$ (**Durrett, 1996**). To handle more general b, σ, it is convenient to use a decomposition of $X_t = M_t + A_t$ into a martingale part M_t and a part with bounded variation A_t, so that increments $X_t - X_s$ may be expressed exactly in terms of increments of M_t, A_t, which lead to Itô and Riemann–Stieltjes integrals, respectively, in the limit of fine partitions (**Karatzas and Shreve, 1991**).

Furthermore, by the construction of the Itô integral,

$$\sum_j g'(t_j)\sigma(t_j)\Delta W_j \xrightarrow{m.s.} \int_0^t g'(X_s)\sigma(s)dW_s \qquad \text{as } |\delta| \to 0.$$

For the second term,

$$\frac{1}{2}g''(\xi_j)(\Delta X_j)^2 = \sum_j \frac{1}{2}g''(\xi_j)\left(b^2(t_j)(\Delta t_j)^2 + 2b(t_j)\sigma(t_j)\Delta t_j\Delta W_{t_j} + \sigma^2(t_j)(\Delta W_{t_j})^2\right).$$

The first two terms go to 0 almost surely as $|\delta| \to 0$. Indeed, letting K be a bound for b, σ, g'' on $[0, T]$, we have

$$\left|\sum_j g''(\xi_j)b^2(t_j)(\Delta t_j)^2\right| \le K \sum_j |\Delta t_j|^2 \le KT \sup_j \Delta t_j \to 0 \quad \text{a.s.}.$$

$$\left|\sum_j g''(\xi_j)b(t_j)\sigma(t_j)\Delta t_j\Delta W_{t_{j+1}}\right| \le K \sum_j |\Delta t_j \Delta W_{t_j}| \le KT \sup_j |\Delta W_{t_j}| \to 0 \quad \text{a.s.}.$$

The fact that $\sup_j |\Delta W_{t_j}| \to 0$ as $\sup_j |\Delta t_j| \to 0$ follows because W is continuous with probability 1 on $[0, T]$ and, hence, uniformly continuous. Finally, Lemma 7.16 and the boundedness of g'' give that

$$\sum_j g''(\xi_j)\sigma^2(t_j)(\Delta W_{t_j})^2 \xrightarrow{p} \int_0^t g''(X_s)\sigma^2(s)ds \qquad \text{as } |\delta| \to 0.$$

Since mean-square convergence and almost-sure convergence imply convergence in probability, and since convergence in probability implies there exists a subsequence along which there is almost-sure convergence, along this subsequence we have

$$Y_t - Y_0 = \sum_j g'(X_{t_j})\Delta X_j + \sum_j \frac{1}{2}g''(X_{t_j^*})(\Delta X_j)^2$$

$$\to \int_0^t g'(X_s)b(s)ds + \int_0^t g'(X_s)\sigma(s)dW_s + \int_0^t \frac{1}{2}g''(X_s)\sigma^2(s)ds$$

almost surely, which implies (7.17). $\qquad\square$

7.6. Itô calculus in higher dimensions

We may wish to calculate integrals that depend on several independent Brownian motions, such as $\int W_t^{(2)}dW_t^{(1)}$, $\int e^{W_t^{(1)}+W_t^{(2)}}dW_t^{(3)}$, etc. The Itô integral can be extended to this case.

DEFINITION 7.17. Let $W_t = (W_t^{(1)}, \ldots, W_t^{(n)})^T$ be an n-dimensional Brownian motion (a vector of n independent Brownian motions). Let $M = M(t, \omega)$ be a matrix-valued process that is adapted to W_t. The *multi-dimensional Itô integral* of M is

$$(7.19) \qquad \int_0^\infty MdW_t = \int_0^\infty \begin{pmatrix} M_{11} & M_{12} & \cdots & M_{1n} \\ \vdots & & & \vdots \\ M_{m1} & M_{m2} & \cdots & M_{mn} \end{pmatrix}\begin{pmatrix} dW_t^{(1)} \\ \vdots \\ dW_t^{(n)} \end{pmatrix}.$$

That is, the integral is a vector whose kth component is $\sum_{j=1}^n \int_0^\infty M_{kj}(s, \omega)dW^{(j)}(s, \omega)$.

Itô's formula can be extended to higher dimensions.

THEOREM 7.18 (Itô formula, multidimensional). *Let* X_t *solve*

$$(7.20) \qquad\qquad dX_t = b(t,\omega)dt + \sigma(t,\omega)dW_t,$$

where $X_t, b \in \mathbb{R}^n$, $\sigma \in \mathbb{R}^{n\times m}$, $W_t \in \mathbb{R}^m$, *and* b, σ *are adapted to* W_t. *Let* $Y_t = f(X_t)$, *where* $f \in C^2(\mathbb{R}^n)$. *Then*

$$(7.21) \qquad\qquad dY_t = \nabla f(X_t) \cdot dX_t + \frac{1}{2}(dX_t)^T \nabla^2 f(X_t)\, dX_t,$$

where $\nabla^2 f = \left(\frac{\partial^2 f}{\partial x_i \partial x_j}\right)_{i,j}$ *is the Hessian matrix of* f, *and products of increments are evaluated using the rules following (7.16) plus the additional rule*

$$dW_t^{(i)} \cdot dW_t^{(i)} = dt, \qquad dW_t^{(i)} \cdot dW_t^{(j)} = 0 \qquad \text{for } i \neq j.$$

Therefore, Y_t *solves the equation*

$$(7.22) \qquad dY_t = \left(b \cdot \nabla f(X_t) + \frac{1}{2}\sigma\sigma^T : \nabla^2 f(X_t)\right) dt + (\nabla f(X_t))^T \sigma\, dW_t,$$

where $A : B = \mathrm{Tr}(A^T B) = \sum_{i,j} A_{ij} B_{ij}$.

PROOF. Very similar to the 1D case. □

Exercise 7.3. Give a heuristic justification for (7.21) based on Taylor-expansion as in the example in the previous section.

Exercise 7.4. Verify that $(dX_t)^T \nabla^2 f(X_t) dX_t = (\sigma\sigma^T : \nabla^2 f)dt$.

Example 7.19. Let X_t, Y_t solve the equations

$$X_t = -\gamma X_t dt + \sqrt{2\mu}dW_t^{(1)}, \qquad dY_t = -\gamma Y_t dt + \sqrt{2\mu}dW_t^{(2)},$$

where $W_t^{(1)}, W_t^{(2)}$ are independent Brownian motions. (We will see later that X_t, Y_t are independent *Ornstein–Uhlenbeck* processes; see Example 8.7.) Let us find an evolution equation for $A_t = \sqrt{X_t^2 + Y_t^2}$, the amplitude of the process (X_t, Y_t).

To this aim, we apply Itô's formula with $f(x,y) = \sqrt{x^2 + y^2}$. We calculate

$$\nabla f = \begin{pmatrix} \frac{x}{\sqrt{x^2+y^2}} \\ \frac{y}{\sqrt{x^2+y^2}} \end{pmatrix}, \qquad \nabla^2 f = \begin{pmatrix} \frac{1}{\sqrt{x^2+y^2}} - \frac{x^2}{(x^2+y^2)^{3/2}} & -\frac{xy}{(x^2+y^2)^{3/2}} \\ -\frac{xy}{(x^2+y^2)^{3/2}} & \frac{1}{\sqrt{x^2+y^2}} - \frac{y^2}{(x^2+y^2)^{3/2}} \end{pmatrix}.$$

We have $b(x,y) = (-\gamma x, -\gamma y)^T$, $\sigma(x,y) = \mathrm{diag}(\sqrt{2\mu}, \sqrt{2\mu})$, and $\frac{1}{2}\sigma\sigma^T = \mathrm{diag}(\mu, \mu)$. Putting this together into Itô's formula and substituting the expression for A_t when appropriate gives

$$(7.23) \qquad dA_t = \left(-\gamma A_t + \frac{\mu}{A_t}\right) dt + \sqrt{2\mu}\frac{X_t}{A_t}dW_t^{(1)} + \sqrt{2\mu}\frac{Y_t}{A_t}dW_t^{(2)}.$$

Now, it turns out this equation can be written only in terms of A_t. (This will not always be the case for a general function of the process.) Write the noise term as

$$\sigma(X_t, Y_t)\begin{pmatrix} dW_t^{(1)} \\ dW_t^{(2)} \end{pmatrix}$$

for a 1×2 matrix

$$\sigma(x, y) = \sqrt{2\mu} \left(\frac{x}{\sqrt{x^2 + y^2}} \quad \frac{y}{\sqrt{x^2 + y^2}} \right).$$

It is a useful fact that for an Itô process of the form (7.20), we can replace the noise matrix σ with *any* matrix $\tilde{\sigma}$ such that $\tilde{\sigma}\tilde{\sigma}^T = \sigma\sigma^T$ and obtain a process which is statistically indistinguishable from the original (it has the same finite-dimensional distributions) (**Øksendal, 2003**, Theorem 8.4.3). Since $\sigma\sigma^T = 2\mu$, we may choose $\tilde{\sigma} = \left(\sqrt{2\mu} \quad 0 \right)$ to write (7.23) as

$$(7.24) \qquad dA_t = \left(-\gamma A_t + \frac{\mu}{A_t} \right) dt + \sqrt{2\mu}\, dW_t^{(1)}.$$

We obtain an equation for A_t which depends only on A_t, and not on the individual processes X_t, Y_t. The solution to this equation is known as the *Rayleigh process*.

7.7. Additional exercises

Exercise 7.5. Let $0 = t_0 < t_1 < \cdots < t_n = t$, let $W_j = W(t_j)$, $\Delta W_j = W(t_{j+1}) - W(t_j)$, $\Delta t_j = t_{j+1} - t_j$. Evaluate the mean-square limits of the following sums directly, as $\sup_j \Delta t_j \to 0$:

    (i) $\sum_{j=0}^{n-1} \frac{1}{2}(W_j + W_{j+1})\Delta W_j$;

    (ii) $\sum_{j=0}^{n-1} W_{j+\frac{1}{2}}\Delta W_j$;

    (iii) $\sum_{j=0}^{n-1} W_j^2 \Delta W_j$.

Hint for (iii): Do Exercise 7.6(i) first, so you can guess the answer.

Exercise 7.6.

    (i) Use Ito's formula to evaluate $\int_0^t W_s^2 dW_s$ (your answer will contain a Riemann integral; you can leave it in this form.)

    (ii) Now calculate $\mathbb{E} \int_0^t W_s^2 dW_s$ and $\mathbb{E} \left(\int_0^t W_s^2 dW_s \right)^2$.

        Hint: You will probably *not* want to use your answer from part (a) to do this.

Exercise 7.7. A stochastic differential equation (SDE) is an equation of the form $dX_t = b(t, X_t)dt + \sigma(t, X_t)dW_t$. Find the SDEs satisfied by the following processes:

    (i) $X_t = W_t/(1 + t)$;

    (ii) $X_t = \sin W_t$;

    (iii) $X_t = a\cos W_t$, $Y_t = a\sin W_t$ where $a \neq 0$ (this is Brownian motion on a circle).

Exercise 7.8. Let X_t, Y_t, be Itô processes, i.e., they can be expressed as

$$dX_t = b_1(t, \omega)dt + \sigma_1(t, \omega)dW_t, \qquad dY_t = b_2(t, \omega)dt + \sigma_2(t, \omega)dW_t,$$

where b_i, σ_i, $i = 1, 2$ are adapted functions. Use Itô's formula to derive the product rule:

$$d(X_t Y_t) = X_t dY_t + Y_t dX_t + dX_t dY_t,$$

where dX_t, dY_t should be replaced by their respective formulas, and $dX_t dY_t$ should be replaced by $\sigma_1 \sigma_2 dt$.

***Exercise* 7.9.** Consider the two-dimensional diffusion in polar coordinates:

$$dR_t = R_t dt + 2R_t dW_t^{(1)}, \qquad d\Theta_t = R_t^\alpha dW_t^{(2)},$$

where $\alpha \geq 0$ is a parameter. Convert this equation to Cartesian coordinates, $X_t = R_t \cos \Theta_t$, $Y_t = R_t \sin \Theta_t$.

***Exercise* 7.10.** Let

$$R_t(\omega) = |B_t(\omega)| = \sqrt{B_1^2 + \ldots + B_n^2},$$

where B_t is an n-dimensional Brownian motion with $n \geq 2$. (The transformation is not C^2 at the origin but this is ok when $n \geq 2$ because the process never hits the origin almost surely.) Show that $dR_t = \frac{1}{R_t} \sum_{i=1}^n B_i dB_i + \frac{1}{2} \frac{n-1}{R_t} dt$. Then, find a transformation of the noise as in Example 7.19 to find an equation for R_t whose coefficients depend only on R_t.

CHAPTER 8

Stochastic Differential Equations

We turn to studying stochastic differential equations (SDEs), which are equations of the form

(8.1) $$dX_t = b(X_t, t)dt + \sigma(X_t, t)dW_t, \qquad X_0 = \xi.$$

Here $X_t, b \in \mathbb{R}^n$, $\sigma \in \mathbb{R}^{n \times n}$, and W is an n-dimensional Brownian motion. The initial condition ξ could be random, and is assumed to be independent of W. Recall that (8.1) is shorthand for the integral equation

(8.2) $$X_t = \xi + \int_0^t b(X_s, s)ds + \int_0^t \sigma(X_s, s)dW_s.$$

Each term in (8.1) has a different interpretation.
- The term $b(X_t, t)dt$ is called the *drift* term. It describes the deterministic part of the equation. When this is the only term, we obtain an ODE.
- The term $\sigma(X_t, t)dW_t$ is called the *diffusion* term. It describes random motion proportional to a Brownian motion. Over small times, this term causes probability to spread out diffusively with a diffusivity locally proportional to σ^2.

If the diffusion term is constant in x, i.e., $\frac{\partial \sigma}{\partial x} = 0$, then the noise is said to be *additive*. If the diffusion term depends on x, $\frac{\partial \sigma}{\partial x} \neq 0$, the noise is said to be *multiplicative*. Equations with multiplicative noise have to be treated more carefully than equations with additive noise.

Often we will consider time-homogeneous SDEs where b, σ only depend on x. Any time-inhomogeneous SDE can be converted to a time-homogeneous one by introducing an additional variable $Y_t = t$, so that $dY_t = dt$.

We learned how to define the stochastic integral in (8.2) in the last chapter. In this chapter we will look at properties of the solutions themselves: When do they exist? Are they unique? And how can we find them analytically to extract useful information?

8.1. Existence and uniqueness

THEOREM 8.1. *Given equation (8.1), suppose $b \in \mathbb{R}^n$, $\sigma \in \mathbb{R}^{n \times m}$ satisfy global Lipschitz and linear growth conditions:*

$$|b(x,t) - b(y,t)| + |\sigma(x,t) - \sigma(y,t)| \le K|x - y|$$
$$|b(x,t)| + |\sigma(x,t)| \le K(1 + |x|)$$

for all $x, y \in \mathbb{R}^n$, $t \in [0, T]$, and some constant $K > 0$. Assume the initial value $X_0 = \xi$ is a random variable with $\mathbb{E}\xi^2 < \infty$ and which is independent of W. Then (8.1) has a unique *solution $X = (X_t)_{0 \leq t \leq T}$, such that X is continuous with probability 1, X is adapted[1] to W, and $\mathbb{E} \int_0^T |X_t|^2 dt < \infty$.*

"Unique" means that if $X^{(1)}, X^{(2)}$ are two solutions satisfying the conditions of the theorem, then $P(X^{(1)}(t, \omega) = X^{(2)}(t, \omega)$ for all$0 \leq t \leq T) = 1$. That is, the two solutions are equal everywhere with probability 1. This is different from the statement that $X^{(1)}$, $X^{(2)}$ are versions of each other—you should think about how.

REMARK 8.2. The global Lipschitz condition and linear growth condition ask for constants K that are independent of t. If b, σ are functions of x only, then the Lipschitz condition implies the linear growth condition. When b, σ are also functions of t, the Lipschitz condition implies the linear growth condition only with additional assumptions on how b, σ behave with t—for example, if they are continuous in t or bounded in t.

This theorem bears a lot in common with existence and uniqueness theorems for ODEs. Counterexamples used for ODEs to show the necessity of each of the conditions can also be used for SDEs.

Example 8.3. To construct an equation whose solution is not unique, we drop the condition of Lipschitz continuity. Consider the ODE

$$dX_t = 3X_t^{2/3} dt, \qquad X_0 = 0,$$

which has solutions

$$X_t = \begin{cases} 0 & t \leq a, \\ (t-a)^3 & t > a \end{cases},$$

for any $a > 0$. This does not violate the theorem because $b(x) = 3x^{2/3}$ is not Lipschitz continuous at 0. For a similar example involving a Brownian motion, consider

$$dX_t = 3X_t^{1/3} dt + 3X_t^{2/3} dW_t, \qquad X_0 = 0.$$

This has (at least) two solutions: $X_t = 0$ and $X_t = W_t^3$.

Example 8.4. To construct an equation which has no global solution, we drop the linear growth conditions. Consider

$$dX_t = X_t^2 dt, \qquad X_0 = x_0.$$

The solution is $X_t = \frac{1}{\frac{1}{x_0} - t}$, which blows up at $t = \frac{1}{x_0}$.

REMARK 8.5. In Example 8.4, the drift $b(x) = x^2$ is not globally Lipschitz continuous. It is locally Lipschitz continuous, however, which is sufficient to show uniqueness (**Karatzas and Shreve, 1991**, Section 5, Theorem 2.5).

PROOF (UNIQUENESS)(**Evans, 2013**, Section 5.B.3). Let $X, \hat{X}$ be two solutions to (8.1). Then for $0 \leq t \leq T$,

$$X_t - \hat{X}_t = \int_0^t \big(b(X_s, s) - b(\hat{X}_s, s) \big) \, ds + \int_0^t \big(\sigma(X_s, s) - \sigma(\hat{X}_s, s) \big) \, dW_s.$$

---

[1]Technically, we ask for something slightly stronger, namely that X be progressively measurable with respect to $\mathcal{F}$, the filtration generated by $(W_t)_{t \geq 0}$

Square each side, use $(a + b)^2 \le 2a^2 + 2b^2$, and take expectations to get

$$\mathbb{E}|X_t - \hat{X}_t|^2 \le 2\mathbb{E}\left|\int_0^t \left(b(X_s, s) - b(\hat{X}_s, s)\right) ds\right|^2 + 2\mathbb{E}\left|\int_0^t \left(\sigma(X_s, s) - \sigma(\hat{X}_s, s)\right) dW_s\right|^2.$$

We estimate the first term on the right-hand side using the the Cauchy–Schwarz inequality $\left|\int_0^t f ds\right|^2 \le t \int_0^t |f|^2 ds \le T \int_0^t |f|^2 ds$. We then use the Lipschitz continuity of b. The result is

$$\mathbb{E}\left|\int_0^t \left(b(X_s, s) - b(\hat{X}_s, s)\right) ds\right|^2 \le T\mathbb{E}\int_0^t \left|b(X_s, s) - b(\hat{X}_s, s)\right|^2 ds$$

$$\le K^2 T \int_0^t \mathbb{E}|X_s - \hat{X}_s|^2 ds.$$

We estimate the second term using the Itô isometry and the Lipschitz continuity of σ:

$$\mathbb{E}\left|\int_0^t \left(\sigma(X_s, s) - \sigma(\hat{X}_s, s)\right) dW_s\right|^2 = \int_0^t \mathbb{E}|\sigma(X_s, x) - \sigma(\hat{X}_s, s)|^2 ds \le K^2 \int_0^t \mathbb{E}|X_s - \hat{X}_s|^2 ds.$$

Putting these estimates together shows that

$$\mathbb{E}|X_t - \hat{X}_t|^2 \le C \int_0^t \mathbb{E}|X_s - \hat{X}_s|^2 ds$$

for some constant C, for $0 \le t \le T$. Now we can use Gronwall's inequality, which says that if we are given a function f and nonnegative numbers $a, b \ge 0$ such that

$$f(t) \le a + b \int_0^t f(s) ds, \qquad \text{then} \quad f(t) \le ae^{bt}.$$

The proof is given in Section 8.8.4. Applying Gronwall's inequality with $f(t) = \mathbb{E}|X_t - \hat{X}_t|^2$ and $a = 0$, $b = C$ shows that

$$\mathbb{E}|X_t - \hat{X}_t|^2 = 0 \qquad \text{for all } 0 \le t \le T.$$

Therefore, for each *fixed* $t \in [0, T]$ we have that $X_t = \hat{X}_t$ a.s. That is, $P(\{\omega \in \Omega : X_t(\omega) \neq \hat{X}_t(\omega)\}) = 0$. It remains to show that $X_t = \hat{X}_t$ for all t simultaneously, except for ω in a set of measure 0.

We can argue that $X_r = \hat{X}_r$ for all *rational* $0 \le r \le T$, almost surely. This is because for any countable set of t-values, such as an enumeration of the rationals $\{t_1, t_2, \ldots\}$, we have

$$P(\{\omega : X_t(\omega) \neq \hat{X}_t(\omega) \exists t \in \{t_1, t_2, \ldots\}) = P(\bigcup_i \{\omega : X_{t_i}(\omega) \neq \hat{X}_{t_i}(\omega)\})$$

$$\le \sum_i P(\{\omega : X_{t_i}(\omega) \neq \hat{X}_{t_i}(\omega)\}) = 0.$$

Therefore, $P(\{\omega : X_t(\omega) = \hat{X}_t(\omega) \ \forall t \in \{t_1, t_2, \ldots\}) = 1$. By assumption $X, \hat{X}$ have continuous sample paths almost surely, so we can extend the equality to all values of t using the fact that the rationals form a dense set in $\mathbb{R}$. Therefore, $P(X_t = \hat{X}_t \ \forall t \in [0, T]) = 1$. $\qquad \square$

PROOF (EXISTENCE). This proof follows (**Evans, 2013**, Section 5.B.3); see also (**Varadhan, 2007**, Theorem 6.1, p. 88). It uses some results from probability theory that can be found in any graduate probability text.

The proof is based on Picard iteration, as for the typical ODE existence proof. For simpler notation, we consider a one-dimensional SDE but the proof is almost identical in higher dimensions. Let the 0th iterate be $X_t^0 = \xi$, and define the $(n + 1)$th iterate as

$$X_t^{n+1} = X_0 + \int_0^t b(X_s^n, s)ds + \int_0^t \sigma(X_s^n, s)dW_s, \qquad n = 1, 2, \ldots, \quad 0 \leq t \leq T.$$

One can verify by induction that X^{n+1} is adapted (and progressively measurable), continuous almost surely, and has $\sup_{0 \leq t \leq T} \mathbb{E}|X_t^{n+1}|^2 < \infty$. This implies that

$$\mathbb{E}\int_0^T |\sigma(X_s^{n+1}, s)|^2 ds < \infty$$

so the next iterate is well defined. Let the mean-squared difference between successive iterates be

$$D^n(t) = \mathbb{E}|X_t^{n+1} - X_t^n|^2.$$

We claim that

$$D^n(t) \leq \frac{(Mt)^{n+1}}{(n+1)!}$$

for some constant M depending on K, T, ξ. We prove this by induction. For $n = 0$, substituting $X_0 = \xi$,

$$D^0(t) = \mathbb{E}|X_t^1 - X_t^0|^2 \leq 2\mathbb{E}\left|\int_0^t K(1 + |\xi|)ds\right|^2 + 2\mathbb{E}\int_0^t K^2(1 + |\xi|)^2 ds \leq \frac{tM}{1!}$$

for some M large enough. The first term uses the linear growth bound on b, and the second term uses the Itô isometry and the linear growth bound on σ. Next, assume the claim holds for $n - 1$ and calculate

$$D^n(t) = \mathbb{E}\left|\int_0^t (b(X_s^n, s) - b(X_s^{n-1}, s))ds + \int_0^t (\sigma(X_s^n, s) - \sigma(X_s^{n-1}, s))dW_s\right|^2$$

$$\leq 2TK^2\mathbb{E}\int_0^t |X_s^n - X_s^{n-1}|^2 ds + 2K^2\mathbb{E}\int_0^t |X_s^n - X_s^{n-1}|^2 ds,$$

following the same calculations as in the proof of uniqueness. Therefore, by the induction hypothesis,

$$D^n(t) \leq 2K^2(1 + T)\int_0^t \frac{M^n s^n}{n!} ds \leq \frac{(Mt)^{n+1}}{(n+1)!},$$

provided $M \geq 2K^2(1 + T)$. We use this result to bound the maximum difference between iterates. By the triangle inequality,

$$\max_{0 \leq t \leq T} |X_t^{n+1} - X_t^n|^2 \leq 2\max_{0 \leq t \leq T}\left|\int_0^t (b(X_s^n, s) - b(X_s^{n-1}, s))ds\right|^2$$

$$+ 2\max_{0 \leq t \leq T}\left|\int_0^t (\sigma(X_s^n, s) - \sigma(X_s^{n-1}, s))dW_s\right|^2.$$

For the first term on the RHS, we have, from Lipschitz continuity,

$$\mathbb{E} \max_{0 \leq t \leq T} \left| \int_0^t (b(X_s^n, s) - b(X_s^{n-1}, s)) ds \right|^2 \leq TK^2 \int_0^T \mathbb{E}|X_s^n - X_s^{n-1}|^2 ds.$$

For the second term on the RHS, we use a martingale inequality, which says that, given a process $M = (M_t)_{t \geq 0}$ which is a martingale[2] with respect to W, we have that $\mathbb{E}\left(\max_{0 \leq s \leq t} |X_s|^p\right) \leq \frac{p}{p-1}\mathbb{E}|X_t|^p$, for $1 < p < \infty$. Applying this inequality with $p = 2$ to the integrand in the second term, which can be shown to be a martingale and then using Lipschitz continuity, gives

$$\mathbb{E} \max_{0 \leq t \leq T} \left| \int_0^t (\sigma(X_s^n, s) - \sigma(X_s^{n-1}, s)) dW_s \right|^2 \leq 2\mathbb{E}\left| \int_0^t (\sigma(X_s^n, s) - \sigma(X_s^{n-1}, s)) dW_s \right|^2$$

$$\leq 4K^2 \int_0^T \mathbb{E}|X_s^n - X_s^{n-1}|^2 ds.$$

Putting this together shows that

$$\mathbb{E} \max_{0 \leq t \leq T} |X_t^{n+1} - X_t^n|^2 \leq C\frac{(MT)^{n+1}}{(n+1)!}$$

for some constant C. We now use this to show that $X_t^0 + \sum_{j=0}^{n-1}(X_t^{n+1} - X_t^n)$ converges in some sense as $n \to \infty$. Chebyshev's inequality implies that

$$P\left(\max_{0 \leq t \leq T} |X_t^{n+1} - X_t^n| > \frac{1}{2^n}\right) \leq 2^{2n}\mathbb{E} \max_{0 \leq t \leq T} |X_t^{n+1} - X_t^n|^2 \leq 2^{2n}C\frac{(MT)^n}{n!}.$$

Since $\sum_{n=1}^{\infty} 2^{2n}C\frac{(MT)^n}{n!} < \infty$, we may apply the Borel–Cantelli lemma to say that

$$P\left(\max_{0 \leq t \leq T} |X_t^{n+1} - X_t^n| > \frac{1}{2^n} \text{ i.o.}\right) = 0.$$

Therefore, for almost every $\omega \in \Omega$,

$$X_t^n = X_t^0 + \sum_{j=0}^{n-1}(X_t^{n+1} - X_t^n)$$

converges uniformly on $[0, T]$ to a process X, which is adapted (and progressively measurable) and almost surely continuous. One can check that X is a solution to (8.1) by passing to the limit in the integrals defining X^n. The final step is to verify that $\mathbb{E}\int_0^T X_t^2 dt < \infty$. We do this by induction. We have

$$\mathbb{E}|X_t^{n+1}|^2 \leq C\mathbb{E}|X_0^2| + C\mathbb{E}\left| \int_0^t b(X_s^n, s) ds \right|^2 + C\mathbb{E}\left| \int_0^t \sigma(X_s^n, s) dW_s \right|^2$$

where C denotes a constant (whose value will change line by line). Applying the linear growth condition and the Itô isometry,

$$\mathbb{E}\left| \int_0^t b(X_s^n, s) ds \right|^2 \leq \mathbb{E}\int_0^t K^2(1 + |X_s^n|)^2 ds,$$

$$\mathbb{E}\left| \int_0^t \sigma(X_s^n, s) dW_s \right|^2 = \int_0^t \mathbb{E}|\sigma(X_s^n, s)|^2 ds \leq \mathbb{E}\int_0^t K^2(1 + |X_s^n|)^2 ds,$$

---

[2] $\mathbb{E}|M_t| < \infty$ and $\mathbb{E}[M_t|(W_u)_{0 \leq u \leq s}] = M_s$ for all $s \leq t$.

so, therefore,

$$\mathbb{E}|X_t^{n+1}|^2 \le C(1 + \mathbb{E}|X_0|^2) + C \int_0^t \mathbb{E}|X_s^n|^2 ds.$$

By induction,

$$\mathbb{E}|X_t^{n+1}|^2 \le (C + C^2 t + \cdots + C^{n+2} \frac{t^{n+1}}{(n+1)!})(1 + \mathbb{E}|X_0|^2) \le C(1 + \mathbb{E}|X_0|^2)e^{Ct}.$$

As $n \to \infty$, we obtain

$$\mathbb{E}|X_t|^2 \le C(1 + \mathbb{E}|X_0|^2)e^{Ct}, \qquad 0 \le t \le T.$$

□

The proof above showed a useful growth bound on the solution.

PROPOSITION 8.6. *Given a solution to* (8.1) *satisfying the conditions of Theorem 8.1, the solution satisfies*

(8.3) $$\mathbb{E}|X_t|^2 \le C(1 + \mathbb{E}|X_0|^2)e^{Ct}, \qquad 0 \le t \le T,$$

where C is a constant depending on T, K.

8.2. Examples of SDEs and their solutions

Example 8.7. The *Ornstein–Uhlenbeck process* (OU process) is the solution to the one-dimensional SDE

(8.4) $$dX_t = -aX_t dt + \sigma dW_t, \qquad X_0 = \xi,$$

where ξ is independent of $(W_t)_{t \ge 0}$ and $a, \sigma \in \mathbb{R}$ are constants with $a > 0$. This process has additive noise. The drift term causes the process to initially decay exponentially to zero, and when it gets close the noise becomes important and causes the process to fluctuate about zero (Figure 8.1).

The OU process is frequently used in models. For example, it is used to model the deviation from rest length X_t of a polymer or ligand in solution (or some other object which behaves approximately like a harmonic spring), where $a = k/\gamma$ is the effective spring constant k of the polymer divided by the hydrodynamic friction coefficient γ; and $\sigma = \sqrt{2k_B T/\gamma}$ captures the thermal fluctuations in the fluid, which depend on temperature T and Boltzmann constant k_B. It is also used to model financial objects, such as stock prices or interest rate fluctuations, where it is known as the Vasicek model of interest rate fluctuations. These models often include an additional term $\mu a dt$ on the right-hand side, which shifts the mean to μ. In general, an OU process arises from linearizing any SDE about a stable fixed point x_0 where the drift goes to zero, $b(x_0) = 0$, but the diffusion term remains bounded away from zero, $\sigma(x_0) > 0$.

Let us solve explicitly for the solution to (8.4). Multiply both sides by e^{at} and integrate from 0 to t:

$$\underbrace{e^{at} dX_t + ae^{at} X_t dt}_{=d(e^{at} X_t)} = \sigma e^{at} dW_t \qquad \Rightarrow \qquad e^{at} X_t - X_0 = \int_0^t \sigma e^{as} dW_s.$$

This gives solution

(8.5) $$X_t = e^{-at} X_0 + \sigma \int_0^t e^{-a(t-s)} dW_s.$$

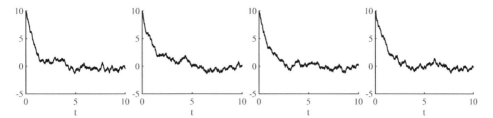

FIGURE 8.1. Realizations of an Ornstein-Uhlenbeck process with $\alpha = \sigma = 1$ and initial condition $X_0 = 10$.

The first term shows the initial condition is "forgotten" exponentially quickly. The second term represents the stochastic fluctuations and is similar to the convolution of an exponential kernel with white noise, $e^{-at} * \dfrac{dW}{dt}$, except the convolution only looks at values in the past. This term is Gaussian, since it is a linear functional applied to a Gaussian process. Hence, if X_0 is Gaussian, then $(X_t)_{t \geq 0}$ is a Gaussian process.

From (8.5) we can calculate the moments of X_t. The mean is

$$\mathbb{E}X_t = e^{-at}\mathbb{E}X_0.$$

The mean decays exponentially to 0, $\mathbb{E}X_t \to 0$ as $t \to \infty$. The covariance is (recalling the calculations to show (7.11))

$$B(s,t) = \mathbb{E}X_s X_t - \mathbb{E}X_s \mathbb{E}X_t$$

$$= e^{-as}e^{-at}(\mathbb{E}X_0^2 - (\mathbb{E}X_0)^2) + \sigma^2 \int_0^s \int_0^t e^{-a(t-v)}e^{-a(s-u)} \underbrace{\mathbb{E}dW_u dW_v}_{=\delta(u-v)dudv}$$

$$= e^{-a(s+t)} \operatorname{Var}(X_0) + \sigma^2 \int_0^{s\wedge t} e^{-a(s-u)}e^{-a(t-u)}du$$

$$= e^{-a(s+t)} \operatorname{Var}(X_0) + \frac{\sigma^2}{2a}e^{-a(s+t)}\left(e^{2a(s\wedge t)} - 1\right)$$

$$= e^{-a(s+t)} \operatorname{Var}(X_0) + \frac{\sigma^2}{2a}\left(e^{-a|s-t|} - e^{-a(s+t)}\right).$$

If $s, t \to \infty$ with $s - t$ fixed, the covariance approaches $B(s,t) \to \frac{\sigma^2}{2a}e^{-a|s-t|}$, the covariance function for a weakly stationary process.

Now, consider what happens if we take the distribution of X_0 to be normal, with the long-time mean and variance $X_0 \sim N(0, \frac{\sigma^2}{2a})$. The mean and covariance at all times are

$$\mathbb{E}X_t = 0, \qquad B(s,t) = \frac{\sigma^2}{2a}e^{-a|s-t|}.$$

Therefore, X is weakly stationary, and since X is Gaussian, it is also strongly stationary. Further, since X is Gaussian we must have $X_t \sim N(0, \frac{\sigma^2}{2a})$ for all $t \geq 0$. Such a distribution, which does not change with time, is called a *stationary distribution*. We found it here by a clever guess but later we will learn a systematic way to find the stationary distribution.

It turns out the Ornstein–Uhlenbeck process with initial condition as above is the only process that is *stationary, Markov, Gaussian*, and that has *continuous paths*.

Example 8.8. A *Geometric Brownian motion* (GBM) is the solution to the one-dimensional SDE

$$(8.6) \qquad\qquad dN_t = rN_t dt + \alpha N_t dW_t, \qquad N_0 = \xi,$$

where $r, \alpha \in \mathbb{R}$ are parameters. This process has multiplicative noise. It models systems that grow in proportion to their size, such as a population, where N_t is the population size at time t, r is the average growth rate, and αdW_t captures fluctuations in the growth rate. It is also used to model the price of financial assets, such as stocks, where N_t is the price of the stock, r is the rate of return, and α is the volatility.

Let us find an analytic expression for the solution. Divide (8.6) by N_t:

$$\frac{dN_t}{N_t} = rdt + \alpha dW_t.$$

It would be nice to write the LHS as $d(\log N_t)$ but we cannot, since we need to use Itô's formula. Instead, we calculate

$$d(\log N_t) = \frac{1}{N_t}dN_t - \frac{(dN_t)^2}{2N_t^2} = \frac{1}{N_t}dN_t - \frac{\alpha^2}{2}dt.$$

Now, substitute for dN_t using the equation to get

$$d(\log N_t) = (r - \frac{\alpha^2}{2})dt + \alpha dW_t.$$

Integrate and take the exponential to find the solution as

$$(8.7) \qquad\qquad N_t = N_0 e^{(r-\frac{\alpha^2}{2})t + \alpha W_t}.$$

Let us look at properties of this solution. First, notice that it does not change signs. Therefore, if $N_0 > 0$, then $N_t > 0$ for all t. This is in contrast to the OU process, which fluctuates about 0, attaining positive and negative values in equal measure.

Next, let us calculate the mean, $\mathbb{E}N_t$. It is possible to calculate this from the solution formula (8.7) (see Exercise 8.1) but a simpler calculation starts by writing (8.6) in integral form, taking the expectation and using the nonanticipating property to obtain an integral equation,

$$\mathbb{E}N_t = \int_0^t r\mathbb{E}N_s ds + \mathbb{E}N_0.$$

This equation can be solved by taking the time derivative and solving the corresponding ODE to obtain

$$(8.8) \qquad\qquad \mathbb{E}N_t = (\mathbb{E}N_0)e^{rt}.$$

Therefore, the mean grows with the average growth rate.

Exercise 8.1. Derive (8.8) in an alternative way: find the mean of $Y_t = e^{\alpha W_t}$ by calculating dY_t, expressing Y_t as an Itô integral, and then using the nonanticipating property.

Finally, let us examine the trajectories themselves—do they also increase with the average rate? Recall the law of the iterated logarithm, which says that

$$\limsup_{t \to \infty} \frac{W_t}{\sqrt{2t \log \log t}} = 1 \qquad \text{a.s.}$$

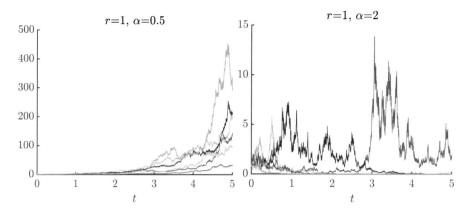

FIGURE 8.2. Trajectories of GBM with different parameters. Left: $r > \alpha^2/2$, so that $N_t \to \infty$ a.s. and $\mathbb{E}N_t \to \infty$. Right: $r < \alpha^2/2$, so that $N_t \to 0$ a.s. but $\mathbb{E}N_t \to \infty$. This is possible because trajectories exhibit large but rare excursions. Each plot shows 6 independent trajectories with parameters shown in titles.

This implies that the supremum of $e^{\alpha W_t}$ grows as $e^{\alpha\sqrt{2t \log \log t}}$ as $t \to \infty$, which is slower than linear in the exponential. Therefore, the trajectory behavior depends on the deterministic growth rate $r - \frac{\alpha^2}{2}$ in the exponential:

• If $r > \frac{\alpha^2}{2}$, then $N_t \to \infty$ a.s. as $t \to \infty$.

• If $r < \frac{\alpha^2}{2}$, then $N_t \to 0$ a.s.

• If $r = \frac{\alpha^2}{2}$, then N_t will fluctuate between values that are arbitrarily large and arbitrarily close to zero, a.s.

Notice that the mean and the trajectory do not always behave the same way at ∞. If $0 < r < \frac{\alpha^2}{2}$, then $\mathbb{E}N_t \to \infty$ while $N_t \to 0$ a.s.! This apparent paradox arises because increasingly large (but rare) fluctuations dominate the expectation (Figure 8.2). It is worth pausing to think about this.

Example 8.9 (Stochastically forced harmonic oscillator). Consider an ODE for a forced, damped harmonic oscillator X:

$$(8.9) \qquad m\frac{d^2 X_t}{dt^2} + \gamma\frac{dX_t}{dt} + kX_t = f(t).$$

Here m is the oscillator's mass, k is its spring constant, γ is a damping coefficient modeling frictional damping, and $f(t)$ is the external forcing. The quantity X_t could represent, for example, the deviation of a spring from its rest length, or the angle of a pendulum such as a swing, under small perturbations from its rest state.

From mechanics, we know that when an undamped ($\gamma = 0$) harmonic oscillator is forced periodically, as $f(t) = \sin \lambda t$, then, when the forcing frequency does not equal the resonant frequency, $\lambda \neq \omega = \sqrt{k/m}$, the oscillations are bounded, and usually quite small—if you pump your legs on a swing too quickly or too slowly, the swing does not move very much. However, when the frequency of the forcing exactly equals

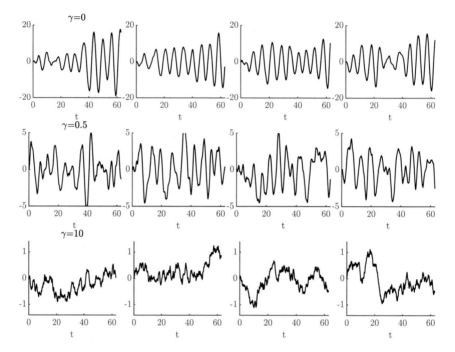

FIGURE 8.3. Realizations of a harmonic oscillator forced with white noise, with $k = 1, m = 1, \sigma = 2$, and different damping parameters $\gamma = 0, 0.5, 10$ (top,middle,bottom). The time period for each is 10 natural periods $(T = 10 \cdot 2\pi/k)$, and the vertical scales are different for each damping parameter since with no damping, the solution eventually diverges.

the resonant frequency, $f(t) = \sin(\omega t)$, the oscillations will grow without bound—on a frictionless swingset, you could make the swing go all the way around the swingset.

What happens when the forcing is stochastic? If you pump your legs completely at random, will you swing?

We answer this by letting $f(t) = \sigma \eta(t)$, where $\eta(t)$ is a white noise, and finding the solution to (8.9). We can write this equation as an SDE by letting $V_t = \frac{dX_t}{dt}$:

$$
\begin{aligned}
dX_t &= V_t dt \\
mdV_t &= (-kX_t - \gamma V_t)dt + \sigma dW_2.
\end{aligned}
$$

This SDE has the form

$$
dU_t = -AU_t dt + BdW_t,
$$

where

$$
U = \begin{pmatrix} X_t \\ V_t \end{pmatrix}, \quad W_t = \begin{pmatrix} W_t^{(1)} \\ W_t^{(2)} \end{pmatrix}, \quad A = \begin{pmatrix} 0 & -1 \\ \frac{k}{m} & \frac{\gamma}{m} \end{pmatrix}, \quad B = \begin{pmatrix} 0 & 0 \\ 0 & \frac{\sigma}{m} \end{pmatrix}.
$$

This is a two-dimensional Ornstein–Uhlenbeck process. We can solve it in the same way as in Example 8.7 using an integrating factor:

$$d(e^{At}U_t) = e^{At}dU_t + Ae^{At}U_t dt$$
$$= e^{At}(-AU_t dt + BdW_t) + Ae^{At}U_t dt$$
$$= e^{At}BdW_t$$

$$\Rightarrow \quad U_t = e^{-At}U_0 + \int_0^t e^{-A(t-s)}BdW_s.$$

In fact, by letting A, B be any $n \times n$ matrices, we have just derived a solution formula for an arbitrary n-dimensional Ornstein–Uhlenbeck process.

Consider how the solution behaves under different assumptions on the damping.

Case $\gamma = 0$ (no damping). Then A has eigenvalues $\lambda = \pm i\omega$ and corresponding eigenvectors $u_1 = (1, -i\omega)^T$, $u_2 = (1, i\omega)^T$. Then $e^{At} = Ue^{Dt}U^{-1}$, with $U = (u_1 \ u_2)$, $D = \text{diag}(i\omega, -i\omega)$. Therefore,

$$e^{At} = \begin{pmatrix} \cos \omega t & -\frac{1}{\omega} \sin \omega t \\ -\omega \sin \omega t & \cos \omega t \end{pmatrix}.$$

If the oscillator initially starts at rest, $X_0 = 0$, $X_0' = 0$, then

$$X_t = \frac{\sigma}{m\omega} \int_0^t \sin \omega(s - t) \, dW_t^{(2)}.$$

What happens to this solution as $t \to \infty$? We claim it grows without bound. To see why, calculate the variance of the solution, observing first that $\mathbb{E}X_t = 0$ by the nonanticipating property of the Itô integral. The variance, therefore, is

$$\mathbb{E}X_t^2 = \frac{\sigma^2}{m^2\omega^2} \int_0^t (\sin \omega(s - t))^2 ds \qquad \text{(Itô isometry)}$$

$$= \frac{\sigma^2}{m^2\omega^2} \left(\frac{t}{2} - \frac{\sin 2\omega t}{4\omega} \right)$$

$$\sim \frac{\sigma^2}{m^2\omega^2} \frac{t}{2} \quad \to \infty \qquad \text{as } t \to \infty.$$

A stochastically forced swingset will swing! If you pump your legs completely at random, you can make a frictionless swing go as high as you want. It is somewhat remarkable that although you are forcing all frequencies equally, and all of these frequencies except one are nonresonant, you still have enough forcing near the resonant frequency to make the oscillations grow. See Figure 8.3 (top) for some realizations with $\gamma = 0$.

Case $\gamma \neq 0$ (with damping). In this case the eigenvalues of A have a real *and* imaginary part. The real part is negative and leads to exponential damping. The imaginary part leads to oscillations, with a frequency that is slightly shifted from the resonant frequency ω.

One way to gain insight into the properties of the solution is to assume that a stationary solution exists, look for its covariance function $C(t)$, and then calculate the spectral density $f(\lambda)$. To this aim, consider (8.9) at times 0 and t, and multiply these equations together to get

$$(mX_t'' + kX_t + \gamma X_t')(mX_0'' + kX_0 + \gamma X_0') = \sigma^2 \eta(t)\eta(0).$$

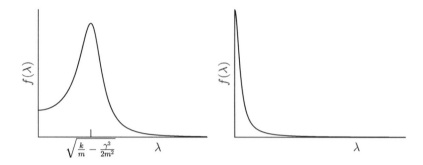

FIGURE 8.4. Spectral density for a stationary swing, with small damping (left, $\gamma = 0.5$), and large damping (right, $\gamma = 10$).

Now, take the expectation and use the relationships

$$\mathbb{E}X'_t X_0 = -\mathbb{E}X_t X'_0 = C'(t), \quad \mathbb{E}X'_t X'_0 = -C''(t), \quad \mathbb{E}X_t X''_0 = \mathbb{E}X''_t X_0 = C''(t),$$

$$\mathbb{E}X''_t X'_0 = -\mathbb{E}X'_t X''_0 = C'''(t), \quad \mathbb{E}X''_t X''_0 = C^{(4)}(t).$$

These relationships are obtained by differentiating $C(t) = \mathbb{E}X_{t+s}X_s = \mathbb{E}X_s X_{s-t}$ in time.
We get

$$m^2 C^{(4)}(t) + k^2 C(t) - \gamma^2 C''(t) + 2mkC''(t) = \sigma^2 \delta(t).$$

Taking the Fourier transform of this equation gives an equation for the spectral density
$f(\lambda)$:

$$m^2 \lambda^4 f(\lambda) + k^2 f(\lambda) + \gamma^2 \lambda^2 f(\lambda) - 2mk\lambda^2 f(\lambda) = \frac{\sigma^2}{2\pi}.$$

Solving for $f(\lambda)$ gives

$$f(\lambda) = \frac{1}{2\pi} \frac{\sigma^2}{(m\lambda^2 - k)^2 + \lambda^2 \gamma^2}.$$

This spectral density is plotted in Figure 8.4 for small and large damping γ. For small
enough damping, the density has a peak at $\tilde{\lambda} = \sqrt{\frac{k}{m} - \frac{\gamma^2}{2m^2}}$, which is less than the resonant frequency $\sqrt{k/m}$. The swing swings, with random oscillations near frequency
$\tilde{\lambda}$, but the oscillations stay bounded (Figure 8.3 (middle)). For large damping, the density is peaked at $\tilde{\lambda} = 0$, and trajectories are much more jagged (Figure 8.3 (bottom)).
When $\gamma = 0$, the spectral density is not integrable, so we would not expect a stationary
solution.

Exercise 8.2. Write down the solution to (8.9) explicitly when $\gamma \neq 0$.

8.3. Stratonovich integral

The Stratonovich integral (Definition 7.3) is another useful stochastic integral.
There is a simple formula that relates it to the Itô integral.

THEOREM 8.10. *Suppose X solves the Stratonovich equation*

(8.10) $$dX_t = b(X_t, t)dt + \sigma(X_t, t) \circ dW_t.$$

Then X also solves the Itô equation

(8.11) $$dX_t = \left(b(X_t, t) + \frac{1}{2}\sigma(X_t, t)\frac{\partial}{\partial x}\sigma(X_t, t)\right)dt + \sigma(X_t, t)dW_t.$$

Conversely, suppose X solves the Itô equation

(8.12) $$dX_t = b(X_t, t)dt + \sigma(X_t, t)dW_t.$$

Then X also solves the Stratonovich equation

(8.13) $$dX_t = \left(b(X_t, t) - \frac{1}{2}\sigma(X_t, t)\frac{\partial}{\partial x}\sigma(X_t, t)\right)dt + \sigma(X_t, t) \circ dW_t.$$

Therefore, a Stratonovich SDE is equivalent to an Itô SDE with an additional drift term. The drift arises only when the noise is multiplicative and it depends on the rate of change of the magnitude of the noise. Heuristically, there is an extra drift because the Stratonovich integral can "see" into the future, so it needs to account for the changing magnitude of the noise.

REMARK 8.11. To transform a Stratonovich SDE to an Itô SDE and vice versa, the diffusion term σ must be differentiable. However, we do not need such an assumption to show existence and uniqueness of the solutions to the SDEs.

PROOF SKETCH (**Pavliotis, 2014**, p. 62). Here is a sketch of the proof. To make it rigorous, one needs to control the error terms. Suppose X solves (8.10), which, as we recall, is shorthand for the integral equation

$$X_t = X_0 + \int_0^t b(X_s, s)ds + \int_0^t \sigma(X_s, s) \circ dW_s.$$

The Riemann integral is unaffected by the definition of the stochastic integral. Therefore, we consider how the Stratonovich integral in the expression above can be transformed into an Itô integral. Let $\{t_j\}_{j=0}^n$ be a partition of $[0, t]$ and write $\sigma_j \equiv \sigma(X_{t_j}, t_j)$ (and similarly for W, X) with increments $\Delta W_j = W_{t_{j+1}} - W_{t_j}$, $\Delta X_j = X_{t_{j+1}} - X_{t_j}$, $\Delta t_j = t_{j+1} - t_j$. Let $\Delta t = \sup_j \Delta t_j$. The Stratonovich integral is

(8.14) $$\int_0^t \sigma(X_s, s) \circ dW_s = \text{m. s.} \lim_{\Delta t \to 0} \sum_j \left[\frac{\sigma_j + \sigma_{j+1}}{2}\right](W_{j+1} - W_j).$$

Now, we estimate σ_{j+1} using a Taylor expansion about σ_j, keeping only terms up to $O(\sqrt{\Delta t_j})$, since we will be multiplying them by $\Delta W_j \sim O(\sqrt{\Delta t_j})$.

$$\sigma_{j+1} = \sigma_j + \frac{\partial \sigma_j}{\partial x}\Delta X_j + O((\Delta X_j)^2)$$

$$= \sigma_j + \frac{\partial \sigma_j}{\partial x}\left(b_j\Delta t_j + \left(\frac{\sigma_j + \sigma_{j+1}}{2}\right)\Delta W_j + O(\Delta t)\right) + O(\Delta t_j)$$

(using (8.10) to approximate ΔX_j)

$$= \sigma_j + \frac{\partial \sigma_j}{\partial x}\left(b_j\Delta t_j + \left(\frac{\sigma_j + \sigma_j + \frac{\partial \sigma_j}{\partial x}\Delta X_j}{2}\right)\Delta W_j\right) + O(\Delta t_j)$$

(substituting for σ_{j+1} from first line)

$$= \sigma_j + \frac{\partial \sigma_j}{\partial x}\sigma_j\Delta W_j + O(\Delta t_j).$$

Now substitute the approximation for σ_{j+1} into (8.14) to obtain

$$\int_0^t \sigma(X_s, s) \circ dW_s = \text{m.s.} \lim_{\Delta t \to 0} \sum_j \left(\sigma_j + \frac{1}{2} \frac{\partial \sigma_j}{\partial x} \sigma_j \Delta W_j \right) \Delta W_j + O((\Delta t_j)^{3/2})$$

$$= \int_0^t \sigma(X_s, s) dW_s + \int_0^t \frac{1}{2} \frac{\partial \sigma(X_s, s)}{\partial x} \sigma(X_s, s) ds.$$

This gives us the extra drift term in (8.11). Therefore, X also solves the Itô equation (8.11).   □

Example 8.12 (Geometric Brownian motion, revisited). Consider the Stratonovich equation

$$dN_t = rN_t dt + \alpha N_t \circ dW_t.$$

This is equivalent to the Itô equation

$$dN_t = (r + \frac{1}{2}\alpha^2)N_t dt + \alpha N_t dW_t,$$

whose solution we found earlier to be $N_t = N_0 e^{rt + \alpha W_t}$. This is also the solution we would have found using the regular chain rule $d(\log N_t) = dN_t / N_t$.

Why use the Stratonovich integral? There are several advantages.
- The regular chain rule holds: $df(X_t) = f'(X_t) \circ dX_t$ (Exercise 8.6).
- If you start with smooth nonwhite noise in a one-dimensional ODE, and take a limit to make the noise white, you typically end up with a Stratonovich SDE. For example, consider the system

$$\frac{dx^\epsilon}{dt} = b(x^\epsilon)dt + \sigma(x^\epsilon)\frac{y^\epsilon(t)}{\epsilon}, \qquad dy_t^\epsilon = -\frac{1}{\epsilon^2}y_t dt + \frac{1}{\epsilon}dW_t,$$

  where $x^\epsilon, y^\epsilon \in \mathbb{R}$. The process x^ϵ solves an ODE, whose right-hand side involves a stochastic process y^ϵ, which has a nonzero correlation in time and, hence, provides a so-called colored noise forcing to the ODE. The stationary covariance function for the noise $\eta_t^\epsilon = y^\epsilon / \epsilon$ is $C^\epsilon(t) = \frac{1}{2\epsilon^2} e^{-\frac{1}{\epsilon^2}|t-s|}$. As $\epsilon \to 0$, this approaches the covariance function for white noise, $C^\epsilon(t) \to \delta(t)$. One can show that x^ϵ approaches the solution to the Stratonovich SDE

$$dX_t = b(X_t) + \sigma(X_t) \circ dW_t.$$

  (See Section 13.13.1 for these calculations.) It is of note that this correspondence between a colored noise process and a Stratonovich SDE only holds in one dimension; in higher dimensions the convergence is more complicated (**Pavliotis, 2014**, Section 5.1).
- If you restrict your process to lie on a submanifold of $\mathbb{R}^n$, the most natural way to do this is through the Stratonovich integral. For example, "Brownian motion" on the surface of a d-dimensional sphere is the solution to

$$dX_t = P(X_t) \circ dW_t,$$

  where $W \in \mathbb{R}^d$ is a d-dimensional Brownian motion and $P(x)$ is the orthogonal projection matrix onto the tangent space to the surface of the sphere at x (See Exercise 8.9).

What are the disadvantages?

- The Itô isometry no longer holds.
- The nonanticipating property no longer holds; the Stratonovich integral "looks into the future."

These losses make rigorously analyzing the Stratonovich integral significantly harder. Mathematically, the Itô integral is a "martingale" but the Stratonovich integral is not; since there are many powerful tools developed for matingales it is more convenient to use the Itô integral to develop the theory of diffusion processes.

Does it matter which integral you use? Not really—you can usually convert from one to the other.

In multiple dimensions the conversion is given as follows.

THEOREM 8.13. *Given $X_t, b \in \mathbb{R}^n, \sigma \in \mathbb{R}^{n \times m}, W_t \in \mathbb{R}^m$. The Stratonovich equation*

$$(8.15) \qquad\qquad dX_t = b(X_t, t)dt + \sigma(X_t, t) \circ dW_t$$

is equivalent to the Itô equation

$$(8.16) \qquad\qquad dX_t = (b(X_t, t) + h(X_t, t))\, dt + \sigma(X_t, t)dW_t.$$

The additional drift term is

$$(8.17) \quad h = \frac{1}{2}\left(\nabla \cdot (\sigma\sigma^T) - \sigma\nabla \cdot \sigma^T\right), \quad \textit{with components} \quad h_i = \frac{1}{2}\sum_{j=1}^{n}\sum_{k=1}^{m}\sigma_{jk}\frac{\partial \sigma_{ik}}{\partial x_j}.$$

The additional drift also satisfies the relationship $h \cdot v = \frac{1}{2}\sigma^T : \nabla(\sigma^T v)$ for all $v \in \mathbb{R}^n$.

A caution on using the Stratonovich correction. To apply the Itô–Stratonovich conversion, it is *very* important that X_t solves an SDE—the coefficients of the equation must depend only on X_t, t and *not* on any other processes, as the following example shows.

Example 8.14. Consider the following one-dimensional equation:

$$(8.18) \qquad dY_t = b(X_t) \circ dW_t, \qquad \text{where} \quad dX_t = \alpha(X_t)dt + \beta(X_t)dW_t.$$

(The same Brownian motion is used for both processes.) It is tempting—but wrong—to convert the equation for Y_t to Itô form using the conversion rule for a one-dimensional diffusion, as

$$(\text{Incorrect!}) \qquad\qquad dY_t = \frac{1}{2}b'(X_t)b(X_t)dt + b(X_t)dW_t.$$

In fact, the conversion rule is

$$(8.19) \qquad\qquad dY_t = \frac{1}{2}b'(X_t)\beta(X_t)dt + b(X_t)dW_t,$$

which can be shown using the multidimensional conversion rule.

***Exercise* 8.3.** Derive the Itô equation (8.19) for Y defined in (8.18). Do this in two ways: (i) start from a discrete approximation of the integrals, as in the derivation of the Stratonivich conversion rule; and (ii) use the Stratonovich conversion rule for multidimensional diffusions.

REMARK 8.15. Here is a more general approach to the Stratonovich integral. Given continuous semimartingales[3] X_t, Y_t, the Stratonovich integral is defined in terms of the Itô integral as

$$\int_0^t Y_t \circ dX_t = \int_0^t Y_t dX_t + \frac{1}{2}\langle X, Y \rangle_t.$$

Here $\langle X, Y \rangle_t$ is the quadratic covariation of X_t, Y_t, defined as

$$\langle X, Y \rangle_t = \underset{\Delta t \to 0}{\text{m. s. lim}} \sum_{j:t_j < t} (X_{j+1} - X_j)(Y_{j+1} - Y_j).$$

The quadratic covariation satisfies $\langle X, Y \rangle_t = \frac{1}{2}([X+Y]_t - [X]_t - [Y]_t)$, where $[X]_t = \langle X, X \rangle_t$ is the quadratic variation of X. For an Itô process $X_t = \int_0^t f(s)ds + \int_0^t g(s)dW_s$, we have $[X]_t = \int_0^t g^2(s)ds$.

To apply this formalism to Example 8.14 we must calculate $\langle b(X), W \rangle_t$. Defining $Z_t = b(X_t)$, the Itô formula gives

$$Z_t = \int_0^t (b'(X_s)\alpha(X_s) + \frac{1}{2}b''(X_s)\beta^2(X_s))ds + \int_0^t b'(X_s)\beta(X_s)dW_t.$$

The quadratic covariation is $\langle Z, W \rangle_t = \int_0^t b'(X_s)\beta(X_s)ds$, leading to

$$Y_t = Y_0 + \int_0^t b(X_t)dW_t + \frac{1}{2}\int_0^t b'(X_s)\beta(X_s)ds \quad \Leftrightarrow \quad dY_t = b(X_t)dW_t + \frac{1}{2}b'(X_t)\beta(X_t)dt.$$

8.4. Additional information: Gronwall's inequality

THEOREM 8.16 (Gronwall's inequality). *Let $\phi(t)$, $b(t) \geq 0$ be nonnegative, continuous functions defined for $0 \leq t \leq T$, and let $a \geq 0$ be a constant. If*

$$\phi(t) \leq a + \int_0^t b(s)\phi(s)ds \qquad \text{for all } 0 \leq t \leq T,$$

then

$$\phi(t) \leq ae^{\int_0^t b(s)ds} \qquad \text{for all } 0 \leq t \leq T.$$

PROOF. (Theorem and proof as stated in (**Evans, 2013**, Section 5.B.3).) Let $\Phi(t) = a + \int_0^t b(s)\phi(s)ds$. Then $\Phi' = b\phi \leq b\Phi$, so

$$\left(e^{-\int_0^t bds}\Phi\right)' = (\Phi' - b\Phi)e^{-\int_0^t bds} \leq (b\phi - b\phi)e^{-\int_0^t bds} = 0.$$

Therefore,

$$\Phi(t)e^{-\int_0^t bds} \leq \Phi(0) = a \qquad \Longrightarrow \qquad \phi(t) \leq \Phi(t) \leq ae^{\int_0^t bds}.$$

$\square$

---

[3]A process X_t is a semimartingale if it can be decomposed as $X_t = M_t + A_t$, where M_t is a local martingale and A_t is a progressively measurable process of locally bounded variation.

8.5. Additional exercises

Exercise 8.4. Convert the following Stratonovich differential equations to Itô differential equations:

(i) $dX_t = aX_t dt + bX_t \circ dB_t$;

(ii) $dX_t = \sin X_t \cos X_t dt + (t^2 + \cos X_t)] \circ dB_t$.

Convert the following Ito differential equations to Stratonovich differential equations:

(iii) $dX_t = rX_t dt + \alpha X_t dB_t$;

(iv) $dX_t = 2e^{-X_t} dt + X_t^2 dB_t$.

Exercise 8.5. Consider geometric Brownian motion (GBM)

$$dX_t = \lambda X_t dt + \sigma X_t dW_t, \qquad X_0 = x_0.$$

(i) Suppose we want to know how the moments evolve. Show that the nth moment $M_n = \mathbb{E}^{x_0} X_t^n$ evolves as

$$\frac{dM_n}{dt} = \left(\lambda n + \frac{\sigma^2}{2} n(n-1)\right) M_n, \qquad M_n(0) = \mathbb{E} x_0^n.$$

(ii) Solve this equation for M_n.

(iii) Under what conditions on λ, σ does the nth moment of GBM converge to 0 as $t \to \infty$?

(iv) Show that if $\sigma \neq 0$ then for any given $\lambda < 0$ you can always find an integer N such that $\mathbb{E} X_t^n \to \infty$ for $n \geq N$.

Exercise 8.6. Verify that the chain rule holds for the one-dimensional Stratonovich equation:

$$df(X_t) = f'(X_t) \circ dX_t,$$

where X_t solves an SDE $dX_t = b(X_t, t)dt + \sigma(X_t, t) \circ dW_t$.

Hint: One way to do this is directly from the definition of the Stratonovich integral as a mean-square limit of certain sums. Another way to do this is to convert the equations to Itô form and back. You can assume that f is invertible, at least locally. Remember that $\frac{\partial}{\partial f} = \left(\frac{\partial f}{\partial x}\right)^{-1} \frac{\partial}{\partial x}$. It will help to define $Y_t = f(X_t)$ and to recall that you can only apply the Itô–Stratonovich correction when Y_t satisfies an SDE.

Exercise 8.7. Let us work out the distributive properties of the different kinds of integrals. Write each of the following equations as a pure Itô equation (for the first 3 cases), or a pure Stratonovich equation (for the last case). You can assume that a, b are continuously differentiable.

(i) $dX_t = a(X_t)(b(X_t) dW_t)$;

(ii) $dX_t = a(X_t)(b(X_t) \circ dW_t)$;

(iii) $dX_t = a(X_t) \circ (b(X_t) dW_t)$;

(iv) $dX_t = a(X_t) \circ (b(X_t) \circ dW_t)$.

Justify your solution at the same level of rigor as the justification of the Itô$\leftrightarrow$ Stratonovich conversion.

An expression of the form $dX_t = a(X_t) \circ dY_t$ should be interpreted, for suitable stochastic processes Y_t (including all those in the question),[4] as $X_t = \int_0^t a(X_s) \circ dY_s$ where the Stratonovich integral was defined in Definition 7.3. For example, the more complete way to write (iii) would be as the system of integral equations

$$X_t = X_0 + \int_0^t a(X_s) \circ dY_s, \qquad Y_t = Y_0 + \int_0^t b(X_s)dW_s.$$

Exercise 8.8. Suppose you use the right-most endpoint to evaluate the Riemann sum in a stochastic integral, as

$$\int_0^T f(t, \omega) * dW_t \equiv \mathrm{m.\,s.} \lim_{\Delta t \to 0} \sum_j f(t_{j+1})(W_{t_{j+1}} - W_{t_j}).$$

Show that the SDE defined by $dX_t = b(X_t, t)dt + \sigma(X_t, t) * dW_t$ is equivalent to the Itô SDE

$$dX_t = (b(X_t, t) + \partial_x \sigma(X_t, t)\sigma(X_t, t))dt + \sigma(X_t, t)dW_t.$$

Exercise 8.9. Suppose we want to study Brownian motion on a circle $C = \{x = (x_1, x_2) : x_1^2 + x_2^2 = 1\}$. One way to do this is to define an orthogonal projection matrix $P(x) = \frac{x}{|x|} \otimes \frac{x}{|x|} = \frac{1}{|x|^2} \begin{pmatrix} x_2^2 & -x_1 x_2 \\ -x_1 x_2 & x_1^2 \end{pmatrix}$, which is such that $P(x)v$ gives the component of v that is perpendicular to x. As for all orthogonal projections, it satisfies $P^2 = P$, $P^T = P$. Show that if $X_0 \in C$ is on the unit circle, then

$$dX_t = P(X_t) \circ dW_t$$

remains on the unit circle. (X_t is, in fact, a "Brownian motion" on the unit circle.)

Exercise 8.10. Let X be an Ornstein–Uhlenbeck process solving $dX_t = -\alpha X_t dt + \sigma dB_t$.
  (i) Suppose that $X_0 \sim N(0, \frac{\sigma^2}{2\alpha})$, so that X is stationary. Compute the spectral density of X.
  (ii) Suppose $A_t = X_t \cos kt + Y_t \sin kt$ is a wave with frequency k, whose amplitudes X_t, Y_t are independent, stationary, identically distributed Ornstein–Uhlenbeck processes. Compute the spectral density of A_t. (This kind of process is sometimes used as a model for different spectral components of a turbulent flow.)

Exercise 8.11. Solve the following SDEs and give an expression for $\mathbb{E}X_t$. For each, you can assume the initial condition is $X(0) = \xi$ with $\mathbb{E}\xi = 0$.
  (i) $dX_t = t\,dt + 2dB_t$;
  (ii) $dX_t = (\sin t)X_t dt + dB_t$;
  (iii) $dX_t = (-X_t + 1)dt + dB_t$.
Hint #1: For (b),(c), find an integrating factor—multiply the equation by a function A_t that is chosen to make the resulting equation simpler. You can find this integrating factor A_t based on your knowledge of how to solve the deterministic equation with no noise term.

---

[4]Y_t must be a semimartingale, and $a(X_t)$ must be a locally bounded predictable process with respect to the filtration generated by Y_t.

Hint #2: Remember the product rule from Exercise 7.8.

Exercise 8.12. Let us solve the SDE

$$dX_t = rdt + \alpha X_t dW_t.$$

One way to do this is by using an integrating factor $G(W_t, t) = e^{-\alpha W_t + \frac{1}{2}\alpha^2 t}$. Let us solve the equation in steps.

  (i) Calculate dG_t and $d(X_t G_t)$.

 (ii) Let $Y_t = X_t G_t$. Write down an equation for $\frac{dY_t}{dt}$ and substitute $X_t = Y_t/G_t$. You should obtain an ODE for Y_t, *not* an SDE; the ODE involves a random, time-dependent function.

(iii) Solve this equation for Y_t. You can solve this equation for each realization of the noise, as you would solve a regular time-dependent ODE. Use this to find the solution for X_t.

Comment: This technique works for SDEs of the form $dX_t = f(X_t, t)dt + c(t)X_t dW_t$, using the integrating factor $G_t = e^{-\int_0^t c(s)dW_s + \frac{1}{2}\int_0^t c^2(s)ds}$ (**Øksendal, 2003**, Exercise 5.16, p. 79). As a further exercise, try solving $dX_t = \frac{1}{X_t}dt + \alpha X_t dW_t$.

Exercise 8.13. Consider the logistic equation with multiplicative noise, interpreted in the Stratonovich sense:

$$dX_t = rX_t\left(1 - \frac{X_t}{K}\right)dt + \sigma X_t \circ dW_t.$$

Let us solve this SDE in the following steps.

  (i) Make the change of variables $Y_t = X_t^{-1}$. Calculate dY_t, remembering that the regular chain rule holds for Stratonovich SDEs (Exercise 8.6). Show that you can write the SDE (heuristically) as

$$\frac{dY_t}{dt} + (r + \sigma\eta(t))Y_t = \frac{r}{K},$$

where $\eta = \frac{dW_t}{dt}$ is white noise. (We can write the SDE this way because we are using Stratonovich calculus, which behaves like regular calculus.)

 (ii) Solve this ODE for $Y(t)$ by finding an integrating factor for this first-order equation. Verify it leads to solution

$$X_t = \frac{X_0 e^{rt + \sigma W_t}}{1 + X_0 \frac{r}{K}\int_0^t e^{rs + \sigma W_s}ds}.$$

Comment: Without the noise term, we have an ODE which is commonly used to describe population growth in a crowded environment. The parameter r is the maximum growth rate, and K is the carrying capacity of the environment. The noise could model a varying growth rate, $r \to r + \sigma\frac{dW}{dt}$. We interpret the noise in the Stratonovich sense here because it makes the SDE easier to solve; but see Exercise 9.9 for a comparison with the Itô interpretation, which leads to a qualitatively different behavior.

CHAPTER 9

Numerically Solving SDEs

Unlike the SDEs we studied in the previous chapter, most SDEs do not have analytical solutions, so to gain information about them we must simulate them numerically. This chapter will introduce the major numerical schemes to solve SDEs and some of the methods used to assess their performance. We will see a lot in common with numerical methods to solve deterministic ODEs. One might expect that for SDEs the additional stochasticity would make the topic richer; however, as we will see, this stochasticity often means that high-order numerical methods are simply too hard to implement, so we will end up studying only some fairly simple numerical methods that are widely used in practice. Two highly recommend additional resources are (**Higham, 2001**), a succinct and pedagogical introduction to SDEs and numerical methods to solve them; and (**Kloeden and Platen, 1992**), the bible on the topic of numerically solving SDEs.

9.1. Stochastic Itô–Taylor expansion to derive basic schemes

We will start by considering the one-dimensional SDE

$$(9.1) \qquad dX_t = b(X_t)dt + \sigma(X_t)dW_t$$

with initial condition X_0, over the interval $t \in [0, T]$. For notational simplicity we consider a time-homogeneous SDE but the theory for a time-inhomogeneous SDE is virtually identical. A simple scheme comes from approximating the Itô integral as a sum of step functions, as in the construction of the Itô integral in Chapter 7.

DEFINITION 9.1 (Euler–Maruyama (EM) scheme). Discretize time as $0 = t_0 < t_1 < \cdots < t_N = T$ with $t_{i+1} - t_i = \Delta t$. Let Y_n be a numerical approximation to X_{t_n}, calculated recursively as

$$(9.2) \qquad Y_{n+1} = Y_n + b(Y_n)\Delta t + \sigma(Y_n)\delta W_n,$$

where $\delta W_n \sim N(0, \Delta t)$ are i.i.d. random variables. For the initial condition choose $Y_0 = X_0$ if X_0 is deterministic, otherwise choose the initial condition to be sufficiently close to the desired one, e.g., $\mathbb{E}(|X_0 - Y_0|^2)^{1/2} \leq C(\Delta t)^{1/2}$ for some constant C.

REMARK 9.2. The random variable δW_n in the EM scheme can be replaced by a random variable with the same mean and variance, such as a uniform random variable or $\xi = \pm\sqrt{\Delta t}$, both of which can be generated more efficiently than Gaussian random variables. Such a modification causes the solution to lose certain strong pathwise convergence properties as $\Delta t \to 0$, but its weaker, statistical properties will converge with the same order, which is sufficient for many applications.

The Euler–Maruyama scheme is the most widely used scheme but also the least accurate. To derive better methods we turn to the *Itô–Taylor expansion*. It is simplest to first introduce this method in the deterministic setting for the solution to an ODE. Suppose X_t solves

$$(9.3) \qquad\qquad \frac{dX_t}{dt} = a(X_t),$$

where $a(x)$ is a function with plenty of bounded, continuous derivatives. Normally, if you were asked to perform a Taylor expansion of X_t about $t = 0$, say, to second order, you would compute it as

$$X_t = X_0 + X'(0)t + \frac{1}{2}X''(0)t^2 + o(t^2) = X_0 + a(X_0)t + \frac{1}{2}a'(X_0)a(X_0)t^2 + o(t^2)$$

where the second step comes from substituting for derivatives of X, using the ODE (9.3) and its derivatives. This approach will not work for an SDE because solutions to SDEs are nowhere differentiable. Therefore, we work with an integrated form of the Taylor expansion, which will allow us to expand a solution up to arbitrary order even if it is not differentiable. To this aim, write (9.3) in integral form as

$$(9.4) \qquad\qquad X_t = X_0 + \int_0^t a(X_s)ds.$$

We need to approximate $a(X_s)$ over a small interval $[0, t]$. We do this using the following observation. For any continuously differentiable function f, the chain rule and (9.3) imply $\frac{d}{dt}f(X_t) = a(X_t)\frac{\partial f(X_t)}{\partial x}$, so integrating gives

$$(9.5) \qquad f(X_t) = f(X_0) + \int_0^t \mathcal{L}f(X_s)ds, \quad \text{where} \quad \mathcal{L} = a(x)\frac{\partial}{\partial x}.$$

Applying this identity to $f = a$ gives $a(X_s) = a(X_0) + \int_0^s \mathcal{L}a(X_s)ds$. Substituting into (9.4) gives

$$(9.6) \qquad X_t = X_0 + a(X_0)\int_0^t ds + \int_0^t \int_0^s \mathcal{L}a(X_u)duds,$$

and, therefore,

$$X_t = X_0 + a(X_0)t + R_2, \qquad R_2 = \int_0^t \int_0^s \mathcal{L}a(X_u)duds.$$

If we ignore R_2 (which we can do, for example, if $|\mathcal{L}a(x)| \le K$, so $|R_2| \le \frac{1}{2}Kt^2 \ll a(X_0)t$ for small t), we obtain a forward Euler approximation for X_t.

To get a better approximation, we continue the expansion, this time choosing $f = \mathcal{L}a$ in (9.5) to approximate $\mathcal{L}a(X_u)$. This gives

$$X_t = X_0 + a(X_0)\int_0^t ds + \mathcal{L}a(X_0)\int_0^t \int_0^s duds + R_3, \qquad R_3 = \int_0^t \int_0^s \int_0^u \mathcal{L}^2a(X_v)dvduds.$$

If we ignore R_3 we obtain another approximation for X_t. In general, we can approximate X_t up to any order by writing

$$(9.7) \quad X_t = X_0 + \sum_{m=1}^r \frac{t^m}{m!}\mathcal{L}^ma(X_0) + R_{r+1}, \qquad R_{r+1} = \int_0^t \cdots \int_0^{s_r} \mathcal{L}^{r+1}a(X_{s_1})ds_1 \cdots ds_{r+1}.$$

This is the Taylor formula in integral form. It expresses X_t as a function of only X_0, t, and a remainder term.

Now, let us consider the *Itô–Taylor expansion*. Consider the SDE (9.1) in integral form:

$$(9.8) \qquad X_t = X_0 + \int_0^t b(X_s)ds + \int_0^t \sigma(X_s)dW_s.$$

For any function $f \in C^2$, Itô's formula gives

$$df(X_t) = \left(b(X_t)\frac{\partial f}{\partial x}(X_t) + \frac{1}{2}\sigma^2(X_t)\frac{\partial^2 f}{\partial x^2}(X_t)\right)dt + \sigma(X_t)\frac{\partial f}{\partial x}(X_t)dW_t.$$

Integrating gives the identity

$$(9.9) \qquad f(X_t) = f(X_0) + \int_0^t \mathcal{L}_0 f(X_s)ds + \int_0^t \mathcal{L}_1 f(X_s)dW_s,$$

where

$$(9.10) \qquad \mathcal{L}_0 = b(x)\frac{\partial}{\partial x} + \frac{1}{2}\sigma^2(x)\frac{\partial^2}{\partial x^2}, \qquad \mathcal{L}_1 = \sigma(x)\frac{\partial}{\partial x}.$$

Applying (9.9) to $f = b$ and $f = \sigma$ in (9.8) gives

$$(9.11) \qquad X_t = X_0 + b(X_0)\int_0^t ds + \sigma(X_0)\int_0^t dW_s + R_1,$$

with

$$R_1 = \int_0^t \int_0^s \mathcal{L}_0 b(X_z)dzds + \int_0^t \int_0^s \mathcal{L}_1 b(X_z)dW_z ds$$
$$+ \int_0^t \int_0^s \mathcal{L}_0 \sigma(X_z)dzdW_s + \int_0^t \int_0^s \mathcal{L}_1 \sigma(X_z)dW_z dW_s.$$

If we evaluate the integrals in (9.11) analytically and ignore the remainder term R_1, we get the Euler–Maruyama scheme, (9.2).

To derive more accurate schemes we continue the expansion. The terms in R_1 have different orders in t depending on the powers of dt, dW_t. The lowest-order term in R_1 is the last one, $\int_0^t \int_0^s \mathcal{L}_1 \sigma(X_z)dW_z dW_s$, which we expect to be $O(t)$; all other terms should be $O(t^{3/2})$ or higher. Apply (9.9) to $f = \mathcal{L}_1 \sigma$ in R_1 to get

$$(9.12) \qquad X_t = X_0 + b(X_0)\int_0^t ds + \sigma(X_0)\int_0^t dW_s + \mathcal{L}_1 \sigma(X_0)\int_0^t \int_0^s dW_z dW_s + R_2,$$

where R_2 is a remainder term. We can compute the double integral analytically:

$$\int_0^t \int_0^s dW_z dW_s = \int_0^t W_s dW_s = \frac{1}{2}(W_t^2 - t).$$

Substituting into (9.12) and ignoring R_2 gives the Milstein scheme.

DEFINITION 9.3 (Milstein scheme). Discretize time as $0 = t_0 < t_1 < t_2 < \cdots < t_N = T$ with $t_{i+1} - t_i = \Delta t$. Let Y_n be a numerical approximation to X_{t_n}, calculated recursively as

$$(9.13) \qquad Y_{n+1} = Y_n + b(Y_n)\Delta t + \sigma(Y_n)\delta W_n + \frac{1}{2}\sigma(Y_n)\sigma'(Y_n)((\delta W_n)^2 - \Delta t),$$

where $\delta W_n \sim N(0, \Delta t)$ are i.i.d. random variables.

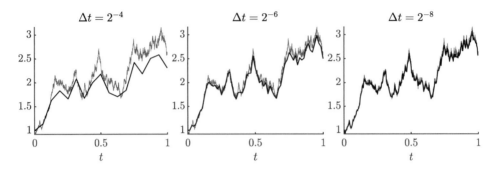

FIGURE 9.1. Numerical approximations of GBM $dX_t = X_t dt + \frac{1}{2}X_t dW_t$ using the Euler–Maruyama method with different timesteps Δt, with the true solution shown in gray. The same realization of Brownian motion is used for each approximation.

Exercise 9.1. Write down the full expression for R_2 in (9.12).

We could continue the Taylor expansion to derive schemes that are even more accurate. This would require calculating integrals of the form

$$\int_0^t dW_{s_1}^{i_1} \int_0^{s_1} dW_{s_2}^{i_2} \cdots \int_0^{s_{k-1}} dW_{s_k}^{i_k},$$

where $i_j \in \{0, 1\}$, and where we write $W_t^1 = W_t$, $W_t^0 = t$. For *scalar* equations, all the Brownian motions above are the same and these integrals can be computed recursively (Exercise 9.5). Therefore, in principle, higher-order schemes can be derived, though they are not often used in practice, since the advantage they give is often not worth the extra programming.

For *vector* equations, deriving more accurate schemes requires calculating multiple integrals against different Brownian motions, such as

$$\int_0^t \int_0^s dW_u^{(1)} dW_s^{(2)},$$

where $W^{(1)}, W^{(2)}$ are independent Brownian motions. There are no known analytic expressions for such multiple integrals, even for the simplest case above. These multiple integrals can be approximated, for example, using a Karhunen–Loeve expansion or by stochastic simulation, but often for such problems, Euler–Maruyama or a variant of it adapted to the structure of a particular problem, is often the most practical method.

9.2. Strong and weak convergence

How can we judge a scheme's quality? Commonly used notions are
- *Consistency*—whether the mean of the increments and some notion of variance of the increments, converge to those of the Itô process, as $\Delta t \to 0$.
- *Convergence*—whether the global error over a fixed time interval $[0, T]$ converges to zero in some sense as $\Delta t \to 0$.
- *Stability*—whether the numerical method reproduces *qualitatively* the same long-time behavior as the exact solution for a given time step Δt.

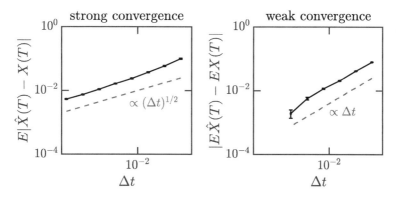

FIGURE 9.2. Demonstrating strong (left) and weak (right) convergence for a GBM $dX_t = rX_t dt + \alpha X_t dW_t$ with $r = 1$, $a = 0.4$, using the Euler–Maruyama discretization with different timesteps Δt. Error bars are 1 standard deviation over M independent samples, where $M = 1000$ for strong convergence, and $M = 4 \times 10^6$ for weak convergence. The total time was $T = 1$ and the initial condition was $X_0 = 1$.

For each of these, there is a strong and a weak form.
- *Strong* forms deal with pathwise results.
- *Weak* forms deal with probability distributions.

In the following, let $Y^{\Delta t} = Y_0^{\Delta t}, Y_1^{\Delta t}, \ldots$ be a discrete approximation to $X = (X_t)_{t \geq 0}$, at times $0 = t_0 < t_1 < \cdots < t_N = T$, with maximum increment $\Delta t = \max_i |t_{i+1} - t_i|$.

DEFINITION 9.4. $Y^{\Delta t}$ *converges strongly* to X at time T *with order* α if there exist constants $C > 0$, $\delta_0 > 0$, independent of Δt, such that

$$\mathbb{E}|Y_N^{\Delta t} - X_T| \leq C(\Delta t)^\alpha \qquad \text{for all } \Delta t < \delta_0.$$

DEFINITION 9.5. $Y^{\Delta t}$ *converges weakly* to X at T *with order* β with respect to a class of functions $\mathcal{C}$ if, for each $f \in \mathcal{C}$, there exist constants $C_f > 0$, $\delta_0 > 0$, independent of Δt, such that

$$|\mathbb{E}f(Y_N^{\Delta t}) - \mathbb{E}f(X_T)| \leq C_f(\Delta t)^\beta \qquad \text{for all } \Delta t < \delta_0.$$

The constant C_f can depend on f but not on Δt.

REMARK 9.6. The set $\mathcal{C}$ may be taken, for example, to be the set of l times continuously differentiable functions whose derivatives at the lth order have at most polynomial growth. This ensures the set contains all polynomials (**Kloeden and Platen, 1992**, p. 327).

The difference between strong and weak convergence is that strong convergence requires the individual paths to converge as the timestep gets smaller, for a *fixed* realization of Brownian motion. Therefore, when testing for strong convergence numerically, the same realization of Brownian motion must be used for all approximations (Figure 9.1). Weak convergence requires only the probability distributions to converge. Therefore, a different Brownian motion can be used for each numerical approximation, or even a random process that is not Brownian motion but has increments with the same mean and variance.

PROPOSITION 9.7. *If $\mathcal{C}$ is restricted to Lipschitz continuous functions, then $\beta \geq \alpha$ (weak order $\geq$ strong order).*

PROOF. Suppose f has Lipschitz constant K. Then

$$|\mathbb{E}f(Y_N^{\Delta t}) - \mathbb{E}f(X_T)| \leq \mathbb{E}|f(Y_N^{\Delta t}) - f(X_T)| \leq K\mathbb{E}|Y_N^{\Delta t} - X_T|.$$

Therefore, if $Y^{\Delta t} \to X$ with strong order α, it also converges to X with weak order at least α. □

THEOREM 9.8. *Given an SDE satisfying the same conditions as in Theorem 8.1 (plus additional smoothness conditions for Milstein),[1] and provided the initial condition is sufficiently close in distribution to the desired initial condition, we have*

	Strong Order	Weak Order
Euler–Maruyama	1/2	1
Milstein	1	1

REMARK 9.9. For additive noise ($\sigma =$ const), the EM and Milstein schemes are equivalent, since $\sigma\sigma' = 0$. Therefore, for additive noise EM will converge with strong and weak order 1.

We will prove strong convergence for the EM scheme and will provide a partial proof of weak convergence. The key to the proof is the following lemma.

LEMMA 9.10. *Consider a process X solving an SDE satisfying the same conditions as in Theorem 8.1 over a time interval $[0, T]$. Let $0 < t < r < T$ and let $\Delta t = r - t$. For all $\Delta t \leq \Delta t_0$ where Δt_0 is some fixed maximum separation, we have the following bound:*

$$(9.14) \qquad\qquad \mathbb{E}|X_r - X_t|^2 \leq C\Delta t,$$

where the constant C depends on $T, K, \Delta t_0, \mathbb{E}X_0^2$ (recall K serves as the Lipschitz constant and linear growth bound).

PROOF. From Itô's formula,

$$|X_r - X_t|^2 = \left|\int_t^r b(X_s)ds + \int_t^r \sigma(X_s)dW_s\right|^2 \leq 2\left(\int_t^r b(X_s)ds\right)^2 + 2\left(\int_t^r \sigma(X_s)dW_s\right)^2.$$

Taking the expectation, applying Cauchy–Schwartz and the Itô isometry, and then using linear growth bounds gives

$$\mathbb{E}|X_r - X_t|^2 \leq 2\Delta t \int_t^r \mathbb{E}b^2(X_s)ds + 2\int_t^r \mathbb{E}\sigma^2(X_s)ds$$

$$\leq 2K^2(\Delta t + 1)\int_t^r \mathbb{E}(1 + |X_s|)^2 ds.$$

---

[1] For the full list of conditions, see the following theorems in (**Kloeden and Platen, 1992**): Theorem 10.2.2, for strong convergence of EM, Theorem 10.3.5 for strong convergence of Milstein, Theorem 10.6.3 for strong convergence of a general order γ scheme, and Theorem 14.5.1 for weak convergence of a general order γ scheme.

Using Proposition 8.6 we may bound $\mathbb{E}|X_s|^2$ using a constant C_1 depending on T, K, X_0, and, hence, we may bound $\mathbb{E}(1 + |X_s|)^2$ using a constant C_2 depending on $T, K, \mathbb{E}X_0^2$. Therefore,

$$\mathbb{E}|X_r - X_t|^2 \le 2K^2 C_2(\Delta t + 1)\Delta t \le C\Delta t$$

for some constant C depending on $T, K, \Delta t_0, \mathbb{E}X_0^2$. $\square$

PROOF OF STRONG CONVERGENCE, EM, 1 DIMENSION. (This proof and the next build on the heuristic arguments given in (**Gardiner, 2009**, Section 15.1.4).) For notational simplicity write $Y_n = Y_n^{\Delta t}$ for the numerical solution and with an abuse of notation write $X_n = X_{t_n}$ for the true solution. Let the error between the numerical and true solutions be $e_n = \mathbb{E}|Y_n - X_n|^2$. We suppose that $e_0 = \mathbb{E}|Y_0 - X_0|^2 \le K_2 \Delta t$ for some constant K_2. We wish to bound e_N where $T = N\Delta t$ is some finite time. We compute:

$$e_{n+1} = \mathbb{E}\Big|Y_{n+1} - Y_n - (X_{n+1} - X_n) + Y_n - X_n\Big|^2$$

$$= \mathbb{E}\Big|b(Y_n)\Delta t + \sigma(Y_n)\delta W_n$$

$$- \left(\int_{n\Delta t}^{(n+1)\Delta t} b(X_r)dr + \int_{n\Delta t}^{(n+1)\Delta t} \sigma(X_r)dW_r\right) + Y_n - X_n\Big|^2$$

$$(9.15) \quad \le 2\mathbb{E}\Big|\int_{n\Delta t}^{(n+1)\Delta t} (b(X_r) - b(Y_n))dr\Big|^2 + 2\mathbb{E}\Big|\int_{n\Delta t}^{(n+1)\Delta t} (\sigma(X_r) - \sigma(Y_n))dW_r\Big|^2 + e_n.$$

Let us bound the first two terms in (9.15) separately. For the first term, we use Cauchy–Schwartz, the triangle inequality, and the inequality $(a+b)^2 \le 2(a^2 + b^2)$, and then we use Lipschitz continuity to obtain[2]

$$\mathbb{E}\Big|\int_{n\Delta t}^{(n+1)\Delta t} (b(X_r) - b(Y_n))dr\Big|^2 \le 2\Delta t \int_{n\Delta t}^{(n+1)\Delta t} \mathbb{E}|b(X_r) - b(X_n)|^2 dr$$

$$+ 2\Delta t \int_{n\Delta t}^{(n+1)\Delta t} \mathbb{E}|b(X_n) - b(Y_n)|^2 dr$$

$$\le 2K^2 \Delta t \int_{n\Delta t}^{(n+1)\Delta t} \mathbb{E}|X_r - X_n|^2 dr$$

$$+ 2K^2 \Delta t \int_{n\Delta t}^{(n+1)\Delta t} \mathbb{E}|Y_n - X_n|^2 dr.$$

We use Lemma 9.10 to bound $\mathbb{E}|X_r - X_n|^2 \le C_1 \Delta t$, where C_1 depends on $T, K, \mathbb{E}X_0^2$, and an upper bound for Δt, obtaining

$$\mathbb{E}\Big|\int_{n\Delta t}^{(n+1)\Delta t} (b(X_r) - b(Y_n))dr\Big|^2 \le C(\Delta t)^3 + C(\Delta t)^2 e_n.$$

---

[2]In more detail:

$$\mathbb{E}\Big|\int_{n\Delta t}^{(n+1)\Delta t} (b(X_r) - b(Y_n))dr\Big|^2 \le \mathbb{E}\Big|\sqrt{\Delta t}\|b(X_r) - b(Y_n)\|_2\Big|^2 \le \Delta t\mathbb{E}\big|\|b(X_r) - b(X_n)\|_2 + \|b(X_n) - b(Y_n)\|_2\big|^2$$

$$\le 2\Delta t\mathbb{E}\|b(X_r) - b(X_n)\|_2^2 + 2\Delta t\mathbb{E}\|b(X_n) - b(Y_n)\|_2^2$$

where $\|\cdot\|_2$ is the L^2-norm on the interval $[n\Delta t, (n+1)\Delta t]$.

We use the Itô isometry and similar steps as above to bound the second term in (9.15):

$$\mathbb{E}\left| \int_{n\Delta t}^{(n+1)\Delta t} (\sigma(X_r) - \sigma(Y_n)) dW_r \right|^2 = \int_{n\Delta t}^{(n+1)\Delta t} \mathbb{E}|\sigma(X_r) - \sigma(Y_n)|^2 dr$$

$$\leq C(\Delta t)^2 + C\Delta t e_n.$$

Putting these bounds together into (9.15) and assuming Δt is small enough that we can bound the Δt^3 term with a lower-order term and use Lemma 9.10, gives

$$(9.16) \qquad\qquad e_{n+1} \leq (C(\Delta t)^2 + C\Delta t + 1)e_n + C(\Delta t)^2.$$

Solving this recurrence relation, the error after $N = T/\Delta t$ steps satisfies

$$e_N \leq (C(\Delta t)^2 + C\Delta t + 1)^{T/\Delta t} e_0 + \frac{(C(\Delta t)^2 + C(\Delta t) + 1)^{T/\Delta t} - 1}{(C(\Delta t)^2 + C(\Delta t) + 1) - 1} C(\Delta t)^2 \leq C_2 \Delta t$$

where C_2 depends on $T, K, K_2, \mathbb{E}X_0^2$, and an upper bound for Δt. Therefore, $\mathbb{E}|X_N - Y_N| \leq (\mathbb{E}|X_N - Y_N|^2)^{1/2} \leq C_3(\Delta t)^{1/2}$, which shows strong convergence with order $1/2$. $\qquad\square$

REMARK 9.11. At a high level, what this proof shows is that the squared error in each time step, e_n, increases by an amount proportional to $(\Delta t)^2$. Indeed, (9.16) says (roughly) that

$$e_{n+1} \leq (1 + \text{small number})e_n + C(\Delta t)^2.$$

Since there are $N = T/\Delta t$ time steps, the total squared error at time T should be about $C(\Delta t)^2 \frac{T}{\Delta t} \propto \Delta t$. Therefore, the nonsquared error should be $\propto \sqrt{\Delta t}$.

Which term contributes most to this error? The proof shows that it comes from the integral $\int_{n\Delta t}^{(n+1)\Delta t}(\sigma(X_r) - \sigma(X_n))dW_r$. Lemma 9.10 showed that over an interval of length Δt, X_t varies in mean-square by $O(\Delta t)$, and, hence, so does any smooth function of X_t such as $\sigma(X_t)$. The mean-squared error in the numerical scheme is mainly controlled by the integral of this mean-squared variation over a grid box, since this controls how far the true solution wanders away from the numerical solution without the numerical scheme "seeing" it. The integral of the variation over one grid box is $O((\Delta t)^2)$, so summing over all grid boxes, the mean-squared error is $O(\Delta t)$. In a higher-order scheme, the error would be controlled by double integrals resembling the remainder terms in R_1 (see (9.11)), which depend on higher powers of Δt.

PARTIAL PROOF OF WEAK CONVERGENCE OF EM, 1 DIMENSION. Proving weak convergence is best done using the PDE theory of diffusion processes, which we will learn in subsequent chapters. Here, we show weak convergence for the function $f(x) = x$, under the assumption that the drift b has two bounded continuous derivatives. Let the error be $\epsilon_n = \mathbb{E}(Y_n - X_n)$. We wish to bound $|\epsilon_N|$ where $N = T/\Delta t$. We have, using the nonanticipating property of the Itô integral,

$$\epsilon_{n+1} = \epsilon_n + \mathbb{E}\int_{n\Delta t}^{(n+1)\Delta t} (b(X_r) - b(Y_n))dr$$

$$= \epsilon_n + \mathbb{E}\int_{n\Delta t}^{(n+1)\Delta t} (b(X_r) - b(X_n))dr + \mathbb{E}\int_{n\Delta t}^{(n+1)\Delta t} (b(X_n) - b(Y_n))dr.$$

For the first term, we have, using (9.9) and the nonanticipating property,

$$\mathbb{E} \int_{n\Delta t}^{(n+1)\Delta t} (b(X_r) - b(X_n))dr = \int_{n\Delta t}^{(n+1)\Delta t} \int_{n\Delta t}^{r} \mathbb{E}\mathcal{L}_0 b(X_s) ds dr.$$

Provided that b has two bounded continuous derivatives, we may bound the absolute value of this term with $C(\Delta t)^2$. For the second term, we Taylor expand b as

$$b(Y_n) - b(X_n) = b'(X_n)(Y_n - X_n) + b''(X_r)(Y_n - X_n)^2/2,$$

where $r \in [n\Delta t, (n+1)\Delta t]$. Therefore, using the boundedness of b', b'' and our estimates of $e_n = \mathbb{E}(Y_n - X_n)^2$ from the proof of strong convergence, we have

$$|\mathbb{E}(b(Y_n) - b(X_n))| \leq C|\mathbb{E}(Y_n - X_n)| + C\mathbb{E}(Y_n - X_n)^2/2 \leq C|\epsilon_n| + C\Delta t.$$

Putting this all together gives

$$|\epsilon_{n+1}| \leq |\epsilon_n| + C|\epsilon_n|\Delta t + C(\Delta t)^2.$$

As in the proof of strong convergence, this recurrence relation leads to a bound for ϵ_N of the form

$$|\epsilon_N| \leq C_2 \Delta t,$$

which shows weak convergence (for $f(x) = x$) with order 1. $\qquad\square$

How can you demonstrate the order of convergence numerically? Here are some possibilities.

(1) Compare to the true solution, if it is known. For example, there are analytical solutions available for the Ornstein–Uhlenbeck process, geometric Brownian motion, and several other equations, which can be evaluated exactly because we can generate exact realizations of W at a finite set of time points.
(2) Compare to a very high resolution simulation.
(3) Look at the difference between solutions as you double the resolution. We expect

$$\frac{\|Y^{\Delta t} - Y^{\Delta t/2}\|}{\|Y^{\Delta t/2} - Y^{\Delta t/4}\|} = 2^\alpha + O(\Delta t),$$

where α is the order and $\| \cdot \|$ is some norm.

Options (2),(3) would show the solution converges to something; however, there is no guarantee that the solution it converges to is the correct one.

To demonstrate strong convergence, one has to compare paths with different time steps using the *same* Brownian motion for each path. To demonstrate weak convergence, one typically picks a function, such as $f(x) = x$, and then estimates $\mathbb{E}f(Y_T^{\Delta t})$ by generating many trajectories with a fixed timestep and computing the empirical average (Figure 9.2).

The numerically measured error will also contain sampling error, since you have a finite number of samples. Therefore, the number of samples must be large enough to make the sampling error smaller than the error due to discretization. It is good practice to construct error bars on each estimate, for example, using the standard deviation of the estimate over independent samples. There will also be errors due to the bias in the random number generator and due to rounding operations to account for machine precision. Interestingly, it is the bias in the random number generator that becomes important first, when Δt is small enough and the number of samples is large enough (**Higham, 2001**)!

9.3. Stochastic stability

Convergence rates bound the error over time intervals $[0, T]$ using a constant $C(T)$. But typically, $C(T) \nearrow \infty$ as $T \nearrow \infty$. In many situations, such as first-passage problems, or to study long-time behavior, we need to simulate the equation indefinitely. In such a situation, we may ask that the numerics reproduce the correct *qualitative* behavior.

One way to do this is with the notion of asymptotic stability.[3] Typically, we pick a particular class of equations on which to study this concept. One common choice is to look at the behavior near fixed points of linear equations.

Recall the concept of linear stability for deterministic ODEs:
  – We typically study the behavior of $\frac{dX}{dt} = \lambda X$, where λ is a complex number.
  – The fixed point $X = 0$ is *asymptotically stable* if $\lim_{t \to \infty} X(t) = 0$. This happens for the equation above when $Re\{\lambda\} < 0$.
  – If we discretize, we ask when the numerical scheme reproduces this same behavior: that $Y_n^{\Delta t} \to 0$ as $n \to \infty$. The set of values of $\lambda \Delta t$ for which this occurs forms the *domain of linear stability* of the scheme.

For SDEs, stability is commonly studied for a geometric Brownian motion,[4]

$$(9.17) \qquad dX_t = \lambda X_t dt + \mu X_t dW_t, \qquad \lambda, \mu \in \mathbb{R}.$$

Such an equation arises from linearizing a nonlinear SDE about a point where the drift and noise both vanish. Since we are now dealing with random variables, which are infinite-dimensional objects, norms are not equivalent in general and there are different notions of "$X_t \to 0$." Two common ones are the following.

DEFINITION 9.12. The solution $X_t = 0$ is *mean-square stable* (for a given pair λ, μ) if $\lim_{t \to \infty} \mathbb{E} X_t^2 = 0$ for any X_0.

DEFINITION 9.13. The solution $X_t = 0$ is *asymptotically stable* if $P\left(\lim_{t \to \infty} X_t = 0\right) = 1$ for any X_0.

Recall from Chapter 8 the solution to (9.17) is

$$X_t = X_0 e^{(\lambda - \frac{\mu^2}{2})t + \mu W_t}.$$

We showed in Example 8.8 and Exercise 8.5 that
  • GBM is mean-square stable $\Leftrightarrow \lambda + \frac{1}{2}\mu^2 < 0$;
  • GBM is asymptotically stable $\Leftrightarrow \lambda - \frac{1}{2}\mu^2 < 0$.

Therefore, for GBM, mean-square stability $\Rightarrow$ asymptotic stability but not the reverse.

---

[3]Note that *numerical stability* is another concept, related to but different from that discussed here, which asks whether two nearby trajectories tend to stay together or to diverge. See (**Kloeden and Platen, 1992**, Section 9.8).

[4]We take $\lambda, \mu \in \mathbb{R}$ here for simplicity, but one often considers $\lambda, \mu \in \mathbb{C}$, which does not change very much of what is written here.

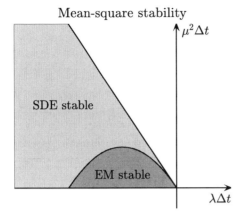
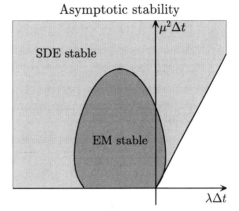

FIGURE 9.3. Regions of mean-square and asymptotic stability for a geometric Brownian motion (9.17), for the true solution to the SDE and the Euler–Maruyama approximation to the solution. The region of asymptotic stability for the EM scheme was determined by evaluating the expectation in (9.19) numerically, by integrating over the standard normal density.

When does a numerical method give the same type of stability as the true solution? Consider the Euler–Maruyama scheme,

$$Y_{n+1} = Y_n(1 + \lambda \Delta t + \mu \Delta W_n).$$

Squaring gives

$$\mathbb{E}Y_{n+1}^2 = \left(|1 + \lambda \Delta t|^2 + |\mu|^2 \Delta t\right) \mathbb{E}Y_n^2.$$

Therefore, mean-square stability is equivalent to the condition

(9.18) $$(1 + \lambda \Delta t)^2 + \mu^2 \Delta t < 1 \quad \Rightarrow \quad \Delta t < \frac{-(\frac{1}{2}\mu^2 + \lambda)}{\lambda^2/2}.$$

We obtain an upper bound on the step size for the solution to be mean-square stable. To see how this compares to the mean-square stability region for the true solution, let $x = \lambda \Delta t$, $y = \mu^2 \Delta t$. The solutions are mean-square stable when

$$\text{EM:} \quad y < -x(2 + x), \qquad \text{True:} \quad y < -2x.$$

The region where the EM solution is mean-square stable is smaller than—and contained in—the region where the true solution is mean-square stable, as shown in Figure 9.3.

What about asymptotic stability? We may write the EM solution as

$$Y_n = Y_0(-1)^{s_n} e^{\sum_{j=0}^{n-1} A_j}, \qquad \text{where } A_j = \log|1 + \lambda \Delta t + \mu \Delta W_j|,$$

and s_n counts the number of all j for which $1 + \lambda \Delta t + \mu \Delta W_j < 0$. Observe that the argument of the exponential is a sum of i.i.d. random variables. The strong law of large numbers says that $\sum_{j=0}^{n-1} A_j/n \xrightarrow{a.s.} \mathbb{E}A_1$ as $n \to \infty$, so $\sum_{j=0}^{n-1} A_j \xrightarrow{a.s.} \pm\infty$ depending on the sign of $\mathbb{E}A_1$. Therefore, the numerical solution is asymptotically stable when

(9.19) $$\mathbb{E}_Z \log|1 + \Delta t \lambda + \sqrt{\Delta t}\mu Z| < 0,$$

where $Z \sim N(0, 1)$ is a standard normal. The regions of stability for the true solution and numerical solution, are shown in Figure 9.3.

9.4. Implicit methods

For ODEs, implicit methods often have better stability properties than explicit methods, allowing for significantly larger time steps at the expense of solving a nonlinear system of equations. Let us briefly take a look at some additional considerations when constructing implicit methods for SDEs, keeping in mind a warning from (**Gardiner, 2009**, p. 401) that

> "…Unfortunately, uninformed intuition in this field can lead to considerable difficulty, extensive waste of time, or even complete failure to solve the problem under study."

Consider a discretization of the GBM in (9.17) using a fully implicit Euler scheme,

$$(9.20) \qquad Y_{n+1} = Y_n + \lambda Y_{n+1} \Delta t + \mu Y_{n+1} \Delta W_n .$$

We can solve to obtain

$$Y_{n+1} = Y_n \frac{1}{1 - \lambda \Delta t - \mu \Delta W_n} .$$

There are two problems here. One is that the factor multiplying Y_n can approach ∞ or change sign. But a GBM cannot change sign! This problem occurs no matter how small we choose Δt because the probability density for ΔW has unbounded support. Indeed, $\mathbb{E}|Y_{n+1}/Y_n| = \infty$ (Exercise 9.2). Therefore, it is usually not possible to have a fully implicit strong scheme for an SDE.

Exercise 9.2. Let $S \sim N(\mu, \sigma^2)$, for $\mu, \sigma \in \mathbb{R}$, $\sigma > 0$. Show that $\mathbb{E}|S|^{-1} = \infty$.

We may nevertheless construct a numerical scheme that gives a weak approximation to the true solution by replacing ΔW with a bounded random variable with the same mean and variance, such as $\Delta \tilde{W} = \pm \sqrt{\Delta}$ with equal probability. But there is still a second problem with (9.20): it is not even a consistent approximation of the SDE (see Exercise 9.3). To obtain a consistent approximation one must modify the drift. A weakly convergent fully implicit Euler approximation for (9.1) is (**Kloeden and Platen, 1992**, p. 337)

$$(9.21) \qquad Y_{n+1} = Y_n + \left(b(Y_{n+1}) - \sigma(Y_{n+1})\frac{\partial \sigma}{\partial x}(Y_{n+1})\right)\Delta t + \sigma(Y_{n+1})\Delta \tilde{W}_n.$$

Exercise 9.3. The mean of a numerical approximation is consistent[5] if

$$\mathbb{E}\left|\mathbb{E}\left[\frac{Y_{n+1}^{\Delta t} - Y_n^{\Delta t}}{\Delta t}\Big|Y_n^{\Delta t}\right] - b(Y_n^{\Delta t})\right|^2 \to 0 \qquad \text{as } \Delta t \to 0.$$

(i) Show that the mean of approximation (9.20) is not consistent.
(ii) Show that the mean of approximation (9.21) applied to GBM is consistent.

---

[5]We neglect an additional condition on the variance of the increment that is necessary for consistency; see (**Kloeden and Platen, 1992**, p. 324) for strong consistency, and (**Kloeden and Platen, 1992**, p. 328) for weak consistency.

For a strongly convergent numerical approximation, one can typically only use implicit methods for the deterministic parts of the equation. For example, a semi-implicit method to solve (9.17) would be (**Pavliotis, 2014**, Section 5.2.1)

$$(9.22) \qquad Y_{n+1} = Y_n + (\theta \lambda Y_{n+1} + (1 - \theta)\lambda Y_n)\,\Delta t + \mu Y_n \Delta W_n,$$

where θ is a parameter governing the ratio of implicit terms to explicit terms. This scheme is called the *stochastic theta method*.

***Exercise* 9.4.** Show that when $\theta \in [\frac{1}{2}, 1]$, the stochastic theta method in (9.22) is mean-square stable for all time steps Δt, provided the true solution is mean-square stable. (It is *A-stable*.) Derive the region of mean-square stability for $\theta \in [0, \frac{1}{2})$.

9.5. Additional exercises

***Exercise* 9.5.** (Multiple stochastic integrals)
  (i) Calculate $\int_0^t \int_0^{s_1} \int_0^{s_2} dW_{s_3}\,dW_{s_2}\,dW_{s_1}$ explicitly in terms of W_t, t.
  (ii) Let $I_t^{(k)} = \int_0^t dW_{s_1} \int_0^{s_1} dW_{s_2} \cdots \int_0^{s_{k-1}} dW_{s_k}$. Show (by induction) that

$$I_t^{(k)} = \frac{1}{k}\left(W_t I_t^{(k-1)} - t I_t^{(k-2)}\right).$$

Comment: Part (b) is the same recurrence relation as for the Hermite polynomials $H_n(x) = (-1)^n e^{x^2/2} \frac{d^n}{dx^n} e^{-x^2/2}$. Therefore, the multiple stochastic integral can also be expressed as $I_t^{(k)} = \frac{t^{n/2}}{n!} H_k(W_t/\sqrt{t})$ (and similar recurrence relations can be found when some of the increments are ds_i).

***Exercise* 9.6.** Derive an Itô scheme for a scalar SDE that you expect to have strong order 1.5 of convergence.
  Explain how to calculate explicitly all random variables in the scheme, including their correlations, if any. You can use the fact that the random variable $Z_t = \int_0^t \int_0^{s_1} dW_{s_2}\,ds_1$ has the following properties: $Z_t \sim N(0, \frac{1}{3}t^3)$, and that $\mathbb{E}Z_t W_t = \frac{1}{2}t^2$.

***Exercise* 9.7.** Analytically compute the region of mean-square stability of geometric Brownian motion (9.23) for the Milstein scheme. Sketch the region on a graph, along with the stability region for the EM scheme and for the SDE.

***Exercise* 9.8** (*Computation required*). Let us numerically compute trajectories of geometric Brownian motion (GBM) by solving the following SDE:

$$(9.23) \qquad dX_t = \lambda X_t dt + \mu X_t dW_t, \qquad X_0 = 1,$$

where λ, μ are parameters.
  (i) Implement the Euler–Maryama scheme for $(\lambda, \mu) = (3, 1.5)$. Demonstrate its orders of strong and weak convergence over a time interval of length $T = 1$.
  (ii) Repeat (i), for the Milstein scheme.
  (iii) Numerically verify the region of mean-square stability you computed for the Milstein scheme in Q3 for parameters $(\lambda, \mu) = (-3, \sqrt{3})$. (The true solution is mean-square stable for these parameters.) Find a timestep Δ_0 for which the scheme is predicted to be mean-square stable and demonstrate numerically that it is stable. Find a timestep Δ_1 for which the scheme is predicted to be

unstable and demonstrate numerically that it is unstable. Choose Δ_0, Δ_1 to be reasonably close to the stability boundary, $\Delta_1 - \Delta_0 \lesssim 0.2$.

(iv) Repeat (iii), but this time for asymptotic stability with parameters $(\lambda, \mu) = (\frac{1}{2}, \sqrt{6})$. (The true solution is asymptotically stable, but not mean-square stable, for these parameters.) Since you do not know the theoretical stability boundary, you will have to explore different timesteps to find it.

Exercise 9.9 (*Computation required*). Consider the logistic equation describing population growth in a crowded environment with multiplicative noise (Exercise 8.13), which we can interpret in either the Itô sense:

$$(9.24) \qquad dX_t = rX_t\left(1 - \frac{X_t}{K}\right)dt + \sigma X_t dW_t;$$

or the Stratonovich sense:

$$(9.25) \qquad dX_t = rX_t\left(1 - \frac{X_t}{K}\right)dt + \sigma X_t \circ dW_t.$$

(i) Write code to simulate each of (9.24) and (9.25), using an Euler–Maruyama method. Plot several realizations for parameters $r = K = 1, X_0 = 0.1$, and several different values of σ.

(ii) Above a certain value of the noise, say, $\sigma > \sigma_c$, the long-time behavior of the solutions becomes qualitatively different. Explain how they differ and estimate the value of σ_c at which the transition occurs (or use (iii) below).

(iii) The solution to the Stratonovich equation (9.25) was shown (Exercise 8.13) to be

$$X_t = \frac{X_0 e^{rt + \sigma W_t}}{1 + X_0 \frac{r}{K} \int_0^t e^{rs + \sigma W_s} ds}.$$

Write down the solution to the corresponding Itô equation. Use these analytical solutions to explain your observations in (ii).

CHAPTER 10

Forward and Backward Equations for SDEs

Consider the multidimensional SDE

$$(10.1) \qquad dX_t = b(X_t, t)dt + \sigma(X_t, t)dW_t, \qquad X_t, W_t \in \mathbb{R}^n.$$

We have studied how to solve for solutions to (10.1), both analytically and numerically. But sometimes we do not want to study individual trajectories; rather, we want to study statistical properties of ensembles of trajectories. Such questions can be studied using partial differential equations associated with each SDE, an approach we follow in this and in the remaining chapters.

10.1. Markov property and transition densities

We start with an important observation: *solutions to* (10.1) *are Markov processes* (recall Definition 4.1 with associated footnote and Equation (6.11)). We will not prove this but rather point out that it is a natural consequence of the fact that increments $X_t - X_s = \int_s^t b(X_u, u)du + \int_s^t \sigma(X_u, u)dW_u$ can be calculated using only $(X_u)_{s \leq u < t}$ and do not require knowing $\{X_u\}_{u<s}$. In fact, a stronger result holds, which is that solutions to (10.1) satisfy the strong Markov property (recall Theorem 4.15).

Because X is a continuous Markov process, we can describe its time-evolution by a transition density $p(x, t|y, s)$, which is a function defined such that for any event $A \subset \mathbb{R}^n$,

$$(10.2) \qquad P(X_t \in A | X_s = y) = \int_A p(x, t|y, s)dx.$$

Clearly, p must be nonnegative, integrable in x, and, furthermore,

$$(10.3) \qquad p(x, t|y, t) = \delta(x - y).$$

From the transition density we can express the average of a function f of the process with a starting point $X_s = y$—call this $\mathbb{E}^{y,s} f(X_t) = \mathbb{E}[f(X_t)|X_s = y]$—by integrating against the first spatial argument of the density, as

$$(10.4) \qquad u(y, s) = \mathbb{E}^{y,s} f(X_t) = \int f(x)p(x, t|y, s)dx.$$

Compare this to a discrete Markov process with transition matrix $P(t)$, where we calculated expectations as $\mathbb{E}^{x,0} f(X_t) = P(t)u^{(0)}$, where $u^{(0)} = (f(1), f(2), \ldots)^T$. That is, we multiplied the transition matrix by a vector on the right, summing over the columns. Therefore, the argument x of $p(x, t|y, s)$ is analogous to the variable indexing the columns of a transition matrix.

We can also compute the probability density $\rho(x, t)$ of X_t—given an initial density $X_0 \sim \rho_0$—by integrating against the second spatial argument, as

$$(10.5) \qquad \rho(x, t) = \int p(x, t | y, 0) \rho_0(y) dy.$$

Compare this to a discrete Markov process, for which the probability distribution at time t is $\mu(t) = \mu(0)P(t)$: we multiply the transition matrix on the left by a row vector, summing over the rows. Therefore, the argument y of $p(x, t | y, s)$ is analogous to the variable indexing the rows of a transition matrix.

We will derive evolution equations for u and ρ, called the Kolmogorov backward and forward equations, respectively. These are analogous to the equations we studied for Markov chains. We will study these equations in domains $D \subset \mathbb{R}^n$ that are both unbounded (Sections 10.10.3, 10.10.4) and bounded (Section 10.10.5), over a time interval $[0, T]$. Our presentation will require a number of assumptions on the coefficient functions over $D \times [0, T]$, including

(A1) $b_i(x, t), \sigma_{ij}(x, t)$ are bounded, continuous in (x, t), uniformly Lipschitz continuous in their spatial variables, and satisfy linear growth conditions in the spatial variables.

(A2) All the partial derivatives $\partial_i a_{ij}(x, t), \partial_{ij}^2 a_{ij}(x, t), \partial_i b_i(x, t)$ are bounded, continuous in (x, t), and uniformly Lipchitz continuous in their spatial variables.

(A3) The diffusion tensor $a(x, t) = \frac{1}{2}\sigma(x, t)\sigma^T(x, t)$ is *uniformly elliptic*: there is a constant $\lambda_0 > 0$ such that

$$(10.6) \quad y^T a(x, t) y \geq \lambda_0 \qquad \text{for all } y \in \mathbb{R}^n \text{ such that } y^T y = 1, \ (x, t) \in D \times [0, T].$$

That is, the minimum eigenvalue of $a(x, t)$ is bounded below by λ_0, uniformly in $D \times [0, T]$.

Some of these assumptions are stronger than one needs for the results below to be true but they simplify the presentation.[1] Our derivations will be mainly formal; we refer the reader to (**Friedman, 1964**), (**Friedman, 2006**), and (**Koralov and Sinai, 2007**) for rigorous proofs and a more complete discussion of existence, uniqueness, and maximum principles for the underlying PDEs (a selection of results is given in Appendix A.A.5). The existence of and analytic properties of transition probabilities are developed in (**Friedman, 1964**), (**Stroock, 2008**), and (**Stroock and Varadhan, 1979**).

---

[1] We follow the presentation in (**Koralov and Sinai, 2007**, Chapter 21), which is closely related to the fairly complete theories developed in (**Friedman, 2006**) and (**Friedman, 1964**). Note that these latter two references require the coefficients of the SDE and sometimes their derivatives to be bounded, as in (A1); however, (**Koralov and Sinai, 2007**, Remark 21.15) argues that one can replace this condition with a linear growth bound provided one assumes the coefficients are uniformly Lipschitz.

10.2. Generator of a diffusion process

Consider a process $X \in \mathbb{R}^n$ solving (10.1), and a function $f \in C^2(\mathbb{R}^n)$. Applying Itô's formula to $f(X_t)$ and integrating from s to t gives

$$f(X_t) - f(X_s) = \int_s^t \left(b(X_u, u) \cdot \nabla f(X_u) + \frac{1}{2}\sigma(X_u, u)\sigma^T(X_u, u) : \nabla^2 f(X_u) \right) du$$

$$+ \int_s^t \nabla f(X_u)^T \sigma(X_u, u) dW_u.$$

Take the expectation conditional on $X_s = y$ to obtain

$$(10.7) \qquad \mathbb{E}^{y,s} f(X_t) - f(y) = \mathbb{E}^{y,s} \int_s^t \mathcal{L}f(X_u) du,$$

where the linear operator $\mathcal{L}$ is given by

$$(10.8) \qquad (\mathcal{L}f)(x) = b(x,t) \cdot \nabla f(x) + a(x,t) : \nabla^2 f(x)$$

where we write $a(x,t) : \nabla^2 f(x) = \sum_{i,j} a_{ij}\partial_{ij}f$, and with

$$a(x,t) = \frac{1}{2}\sigma(x,t)\sigma^T(x,t).$$

DEFINITION 10.1. The *generator* of a diffusion process of the form (10.1) is the linear operator $\mathcal{L}$ defined in (10.8).

The generator $\mathcal{L}$ is exactly analogous to the infinitesimal generator of a continuous-time Markov chain. Recall (Exercise 4.2) that for a time-homogeneous, continuous-time Markov chain, the generator may be defined as the matrix Q such that for a bounded function $f : S \to \mathbb{R}$,

$$\lim_{t \to 0+} \frac{\mathbb{E}^{x,0} f(X_t) - f(x)}{t} = (Q\underline{f})_x,$$

where $\underline{f} = (f(x))_{x \in S}$ is a vector and $(Q\underline{f})_x$ equals the vector $Q\underline{f}$ evaluated at component x. The generator was a linear operator acting on a finite– or countable-dimensional vector space. Consider the same calculation for a time-homogeneous diffusion process (**Koralov and Sinai, 2007**, p. 323). Let $f : \mathbb{R}^n \to \mathbb{R}$ be a bounded function which, for simplicity, we assume has bounded and continuous first and second derivatives. Using (10.7),

$$\lim_{t \to 0+} \frac{\mathbb{E}^{x,0} f(X_t) - f(x)}{t}$$

$$= \lim_{t \to 0+} \mathbb{E}^{x,0} \frac{1}{t} \int_0^t \mathcal{L}f(X_u) du$$

$$= \mathbb{E}^{x,0} \lim_{t \to 0+} \frac{1}{t} \int_0^t \mathcal{L}f(X_u) du \qquad \text{dominated convergence theorem}$$

$$= \mathbb{E}^{x,0} \mathcal{L}f(X_0) \qquad\qquad\qquad\quad \text{mean value theorem}$$

$$= (\mathcal{L}f)(x).$$

The generator $\mathcal{L}$ is now a linear operator acting on functions, a continuous generalization of a matrix acting on vectors.

This calculation foreshadows a more general definition of generator that is used in the probability literature, included here for completeness.

DEFINITION 10.2. The *infinitesimal generator* of a time-homogeneous Markov process is the operator $\mathcal{A}$ acting on functions in $L^\infty = \{f : \|f\|_\infty < \infty\}$ with $\|f\|_\infty = \sup_x |f(x)|$, defined by

$$(10.9) \qquad (\mathcal{A}f)(x) = \lim_{t\to 0} \frac{\mathbb{E}^x f(X_t) - f(x)}{t}.$$

The set $D(\mathcal{A}) \subset L^\infty$ on which this limit exists is the *domain* of $\mathcal{A}$. The convergence above is understood as norm convergence, i.e., there exists a function $g \in L^\infty$, which is identified as $\mathcal{A}f$, such that

$$\lim_{t\to 0} \left\| \frac{\mathbb{E}^{\cdot,0} f(X_t) - f}{t} - g \right\|_\infty = 0.$$

Clearly, when f is sufficiently smooth the generator is $\mathcal{A}f = \mathcal{L}f$ as in (10.8).

REMARK 10.3. Definition 10.2 applies to general Markov processes, not just the ones we have studied: their dynamics are characterized by a generator, which is always a linear functional. For diffusion processes, the functional is a partial differential operator; for processes containing jumps, the generator will contain an integral operator. The *Hille–Yosida theorem* provides the conditions for a closed linear operator $\mathcal{L}$ on a Banach space to be the infinitesimal generator of a Markov process.

REMARK 10.4. The coefficients of the operator $\mathcal{L}$ can be obtained from the moments of the diffusion process and the definition above, as

$$b_i(x) = \lim_{t\to 0} \frac{\mathbb{E}^x[(X_t)_i - x_i]}{t}, \qquad a_{ij}(x) = \lim_{t\to 0} \frac{\mathbb{E}[((X_t)_i - x_i)((X_t)_j - x_j)]}{t}.$$

See, e.g., (**Gardiner, 2009; Pavliotis, 2014; Karlin and Taylor, 1981**).

10.3. Backward Kolmogorov equation

One use of the generator is in the backward equation. We show three versions of this equation: one for a time-inhomogeneous process, one for a time-homogeneous process, and one for the transition density. We start with the time-inhomogeneous backward equation, since it is the most straightforward to prove.

THEOREM 10.5 (Kolmogorov Backward equation, time-inhomogeneous). *Let X solve SDE (10.1), whose coefficients satisfy (A1), (A3). Let $f : \mathbb{R}^n \to \mathbb{R}$ be bounded and continuous. Define*

$$(10.10) \qquad u(y,s) = \mathbb{E}^{y,s} f(X_t) = \mathbb{E}[f(X_t)|X_s = y].$$

Then u solves

$$(10.11) \qquad \partial_s u(y,s) + \mathcal{L}u(y,s) = 0, \quad 0 \le s < t, \qquad u(y,t) = f(y),$$

where $\mathcal{L}$ is the generator of the diffusion, defined in (10.8).

REMARK 10.6. Recall that for a continuous-time Markov chain, the vector $u(t)$—defined as in (4.15)—evolves as $\frac{du}{dt} + Qu = 0$, which is the discrete version of (10.11). As for Markov chains, the backward equation imposes a terminal condition at time t and solves an elliptic equation backward in time.

REMARK 10.7. The time-inhomogeneous backward equation is used frequently in finance. Suppose X_t represents the price of a financial asset, such as a stock, and $f(X_t)$ is the payout one gets when selling the stock at time t. Then $u(y, s)$ is the expected payout if the stock has value y at time s.

PROOF. (*Theorem* 10.5) Showing that the function u defined by (10.10) satisfies (10.11) is technical, as it requires showing that u has two derivatives in x and one derivative in t (e.g., (**Durrett, 1996**, Section 7)). Instead, we show that if u is a bounded solution to (10.11), then u satisfies (10.10).[2] We show this for a scalar SDE but a multidimensional one follows in the same way. Let t be fixed and let $Z_s = u(X_s, s)$. From Itô's formula we have (all functions below are evaluated at (X_s, s))

$$dZ_s = u_t ds + u_x dX_s + a u_{xx} ds$$
$$= (u_t + b u_x + a u_{xx}) ds + u_x \sigma dW_s$$
$$= u_x \sigma dW_s,$$

since u solves the PDE by assumption. Integrating from s to t gives

$$Z_t = Z_s + \int_s^t u_x(X_r, r) \sigma(X_r) dW_r.$$

Taking expectations shows that $\mathbb{E}^{y,s} Z_s = \mathbb{E}^{y,s} Z_t$ for all $0 \le s \le t$. We have $\mathbb{E}^{y,s} Z_s = \mathbb{E}^{y,s} u(X_s, s) = u(y, s)$, and, using the initial condition of the PDE, $\mathbb{E}^{y,s} Z_t = \mathbb{E}^{y,s} u(X_t, t) = \mathbb{E}^{y,s} f(X_t)$. Therefore, $u(y, s) = \mathbb{E}^{y,s} f(X_t)$. □

The proof above shows that solutions to an SDE can be thought of as characteristics for a PDE. When $\sigma = 0$ so that (10.1) is a deterministic equation, the backward equation is the first-order PDE $\partial_t u + b(x) \cdot \nabla u = 0$. Characteristics for this equation satisfy $\frac{dx}{ds} = b(x)$, which is SDE (10.1) with no noise. Our proof then implies the solution $u(x, t)$ to the PDE (10.11) with no diffusion term is constant on characteristics. Indeed, we can calculate this easily using the chain rule and (10.11):

$$\frac{du(x(s), s)}{ds} = u_x \frac{dx}{ds} + u_t = b(x) u_x + u_t = 0.$$

Therefore, along some characteristic $x(s)$, we must have $u(x(s), s) = f(x(t))$.

When we have noise, $\sigma \ne 0$, then the PDE (10.11) no longer has deterministic characteristics but rather it has noisy characteristics, the solutions to SDE (10.1). The solution to the PDE can be expressed in (10.10), not as the *value* of f along characteristics, but instead as the *average* of f, averaged over the ensemble of characteristics with a given starting point, stopped at some common final time t.

If the process is time-homogeneous, then by a change of the time variable we may solve an elliptic equation forward in time instead.

THEOREM 10.8 (Backward equation, time-homogeneous). *Let X solve a time-homogeneous SDE (10.1) whose coefficients satisfy (A1), (A3). Let $f : \mathbb{R}^n \to \mathbb{R}$ be bounded and continuous. Define*

(10.12) $u(x, t) = \mathbb{E}^x f(X_t) = \mathbb{E}[f(X_t) | X_0 = x].$

---

[2]This argument can be found in (**Koralov and Sinai, 2007**, Theorem 21.14); (**Friedman, 2006**, Theorem 6.5.3); (**Varadhan, 2007**, pp. 95–96).

For $t \geq 0$, u satisfies

(10.13) $$\partial_t u = \mathcal{L}u, \qquad u(x, 0) = f(x),$$

where $\mathcal{L}$ is the generator of the diffusion process, defined in (10.8).

PROOF. Change variables $s \to t - s$ in (10.11), assuming time-homogeneous coefficients in the SDE (10.1). Alternatively, let $Z_s = u(X_s, t - s)$, and show that $\mathbb{E}^x Z_s = \mathbb{E}^x Z_0$ for all $0 \leq s \leq t$, as in the proof of Theorem 10.5. $\square$

REMARK 10.9. The assumptions of the theorems ensure there is a unique solution u to (10.13) on $\mathbb{R}^n \times \mathbb{R}^+$, that is bounded and continuous on its domain, with continuous first derivatives in t, and continuous second derivatives in x for $t > 0$ (**Koralov and Sinai, 2007**, Theorem 21.12). One may weaken these assumptions and obtain weaker forms of solutions (as will be the case in all the theorems we state); for example, f may have polynomial growth (Appendix A.A.5). We do not further explore the extent to which we may vary the assumptions.

Example 10.10 (Ornstein–Uhlenbeck process). Consider an OU process $dX_t = -\alpha X_t dt + \sigma dW_t$. The generator is $\mathcal{L}f = -\alpha x \partial_x f + \frac{1}{2}\sigma^2 \partial_{xx} f$ so the time-homogeneous backward equation is

$$\partial_t u = -\alpha x \partial_x u + \frac{1}{2}\sigma^2 \partial_{xx} u, \qquad u(x, 0) = f(x).$$

Example 10.11 (Geometric Brownian motion). A GBM $dX_t = rX_t dt + \sigma X_t dW_t$ has generator $\mathcal{L}f = rx \partial_x f + \frac{1}{2}\sigma^2 x^2 \partial_{xx} f$ so the time-homogeneous backward equation is

$$\partial_t u = rx \partial_x u + \frac{1}{2}\sigma^2 x^2 \partial_{xx} u, \qquad u(x, 0) = f(x).$$

Example 10.12 (Two-dimensional diffusion process). For the sake of illustration, consider a time-homogeneous diffusion process (X_t, Y_t) that evolves as

$$dX_t = -Y_t dt + dW_t^{(1)}, \qquad dY_t = X_t Y_t dt + X_t dW_t^{(1)} + Y_t dW_t^{(2)}.$$

The drift vector is

$$b(x, y) = \begin{pmatrix} -y \\ xy \end{pmatrix}.$$

The noise matrix is

$$\sigma(x, y) = \begin{pmatrix} 1 & 0 \\ x & y \end{pmatrix},$$

so the diffusivity matrix is

$$a(x, y) = \frac{1}{2}\sigma\sigma^T = \frac{1}{2}\begin{pmatrix} 1 & x \\ x & x^2 + y^2 \end{pmatrix}.$$

The generator is, therefore,

$$\mathcal{L}f = -y\partial_x f + xy\partial_y f + \frac{1}{2}\partial_{xx} f + x\partial_{xy} f + \frac{1}{2}(x^2 + y^2)\partial_{yy} f.$$

Suppose we wish to compute $u(x, y, t) = \mathbb{E}[\sqrt{X_t^2 + Y_t^2} | X_0 = x, Y_0 = y]$. Then we would solve the following backward equation:

$$\partial_t u = -y\partial_x u + xy\partial_y u + \frac{1}{2}\partial_{xx} u + x\partial_{xy} u + \frac{1}{2}(x^2 + y^2)\partial_{yy} u, \qquad u(x, y, 0) = \sqrt{x^2 + y^2}.$$

There is a link between the Green's function for the inhomogeneous backward equation and the transition density for the stochastic process. Formally applying ∂_s, $\mathcal{L}$ to the right-hand side of (10.4) and moving the derivatives under the integral gives

$$\int f(x)(\partial_s p(x,t|y,s) + \mathcal{L}_y p(x,t|y,s))dx = 0,$$

where the operator $\mathcal{L}_y$ acts on the y-variables of p. Since this hold for all functions $f \in C_0^\infty(\mathbb{R}^n)$ (infinitely differentiable functions with compact support)—a set of functions we call *test functions*—we obtain a version of the backward equation for the transition density.

THEOREM 10.13 (Backward equation, transition density). *Let X solve SDE* (10.1), *whose coefficients satisfy* (A1), (A3). *The transition density* $p(x,t|y,s)$ *evolves jointly in* y, s *as*

(10.14) $$\partial_s p + \mathcal{L}_y p = 0, \quad 0 \le s < t, \qquad p(x,t|y,t) = \delta(x-y),$$

where $\mathcal{L}_y$ *acts on the y-variable of p.*

In other words, the transition density is the Green's function for the inhomogeneous backward equation (**Koralov and Sinai, 2007**, Lemma 21.17).

Example 10.14. A Brownian motion has transition density

$$p(x,t|y,s) = \frac{1}{\sqrt{2\pi(t-s)}} e^{-\frac{(x-y)^2}{2(t-s)}},$$

which one can verify solves (10.14).

Example 10.15. Consider the OU process $dX_t = -\alpha X_t dt + dW_t$. The transition density can be shown to be

$$p(x,t|y,s) = \frac{1}{\sqrt{2\pi\sigma^2(t-s)}} \exp\left(-\frac{(x - e^{-\alpha(t-s)}y)^2}{2\sigma^2(t-s)}\right),$$

where $\sigma^2(t) = (1 - e^{-2\alpha t})/(2\alpha)$ is the variance at time t. (Exercise: Verify this density satisfies (10.14).)

Deriving the backward equation using semigroup notation. We end this section with an alternative (and optional) derivation of the time-homogeneous backward equation, (10.13), using abstract semigroup notation (though we omit details needed to make the arguments rigorous). We start from the *Chapman–Kolmogorov equations*, which hold in some form for any Markov process:

(10.15) $$p(x,t|y,s) = \int p(x,t|z,u)p(z,u|y,s)dz, \qquad s \le u \le t.$$

Introduce the operator

(10.16) $$T_t f(x) = \mathbb{E}^x f(X_t) = \int_y f(y)p(y,t|x,0)dy,$$

so that $T_t f(x) = u(x,t)$ where u is defined as in (10.12). The domain of T_t is the set of bounded, measurable functions $f : \mathbb{R} \to \mathbb{R}$. We claim that

(10.17) $$T_{s+t}f = (T_s \circ T_t)f.$$

This property is proved from, and indeed is a succinct form of, the Chapman–Kolmogorov equations (10.15). Notice the relationship to the Chapman–Kolmogorov equations $P(s + t) = P(s)P(t)$ for Markov chains. To show this property, calculate

$$
\begin{aligned}
T_{s+t}f = \mathbb{E}^x f(X_{t+s}) &= \int_y f(y)p(y, t+s|x, 0)dy \\
&= \int_y \int_z f(y)p(y, t+s|z, s)p(z, s|x, 0)dzdy \qquad \text{CK eqns (10.15)} \\
&= \int_y \int_z f(y)p(y, t|z, 0)p(z, s|x, 0)dzdy \qquad \text{time-homogeneity} \\
&= \int_z p(z, s|x, 0)\left[\int f(y)p(y, t|z, 0)dy\right]dz \qquad \text{Fubini's theorem} \\
&= T_s(T_t f).
\end{aligned}
$$

We use this property to derive the backward equation:

$$
\begin{aligned}
\frac{\partial u(x, t)}{\partial t} &= \lim_{h\to 0} \frac{\mathbb{E}^x f(X_{t+h}) - \mathbb{E}^x f(X_t)}{h} = \lim_{h\to 0} \frac{T_{t+h}f - T_t f}{h} \\
&= \lim_{h\to 0} \frac{(T_h \circ T_t)f - T_t f}{h} = \lim_{h\to 0} \frac{T_h u - u}{h} \\
&= \mathcal{L}u.
\end{aligned}
$$

REMARK 10.16. Property (10.17) combined with $T_0 = I$ (where I is the identity operator) is the *semigroup property* for the set of operators $\{T_t\}_{t\geq 0}$, hence, the set is called the *transition semigroup* ((**Durrett, 1996**, Chapter 7), (**Varadhan, 2007**), (**Lax, 1997**, Chapter 36)). The operators T_t defined in (10.16) form a semigroup, as do the transition probabilities $P(t)$ for a continuous-time Markov chain, where $P(t)$ is thought of as an operator mapping vectors to vectors. The transition semigroup is obtained from the generator as $T_t = e^{\mathcal{L}t} \equiv I + t\mathcal{L} + \frac{t^2}{2}\mathcal{L}^2 + \cdots$. Studying abstract semigroups of operators, sometimes with additional properties like continuity or uniform continuity at $t = 0$, is another approach to studying Markov processes. For more details, see, e.g., (**Grimmett and Stirzaker, 2001**, p. 256) for ctMCs, (**Pavliotis, 2014**) for a heuristic study for diffusion processes, and (**Gikhman and Skorokhod, 2004**; **Durrett, 1996**) for a rigorous study of Markov processes using semigroup formulation.

Exercise **10.1.** Use the Chapman–Kolmogorov equations (10.15) to show that

$$
\int_{\mathbb{R}^n} u(y, s)\rho(y, s)dy = \mathbb{E}[f(X_t)|X_0 \sim \rho_0] \quad \text{for } 0 \leq s \leq t,
$$

where u is defined in (10.4) and $\rho(x, t)$ is defined in (10.5). Notably, this inner product is independent of s.

10.4. Forward Kolmogorov equation (Fokker–Planck equation)

Now we consider the forward equation, also known as the *Fokker–Planck equation*. It will be formulated in terms of $\mathcal{L}^*$, the formal adjoint of the generator $\mathcal{L}$. This is the operator that satisfies

(10.18)
$$
\langle \mathcal{L}f, g \rangle = \langle f, \mathcal{L}^*g \rangle
$$

for all test functions $f, g \in C_0^\infty(\mathbb{R}^n)$, where $\langle f, g \rangle = \int_{\mathbb{R}^n} fg \, dx$ is the L^2-inner product.

To build intuition, let us first derive the adjoint of the generator for a continuous-time Markov chain with generator Q. We ask for a matrix Q^* such that $\langle Qx, y \rangle = \langle x, Q^*y \rangle$ for all vectors x, y. Writing the inner product as

$$\langle Qx, y \rangle = y^T Q x = x^T Q^T y = \langle x, Q^T y \rangle,$$

we see that $Q^* = Q^T$, hence, the adjoint of the generator is its transpose.

Let us now compute the adjoint of the generator $\mathcal{L}^*$ for a diffusion process. We will use the notation $\nabla \cdot A$ for a matrix A to mean the divergence operator applied along rows. That is, $(\nabla \cdot A)_i = \sum_j \partial_j A_{ij}$. We have

$$\langle \mathcal{L}f, g \rangle = \int g(b \cdot \nabla f + a : \nabla^2 f) dx$$

$$= \int \Big(\nabla \cdot (fgb) - f\nabla \cdot (gb) + \nabla \cdot (ga \cdot \nabla f) - \nabla \cdot (f\nabla \cdot (ga)) + f\nabla \cdot \nabla \cdot (ga) \Big) dx$$

$$= \int f \left(-\nabla \cdot (gb) + \nabla \cdot \nabla \cdot (ga) \right) dx + \int \nabla \cdot (fgb + ga \cdot \nabla f - f\nabla \cdot (ga)) \, dx.$$

Since the terms $g(a \cdot \nabla f)$, $f(gb - \nabla \cdot (ga))$ have compact support, we may apply the divergence theorem over a sufficiently large ball to show the last integral vanishes and obtain the adjoint operator as

(10.19) $$\mathcal{L}^*g(x, t) = -\nabla \cdot (b(x, t)g(x)) + \nabla \cdot \nabla \cdot (a(x, t)g(x)).$$

In components, we have

(10.20) $$\mathcal{L}^*g(x, t) = -\sum_i \partial_i(b(x, t)g(x)) + \sum_{i,j} \partial_{ij}(a(x, t)g(x)).$$

The adjoint operator appears in the forward equation, also known as the Fokker–Planck equation. It is easiest to first derive the forward equation for the transition density and then use this to derive the forward equation for an arbitrary initial density.

THEOREM 10.17 (Forward equation, transition density). *Let X solve SDE (10.1), whose coefficients satisfy (A1), (A2), (A3). The transition density $p(x, t|y, s)$ evolves jointly in (x, t) as*

(10.21) $$\partial_t p = \mathcal{L}_x^* p, \qquad p(x, s|y, s) = \delta(x - y),$$

where $\mathcal{L}_x^*$ acts on the x-variable of p.

PROOF. Here is a formal proof (see (**Koralov and Sinai, 2007**, Lemma 21.17) or (**Friedman, 2006**, Theorem 6.5.4) for a more complete discussion). Let $f(x, t)$ be differentiable in time and infinitely differentiable with compact support in x, and consider

$$\mathbb{E}^{y,s} f(X_t, t) - f(y, s) = \int_{\mathbb{R}^n} f(z, t) p(z, t|y, s) dz - f(y, s).$$

Applying Itô's formula to $f(X_t, t)$ shows we can write the LHS above (similar to (10.7)) as

$$\mathbb{E}^{y,s} f(X_t, t) - f(y, s) = \int_s^t \int_{\mathbb{R}^n} (f_r + \mathcal{L}f)(z, r) p(z, r|y, s) dz \, dr.$$

Integrating by parts on the RHS and using (10.18) and (10.3) gives

$$\int_s^t \int_{\mathbb{R}^n} (f_r + \mathcal{L}f)(z,r)p(z,r|y,s)dzdr$$

$$= \int_s^t \int_{\mathbb{R}^n} (-f\partial_r p + f\mathcal{L}_z^* p)dzdr + \int_{\mathbb{R}^n} f(z,r)p(z,r|y,s)|_{r=s}^{r=t}dz$$

$$= \int_s^t \int_{\mathbb{R}^n} f(-\partial_r p + \mathcal{L}_z^* p)dzdr + \int_{\mathbb{R}^n} f(z,t)p(z,t|y,s)dz - f(y,s).$$

Putting both expressions for $\mathbb{E}^{y,s} f(X_t,t) - f(y,s)$ together shows that

$$\int_s^t \int_{\mathbb{R}^n} f(-\partial_r p + \mathcal{L}_z^* p)dzdr = 0.$$

Since we may choose f to be compactly supported and arbitrarily concentrated near any value of z, r, we must have that $-\partial_r p + \mathcal{L}_z^* p = 0$.   □

THEOREM 10.18 (Forward equation/Fokker–Planck equation). *Let X solve SDE (10.1), whose coefficients satisfy (A1), (A2), (A3). Let $X_0 \sim \rho_0(x)$ be the initial probability density and suppose $\mathbb{E}X_0^2 < \infty$. Then X_t has density $\rho(x,t)$ which solves*

$$(10.22) \qquad \partial_t \rho = \mathcal{L}^* \rho \quad (t > 0), \qquad \rho(x,0) = \rho_0(x),$$

where operator $\mathcal{L}^*$ is defined in (10.19). Specifically,

$$(10.23) \qquad \partial_t \rho = -\nabla \cdot (b\rho) + \nabla \cdot \nabla \cdot (a\rho) \quad (t > 0), \qquad \rho(x,0) = \rho_0(x).$$

Furthermore, ρ is bounded on $\mathbb{R}^n \times [0,\infty)$ and lives in $C^{2,1}(\mathbb{R}^n \times (0,\infty))$ (it has one continuous derivative in time and two continuous derivatives in space).

PROOF. Formally, this can be obtained by multiplying (10.21) by $\rho_0(y)$ and integrating over y, using relationship (10.5) between the density ρ and the transition probability to find (10.22).   □

As for the backward equation, the transition density $p(x,t|y,s)$ is the Green's function for the forward equation (10.22), but this time in the (x,t) variables.

To make a link to the forward equation for a continuous-time Markov chain, recall that the probability distribution $\mu(t)$ (a row vector) for a ctMC evolved as

$$\frac{d\mu}{dt} = \mu Q \Leftrightarrow \frac{d\mu^T}{dt} = Q^T \mu^T.$$

This is the discrete version of (10.22), since $Q^* = Q^T$.

REMARK 10.19. The forward equation is weaker than the backward equation— it requires taking derivatives of b, σ, but these are not required to be differentiable for the SDE to have a unique strong solution or for the backward equation to be well posed. Therefore, the forward equation must sometimes be posed in a weak sense (as the derivation of Theorem 10.17 suggested). One situation where the forward equation does not have a strong solution is when the coefficients b, σ have discontinuities in their derivatives. Sometimes they can even involve delta-functions, for example, in Brownian dynamics (looking ahead to Example 12.5) when $U(x)$ is a step function so the drift, $-\nabla U(x)$, is a delta-function. Another situation when the forward equation only exists in a weak sense is when the measure characterizing X_t is singular with respect to the Lebesgue measure, such as when X_t has "sticky" boundary behavior (**Bou-Rabee and Holmes-Cerfon, 2020**). See (**Evans, 2010**) for the construction of weak solutions to partial differential equations.

Example 10.20. Consider an OU process $dX_t = -\alpha X_t dt + \sigma dW_t$. The forward equation is

$$\partial_t \rho = \alpha \partial_x (x\rho) + \frac{1}{2}\sigma^2 \partial_{xx}\rho, \qquad \rho(x, 0) = \rho_0(x).$$

Example 10.21. Consider GBM $dX_t = rX_t dt + \sigma X_t dW_t$. The forward equation is

$$\partial_t \rho = r\partial_x (x\rho) + \frac{1}{2}\sigma^2 \partial_{xx}(x^2\rho), \qquad \rho(x, 0) = \rho_0(x).$$

Example 10.22. Consider the two-dimensional diffusion process from Example 10.12, $dX_t = -Y_t dt + dW_t^{(1)}$, $dY_t = X_t Y_t dt + X_t dW_t^{(1)} + Y_t dW_t^{(2)}$. Suppose that X_0, Y_0 are independent standard normal random variables. The forward equation is

$$\partial_t \rho = \partial_x (y\rho) - \partial_y (xy\rho) + \frac{1}{2}\partial_{xx}\rho + \partial_{xy}(x\rho) + \frac{1}{2}\partial_{yy}((x^2 + y^2)\rho),$$

$$\rho_0(x, y) = \frac{1}{2\pi}e^{-(x^2+y^2)/2}.$$

10.4.1. Physical interpretation of the Fokker–Planck equation. The Fokker–Planck equation has a physical interpretation in terms of the flux of probability. Write (10.22) as

(10.24) $\partial_t \rho + \nabla \cdot \underline{j} = 0,$ where $\underline{j} = b(x, t)\rho - \nabla \cdot (a(x, t)\rho).$

This is a conservation equation for the probability density ρ. The quantity $\underline{j}$, which tells us how probability moves, is called the *probability current* or *probability flux*. It is analogous to the fluxes encountered in fluid dynamics. Consider a passive tracer in a fluid, such as particles of milk in coffee that is being stirred. The particles will be advected by the fluid's velocity but they will also diffuse because they are jiggled about by random collisions with the fluid molecules. If we let

$$\rho(x, t) = \text{concentration of a passive tracer}$$
$$b(x, t) = \text{velocity of fluid}$$
$$a(x, t) = \text{diffusion tensor in fluid,}$$

then the evolution of ρ is governed by the Fokker–Planck equation, which says that the tracer is advected with velocity b, and diffuses with diffusion tensor a. Probability behaves like a passive tracer[3] in a fluid!

From the probability flux, we can compute the total amount of probability that crosses a surface S per unit time. Consider a closed surface S with interior Ω. The change in total probability in Ω per unit time is, by the divergence theorem,

(10.25) $$\frac{d}{dt}\int_\Omega \rho = \int_\Omega -\nabla \cdot \underline{j} = \int_S -\underline{j} \cdot \hat{n},$$

where $\hat{n}$ is the unit outward normal. The flux across S is $\int_S \underline{j} \cdot \hat{n}$.

---

[3]The more familiar equation for a passive tracer is $\partial_t c + u \cdot \nabla c = $ [diffusion] because for many fluids $\nabla \cdot u = 0$.

Choosing $\Omega = \mathbb{R}^n$, this calculation also shows that probability is conserved, provided $j(x, t)$ decays sufficiently quickly as $|x| \to \infty$.

10.5. Boundary conditions for the forward and backward equations

Often, we are interested in stochastic processes that live in a bounded domain $D \subset \mathbb{R}^n$ with boundary ∂D. Examples include a milk particle diffusing in a coffee cup, a bacterium navigating in a petri dish, an ion moving through an ion channel, a protein wiggling around inside a cell, colloidal particles in a microfluidic channel, etc.

When such a process hits the boundary, there are various things that could happen to it—it could be reflected, like a billiard ball; it could be absorbed, like a fly sticking to a fly trap; it could be reflected with some probability and otherwise absorbed, etc. All of these possibilities are captured at the level of the forward and backward equations by imposing boundary conditions on ∂D. We will variously refer to boundary conditions for the forward or backward equation as boundary conditions for $\mathcal{L}^*$ or $\mathcal{L}$. Each of these operators comes with a domain of definition, $\mathcal{D}(\mathcal{L})$, $\mathcal{D}(\mathcal{L}^*)$, which are classes of functions on which each operator is assumed to act. These classes must be related to each other if the adjoint relationship $\langle \mathcal{L}f, g \rangle = \langle f, \mathcal{L}^*g \rangle$ is to hold in a bounded domain, because the boundary terms in the integration by parts used to derive this relationship (see calculations following (10.18)) must vanish.

Our approach to introducing boundary conditions will be to first list some possible boundary conditions for the forward equation, because it has a more physical interpretation, and then derive the corresponding boundary conditions for the backward equation using (10.18).

An alternative, more direct approach would explicitly construct solutions to the SDE with the corresponding boundary behavior and then use Definition 10.2 of the generator to determine the behavior of the generator $\mathcal{L}$ at the boundary. However, explicitly constructing solutions to SDEs with given boundary behavior requires concepts such as local time that are beyond the scope of this course. We will, however, give insight into the origin of the boundary conditions at the level of trajectories in Section 10.10.5.3, by constructing a continuous-time Markov chain which approximates the solution to an SDE.

10.5.1. Boundary conditions for the Forward equation ($\mathcal{L}^*$). Here are common boundary conditions for $\mathcal{L}^*$, each associated with different kinds of boundary behaviors. In what follows, $\hat{n}$ always denotes an outward normal to a boundary and $\underline{j} = b(x, t)\rho - \nabla \cdot (a(x, t)\rho)$ denotes the probability flux.

- *Reflecting boundary.*

$$\underline{j} \cdot \hat{n} = 0 \qquad \text{on } \partial D.$$

This corresponds to trajectories being reflected at the boundary. There is no net flux of probability across the boundary, so the total probability in the domain is conserved: $\frac{d}{dt} \int_D \rho = 0$ (recall (10.25)).

- *Absorbing boundary.*

$$\rho = 0 \qquad \text{on } \partial D.$$

This corresponds to trajectories being absorbed at the boundary and removed from the system immediately. The total probability is *not* conserved.

- *Periodic boundary on an interval* $[a, b]$.

$$\underline{j}|_{b-} = \underline{j}|_{a+}, \qquad \rho|_{b-} = \rho|_{a+}.$$

Trajectories that leave one side immediately re-enter on the other. Total probability is conserved.

- *At a discontinuity.* If the coefficients $b(x, t)$, $a(x, t)$ are discontinuous on some surface S but particles can still cross it, then we actually have separate equations, one on each part of the domain where the coefficients are continuous. We must match the solutions at S with a condition that captures what happens when particles hit this surface. If particles may cross S freely without reflection or adsorption, then we match the solutions with the conditions that both the probability and the normal components of the probability current are continuous across S,

$$\underline{j} \cdot \hat{n}|_{S+} = \underline{j} \cdot \hat{n}|_{S-}, \qquad \rho|_{S+} = \rho|_{S-}.$$

Note that the derivatives of ρ may not necessarily be continuous even if the flux is.

Example 10.23. Consider a particle with position (X_t, Y_t) in a two-dimensional domain $D = \{(x, y) : y > 0\}$, which is advected horizontally by a shear flow $u(x, y) = (y, 0)^T$, moves downwards with constant velocity $-b(0, 1)^T$ (for example, due to gravity), and diffuses isotropically with diffusion coefficient κ:

$$dX_t = Y_t dt + \sqrt{2\kappa}\, dW_t^{(1)}$$
$$dY_t = -b dt + \sqrt{2\kappa}\, dW_t^{(2)}.$$

The Fokker–Planck equation for the probability density of the particle is

$$\partial_t \rho = \partial_x(-y\rho) + \partial_y(b\rho) + \kappa(\partial_{xx}\rho + \partial_{yy}\rho),$$

and, hence, the flux is

$$\underline{j}(x, y, t) = \begin{pmatrix} y \\ -b \end{pmatrix} \rho(x, y, t) - \kappa \begin{pmatrix} \partial_x\rho(x, y, t) \\ \partial_y\rho(x, y, t) \end{pmatrix}.$$

At the boundary $\partial D = \{(x, y) : y = 0\}$, a reflecting boundary condition would be $\underline{j} \cdot \hat{n} = 0$ where $\hat{n} = (0, -1)^T$, and, hence,

$$b\rho + \kappa\partial_y\rho = 0 \qquad \text{at} \quad y = 0.$$

We end with some remarks about infinite domains. Although there is no "boundary" at which we can impose a boundary condition, we still need to impose some conditions on the solution to make the Fokker–Planck equation (10.22) well posed. One may recall that for the heat equation $\partial_t \rho = \Delta\rho$, $\rho(x, 0) = 0$, one can construct infinitely many solutions; however, all but one grow faster than $e^{\alpha|x|^2}$ (**John, 1978**, Chapter 7), (**Friedman, 1964**). Therefore, it is typical to require solutions to decay sufficiently quickly at ∞, either by directly imposing a decay condition or by asking that solutions live in a particular function space. A reasonable requirement is to ask that $|x|^{n-1}|\underline{j}| \to 0$ as $|x| \to \infty$, so that probability is conserved (recall (10.25)).

REMARK 10.24. Such a decay condition can be justified by appealing to PDE theory. Write $\mathcal{L}^*$ in nondivergence form, as

$$\mathcal{L}^*\rho = a : \nabla^2\rho + \tilde{b} \cdot \nabla\rho + c\rho, \qquad \text{where} \quad \tilde{b} = -b + 2\nabla \cdot a, \quad c = -\nabla \cdot b + \nabla \cdot \nabla \cdot a.$$

We may now apply Theorem A.27 from Appendix A.A.5 to show that if we ask for a solution such that $|\rho(x,t)| \leq Be^{\beta|x|^2}$ for $B, \beta > 0$, and if the coefficients $\tilde{b}, c$ are bounded and uniformly Lipschitz continuous and the initial probability density ρ_0 satisfies a mild exponential growth condition, then there exists a unique solution ρ to (10.22). If, furthermore, the initial probability density satisfies $|\rho_0(x)| \leq Ae^{-\alpha|x|^2}$ for $\alpha > 0$, then $|\rho| \leq Kt^{-n/2}e^{-\frac{1}{2t}\delta|x|^2}$, $|\nabla\rho| \leq Kt^{(-n+1)/2}e^{-\frac{1}{2t}\delta|x|^2}$ for some $K, \delta > 0$. That is, ρ and its first derivatives decay exponentially quickly. Therefore, the flux $\underline{j}$ must decay exponentially quickly as well.

10.5.2. Boundary conditions for the backward equation ($\mathcal{L}$). Boundary conditions for the backward equation, or for $\mathcal{L}$, can be derived from those for the forward equation, or $\mathcal{L}^*$, using integration by parts, by asking that (10.18) holds for all functions f, g satisfying the appropriate boundary conditions. Our calculations just after (10.18) showed that for sufficiently differentiable functions f, g,

$$(10.26) \qquad \langle \mathcal{L}f, g \rangle = \langle f, \mathcal{L}^*g \rangle + \int_{\partial D} f\underline{j} \cdot \hat{n} + g(a\nabla f) \cdot \hat{n},$$

where $\underline{j} = b(x,t)g - \nabla \cdot (a(x,t)g)$ as in (10.24). We need the integral over ∂D to vanish for all functions $f \in \mathcal{D}(\mathcal{L})$, i.e., all functions satisfying the boundary conditions associated with $\mathcal{L}$, and for all $g \in \mathcal{D}(\mathcal{L}^*)$, i.e., all functions satisfying the boundary conditions associated with $\mathcal{L}^*$. Given boundary conditions for one of these operators, we use the vanishing of the boundary terms to determine the corresponding boundary conditions for the other operator. Here are some examples.

- *Reflecting boundary.* The boundary condition for $\mathcal{L}^*$ is $\underline{j} \cdot \hat{n} = 0$ on ∂D. Therefore, the first term in the integrand in (10.26) is always zero, so we must only ensure the second term is zero. A condition that ensures this is

$$(a\nabla f) \cdot \hat{n} = 0 \qquad \text{on } \partial D.$$

  In components, $\sum_{i,j} n_i a_{ij} \partial_j f = 0$.
- *Absorbing boundary.* The boundary condition for $\mathcal{L}^*$ is $g = 0$ on ∂D, so the second term in the integrand in (10.26) is always zero. To ensure the first term is also zero, we must choose

$$f = 0 \qquad \text{on } \partial D.$$

Other conditions are left as exercises.

10.5.3. Boundary conditions from a limit of random walks. One way to gain insight into the microscopic origin of the boundary conditions is to construct a continuous-time Markov chain which approximates the solution to the SDE, and then to see how this process behaves at the boundary of its domain ((**Bou-Rabee and Vanden-Eijnden, 2018**), (**Bou-Rabee and Holmes-Cerfon, 2020**)). We illustrate with an example.

Consider a Brownian motion on $[0, \infty)$ with a reflecting boundary condition at 0. The generator is

$$\mathcal{L}f = \frac{1}{2}\partial_{xx}f \qquad \partial_x f|_{x=0} = 0.$$

Let us discretize the domain of the process as $\mathbb{R}^h = \{0, h, 2h, 3h, \ldots\}$, where h is the spacing between neighboring grid points. We will construct a continuous-time Markov chain on $\mathbb{R}^h$, whose generator Q^h is a finite-difference approximation to $\mathcal{L}$. Let $f \in C_0^4(\mathbb{R})$ and let $f_k = f(kh)$, $k = 0, 1, 2, \ldots$ be the values of the function at the grid points as illustrated below.

The white dot is a ghost grid point, which we recruit in our construction. At each interior grid point, a second-order centered finite difference approximation for $\frac{1}{2}\partial_{xx}f$ gives

$$(10.27) \qquad (\mathcal{L}f)(kh) = \frac{f_{k+1} - 2f_k + f_{k-1}}{2h^2} + O(h^2), \qquad k \geq 1.$$

At the boundary grid point, $k = 0$, we do not know the value of the "ghost" point f_{-1} that is needed in (10.27), so we solve for it using the boundary condition. The discretized boundary condition, using a second-order centered finite difference approximation for $\partial_x f$, is

$$\frac{f_1 - f_{-1}}{2h} + O(h^2) = 0 \quad \Leftrightarrow \quad f_{-1} = f_1 + O(h^3).$$

Using this equation to eliminate f_{-1} in (10.27) with $k = 0$ gives an approximation to the generator at the boundary as

$$(10.28) \qquad (\mathcal{L}f)(0) = \frac{2f_1 - 2f_0}{2h^2} + O(h).$$

Now, we construct a continuous-time Markov chain Y_t with state space $\mathbb{R}^h$, whose generator Q^h is the discrete approximation to $\mathcal{L}$:

$$(10.29) \qquad (Q^h f)_k = \begin{cases} \dfrac{f_{k+1} - 2f_k + f_{k-1}}{2h^2}, & k = 1, 2, \ldots, \\ \dfrac{2f_1 - 2f_0}{2h^2}, & k = 0. \end{cases}$$

From the generator we can read off how Y_t behaves in the interior points and at the boundary point (recall the Gillespie algorithm from Chapter 4). At an interior point, $k > 0$, Y_t jumps left or right with equal probability with a holding time $\tau_k \sim \text{Exp}(1/h^2)$, whose average is $\mathbb{E}\tau_k = h^2$. At a boundary point, $k = 0$, Y_t jumps to the right with a holding time $\tau_0 \sim \text{Exp}(1/h^2)$, whose average is $\mathbb{E}\tau_0 = h^2$. Therefore, whenever Y_t hits zero its next step is to the right: it is "reflected" from the boundary.

Now, consider the same discretization but for the absorbing boundary condition $f|_{x=0} = 0$. The discretized generator is

$$(10.30) \qquad (Q^h f)_k = \begin{cases} \dfrac{f_{k+1} - 2f_k + f_{k-1}}{2h^2}, & k = 1, 2, \ldots, \\ 0, & k = 0. \end{cases}$$

Now, when Y_t hits 0, it stays there forever. It is "absorbed" at the boundary point.

REMARK 10.25. Conditions under which a Markov chain with continuous jumps converges to a diffusion process are given in (**Stroock and Varadhan, 1979**, Chapter 11). To show that Q^h converges to a reflecting Brownian motion requires also handling the fact that the Markov chain only jumps to grid points (**Bou-Rabee and Vanden-Eijnden, 2018**).

10.6. Stationary distribution

Suppose the SDE (10.1) is time-homogeneous. Is there a probability density that does not change with time? Recall that for a Markov chain, a stationary distribution π solves $\pi = \pi P(t)$ for all $t \geq 0$. The definition is the same for a diffusion process.

DEFINITION 10.26. A *stationary distribution* or *invariant measure* is a probability distribution $\mu(x)$ such that

$$(10.31) \qquad P(X_t \in A | X_0 \sim \mu(x)) = \mu(A) = \int_{x \in A} \mu(dx)$$

for all measurable sets $A \subset \mathbb{R}^n$. If the process has a probability density ρ, then ρ is a *stationary density* if $\partial_t \rho = 0$, so that $\mathcal{L}^* \rho = 0$.

Explicitly, a stationary density ρ solves the elliptic PDE

$$(10.32) \qquad \nabla \cdot \underline{j} = 0 \quad \Longleftrightarrow \quad \nabla \cdot (b(x)\rho - \nabla \cdot (a(x)\rho)) = 0.$$

Example 10.27 (Brownian motion). Suppose we have a one-dimensional Brownian motion on the interval $[0, 1]$ with reflecting boundary conditions. The stationary distribution solves the equation

$$\rho_{xx} = 0, \qquad \rho_x|_{x=0} = \rho_x|_{x=1} = 0.$$

Integrate once to find $\partial_x \rho = cst$; the boundary conditions imply that the constant is 0. Integrate again to find $\rho(x) = cst$. Since ρ is a probability density, we must have $\int_0^1 \rho(x)dx = 1$, so $\rho(x) = 1$. The stationary distribution is constant—there is equal probability of finding a Brownian motion anywhere in its domain.

Exercise 10.2 Show that the stationary distribution of a Brownian motion with reflecting boundary conditions in any bounded domain $D \subset \mathbb{R}^n$ is constant in that domain.

Example 10.28 (Ornstein–Uhlenbeck process). Consider $dX_t = -\alpha X_t + \sigma dW_t$. The stationary distribution solves

$$\alpha \frac{\partial}{\partial x}(x\rho) + \frac{1}{2}\sigma^2 \frac{\partial^2 \rho}{\partial x^2} = 0.$$

Let us look for a solution with $\underline{j} = 0$. Then

$$\alpha x\rho + \frac{1}{2}\sigma^2 \rho_x = 0 \quad \Rightarrow \quad \frac{\rho_x}{\rho} = -\frac{2\alpha x}{\sigma^2} \quad \Rightarrow \quad \ln \rho = -\frac{\alpha}{\sigma^2} x^2 + C$$

where C is a constant. The stationary distribution is

$$\rho = \frac{1}{\sqrt{2\pi\sigma^2/(2\alpha)}} e^{-\frac{1}{2}\frac{x^2}{\sigma^2/(2\alpha)}}.$$

This stationary distribution is Gaussian, with mean 0 and variance $\sigma^2/2\alpha$.

Example 10.29. Consider a process with a varying diffusivity:

$$dX_t = \sigma(X_t)dW_t,$$

on some interval $[a, b] \subset \mathbb{R}$ with reflecting boundary conditions. The stationary distribution solves

$$\frac{1}{2}\partial_{xx}(\sigma^2\rho) = 0, \qquad \partial_x(\sigma^2\rho) = 0 \quad \text{at } x = a, b.$$

Clearly, a solution is $\rho(x) = Z^{-1}/\sigma^2(x)$, where Z is a normalizing constant. That is, the process spends more time on average in places where the diffusivity $\frac{1}{2}\sigma^2(x)$ is lower and less time on average where the diffusivity is higher. This make sense because when the diffusivity is high the process quickly leaves that region, but when it is low it stays longer.

Example 10.30 (Brownian dynamics). An equation that is widely used to study small objects moving in a fluid with positions (or other configurational variables) $x \in \mathbb{R}^n$ is the *overdamped Langevin equation* or *Brownian dynamics equation*,

$$(10.33) \qquad dX_t = -\frac{\nabla U(X_t)}{\gamma}dt + \sqrt{\frac{2k_B T}{\gamma}}dW_t, \qquad X_t, W_t \in \mathbb{R}^n.$$

Here, $U(x)$ is the potential energy or free energy of the system, γ is a friction coefficient for moving through the fluid, T is the temperature, and k_B is Boltzmann's constant. For example, this SDE could model a spherical particle moving in water with position $x \in \mathbb{R}^3$, with potential energy $U(x) = mgx \cdot e_3$ due to gravity, and with the friction coefficient given by the Stokes–Einstein relation $\gamma = 6\pi\eta R$ where η is the dynamic viscosity of the fluid and R is the particle's radius. The random forcing term arises as an approximation for the fluid, which is composed of a great many discrete molecules. At small enough scales the discreteness of these molecules is relevant and is effectively modeled as a stochastic forcing with a corresponding frictional dissipation.

The corresponding Fokker–Planck equation is

$$\partial_t\rho = \nabla \cdot \left(\frac{1}{\gamma}\nabla U(x)\rho\right) + \frac{k_B T}{\gamma}\Delta\rho.$$

To find the stationary distribution, let us look for a solution with $\underline{j} = 0$:

$$\frac{1}{\gamma}\nabla U(x)\rho + \frac{k_B T}{\gamma}\nabla\rho = 0 \;\Rightarrow\; \frac{\nabla\rho}{\rho} = -(k_B T)^{-1}\nabla U \;\Rightarrow\; \ln\rho = -(k_B T)^{-1}U(x) + C.$$

The stationary distribution is, therefore,

$$\rho(x) = Z^{-1}e^{-U(x)/k_B T}, \qquad \text{with} \quad Z = \int_{\mathbb{R}^n} e^{-U(x)/k_B T}dx,$$

provided $Z < \infty$. This is the *Boltzmann distribution* or *Gibbs measure*. It is known to be the stationary distribution for a physical system in equilibrium, i.e., one with no external, nonconservative forces. Since one criterion for constructing a model is that it has the correct stationary distribution, this calculation verifies that (10.33) may be an appropriate model for a system described by the Boltzmann distribution.

Example 10.31 (Sampling a probability distribution). Suppose we wish to generate samples from a probability distribution π, which could be unnormalized. We may use Example 10.30 to construct a system whose dynamics have the desired stationary distribution. Define $U(x) = -\log \pi(x)$ so that $\pi(x) = e^{-U(x)}$. Following Example 10.30, the stochastic process

$$dX_t = \nabla \log \pi(X_t)dt + \sqrt{2}\, dW_t$$

has stationary distribution π. One can further show that under certain conditions on $U(x)$, the distribution of X_t converges exponentially quickly to π (**Markowich and Villani, 2000; Pavliotis, 2014**). Such dynamical equations are frequently used to sample high-dimensional probability distributions, such as the likelihood functions that arise in Bayesian statistics.

Notice that in all of these examples we looked for a solution with $j = 0$. This is a much stronger condition than $\nabla \cdot j = 0$, so we should not always expect to find such a solution. However, if we do find a solution then we are done, since (usually) the solution is unique. We will see in Chapter 12 that we can tell, from the coefficients of the SDE, when a solution satisfying the stronger condition $j = 0$ will be possible. Such systems with no steady-state flux will correspond to "equilibrium" or reversible systems, which satisfy detailed balance.

Here is an example where we must work with a weaker form of the Fokker–Planck equation.

Example 10.32 (Sticky Brownian motion). Consider a Brownian motion on $[0, 1]$, which can "stick" (spend finite time at) a boundary at $x = 0$, and which reflects off a boundary at $x = 1$. The forward equation is

$$\frac{1}{2}\Delta f = 0, \qquad f_x = \kappa f_{xx} \quad \text{at } x = 0, \quad f_x = 0 \quad \text{at } x = 1.$$

Notice the unusual boundary condition at $x = 0$. Let us show the stationary distribution is $\rho(x) = \frac{1}{1+\kappa}(1 + \kappa\delta(x))$. Notice that we cannot compute $\mathcal{L}^*\rho$ directly, since ρ contains a delta-function (even defining $\mathcal{L}^*$ is tricky). Therefore, we use a weak formulation of the stationary Fokker–Planck equation and show that $\langle \mathcal{L}f, \rho \rangle = 0$ for all test functions f. We compute (leaving out the normalization factor):

$$\langle \mathcal{L}f, \rho \rangle = \int f_{xx}(1 + \kappa\delta(x))dx$$
$$= f_x|_0^1 + \kappa f_{xx}(0)$$
$$= 0 - f_x(0) + \kappa f_{xx}(0)$$
$$= 0.$$

10.7. Additional exercises

Exercise 10.3. The *Rayleigh process* describes the evolution of the amplitude of a 2D Ornstein–Uhlenbeck process with independent, identical components (recall Example 7.19):

$$dA_t = \left(-\gamma A_t + \frac{\mu}{A_t}\right)dt + \sqrt{2\mu}\, dW_t, \qquad A_t \in (0, \infty).$$

(i) Write down the generator $\mathcal{L}$ and its adjoint $\mathcal{L}^*$.

(ii) Find the stationary distribution p_s of this process.

Now, suppose you restrict the process to the interval $[1, 3]$ by imposing reflecting boundary conditions.

(iii) Write down a PDE you could solve for the evolution of the probability density $\rho(x, t)$, given the process starts with a uniform distribution on the interval. Include all boundary conditions and initial conditions.

(iv) Write down a PDE you could solve to obtain the nth moment $M_n(x, t) = E^x A_t^n$. Include all boundary conditions and initial conditions.

Exercise 10.4. In many biological and chemical applications, trajectories of an SDE (representing, for example, a diffusing molecule) are partially reflected and partially absorbed at a boundary. This is described by the radiation boundary condition on the Fokker–Planck operator $\mathcal{L}^*$:

$$\underline{j} \cdot \hat{n} = \kappa \rho \quad \text{on the boundary,}$$

where $\underline{j}$ is the probability flux, ρ is the probability density, and $\kappa \in (0, \infty)$ is a constant related to the probability of being reflected or absorbed at 0.[4] Consider the one-dimensional OU process: $dX_t = -\alpha X_t dt + dW_t$ on $[0, \infty)$ with a radiation boundary condition at $x = 0$.

(i) Calculate the corresponding boundary condition on the generator $\mathcal{L}$.
(ii) Compute an equation for the evolution of the total probability $P_{tot}(t) = \int_0^\infty \rho(x, t) dx$. You should express $\partial_t P_{tot}$ as a function of ρ evaluated only on the boundary. Can P_{tot} ever increase?

Exercise 10.5. Consider a particle diffusing on an interval $[0, L]$ with reflecting boundary conditions at both ends. On the subinterval $[0, d]$ the particle drifts toward the origin with constant velocity $-v$, but outside this subinterval there is no force. Additionally, the particle is forced by a white noise whose strength is a constant σ everywhere.

(i) Write down the two SDEs describing this process. (You do not need to consider boundary conditions in this part.)
(ii) Write down the forward and backward equations, *including all boundary conditions*.
(iii) Show that your Fokker–Planck equation conserves probability.
(iv) Find the stationary distribution $p_s(x)$.

Exercise 10.6. Consider the diffusion

$$dX_t = -b dt + dW_t$$

on $[0, \infty)$ with a reflecting boundary condition at 0, where $b > 0$ is constant. Construct a continuous-time Markov chain discretization of this process, which jumps on a set of grid points $\{0, h, 2h, 3h, \ldots\}$. Discretize the generator of the process using a centered-difference scheme for the second derivative and an upwind scheme for the first derivative: $\partial_x f \approx \frac{f_k - f_{k-1}}{h}$. Provide the generator for your ctMC and explain how

---

[4]See A. Singer, Z. Schuss, A. Osipov, D. Holcman, *Partially reflected diffusion*, SIAM J. Appl. Math., 68(3) 844–868.

you would simulate it: If the chain is at kh, what points does it jump to, with what probabilities, and what is the average waiting time?

Exercise 10.7. Suppose in Exercise 10.6 you use a centered-difference scheme for the first derivative $\partial_x f \approx \frac{f_{k+1} - f_{k-1}}{2h}$. Does this always give you a ctMC? If not, what can go wrong?

Exercise 10.8. The *Langevin equation* describes the motion of a particle $X \in \mathbb{R}$ in a potential energy well that is stochastically forced and linearly damped:

$$m\frac{d^2X_t}{dt^2} + \gamma\frac{dX_t}{dt} + \nabla U(X_t) = \sqrt{2k_B T\gamma}\,\eta(t).$$

Here, m is the mass of the particle, γ is the friction coefficient (for example, representing Stokes drag in a fluid), η is white noise, T is the temperature and k_B is Boltzmann's constant, and $U(x)$ is the potential energy of the particle, which could arise, for example, from gravity, electrical charges, or other types of potentials.

   (i) Write this as a system of SDEs by letting $V_t = \frac{dX_t}{dt}$ be the velocity.

   (ii) Write down the corresponding Fokker–Planck equation.

   (iii) Show the stationary distribution is $\rho_s(x, v) = Z^{-1}e^{-H(x,v)/k_B T}$, where

$$H(x, v) = \frac{mv^2}{2} + U(x)$$

is the Hamiltonian (a sum of potential and kinetic energies), and

$$Z = \int e^{-H(x,v)/k_B T}\,dx\,dv$$

is the normalization constant.

   (iv) Calculate j_s, the steady-state flux, and show that it is not zero.

   (v) Repeat (a)–(c), where $x \in \mathbb{R}^n$ is a system of particles with positions $x = (x_1, x_2, \ldots, x_n)$, $\gamma = \gamma(x)$ is a symmetric positive definite matrix depending on x (the "friction tensor"), and $\sqrt{\gamma}$ is any matrix such that $\sqrt{\gamma}(\sqrt{\gamma})^T = \gamma$. You can assume that the masses of all the particles are the same.[5]

Comment #1: Even though $j_s \neq (0, 0)$, this system still satisfies detailed balance— when one accounts for the different properties under time-reversal of the different variables. That is, under time reversal, position-like variables (so-called "even" variables) remain unchanged, $x \to x$, but velocity-like variables (so-called "odd" variables) must have their sign flipped, $v \to -v$. See Section 12.12.5.

Comment #2: Langevin equations like this one are commonly used in sampling problems to sample from a density $\pi(x)$, by defining $U(x) = -\log \pi(x)$. It turns out the sampling can be significantly more efficient by introducing an extra variable, the "velocity", and then marginalizing over velocity.

---

[5] If they are not, then the correct Hamiltonian is $\frac{1}{2}v^T M v + U(x)$, where M is the mass matrix, a diagonal matrix with the particle masses on its diagonal.

CHAPTER 11

Some Applications of the Backward Equation

In this chapter we will look at some applications of the backward equation. First, we will learn how to solve for first-passage time distributions. In particular, we will show how to solve for the mean first-passage time (MFPT) by solving an elliptic equation with Dirichlet boundary conditions. Then, we will show how to solve more general boundary-value elliptic PDEs using stochastic processes. Finally, we will learn about the Feynman–Kac formula, which generalizes the backward equation to include a source term.

11.1. First-passage times

Consider a time-homogeneous process

$$(11.1) \qquad dX_t = b(X_t)dt + \sigma(X_t)dW_t \,,$$

which lives in a bounded domain $D \subset \mathbb{R}^n$ with boundary ∂D. How long does it take to reach the boundary? This question has a number of applications, such as:

- an organism looking for food, where ∂D is the boundary of the food source;
- a chemical reaction; where ∂D is the boundary of another molecular conformation;
- a ligand looking for a binding site at location ∂D;
- the stock market, e.g., the time it takes for an investment to double its value;
- the time when average sea level has risen by 3 feet;

and many others. In these applications we are interested in solving for the *first-passage time*, the time it takes a trajectory starting at x to hit ∂D for the first time, defined as

$$(11.2) \qquad T(x) = \inf\{t \,:\, X_t \in \partial D | X_0 = x\}.$$

We can answer questions about first-passage times with a variant of the backward equation. In this section we outline how to do this, assuming all functions defined are nice enough that we can differentiate them as many times as we need and interchange derivatives and integrals. See Appendix A.A.5 for theorems regarding when the PDEs involved are well posed.

We start by putting an *absorbing* boundary condition at ∂D, so that trajectories are removed from the system as soon as they reach the boundary: $p(y,t|x,s) = 0$ for $x \in \partial D$. Let $G(x,t)$ be the probability that a process is still in D at time t, given that it started at x at time 0. We can express G in terms of the transition density as

$$(11.3) \qquad G(x,t) = P(T(x) > t) = \int_D p(y,t|x,0)dy \,.$$

To solve for $G(x,t)$ we need an equation that relates its evolution in t to its evolution in x. The forward equation gives the evolution of $p(y,t|x,s)$ in (y,t) and the backward equation gives the evolution of $p(y, t|x, s)$ in (x, s). However, for a time-homogeneous process, $p(y, t|x, 0) = p(y, 0|x, -t)$, so the backward equation becomes

$$\partial_t p(y, t|x, 0) = \mathcal{L}_x p(y, t|x, 0).$$

Integrate over y to get

(11.4) $\partial_t G = \mathcal{L} G$ (in D), $G(x, 0) = 1$ $(x \in D)$, $G(x, t) = 0$ $(x \in \partial D)$.

If we solve this parabolic equation for G, we can recover the full distribution of T from (11.3).

To find moments of T, we can solve an elliptic equation instead. Consider the *mean first-passage time* (MFPT) $T_1(x) = \mathbb{E}T(x)$. Since the probability density of $T(x)$ is $-\partial_t G(x, t)$, we have

$$T_1(x) = \mathbb{E}T(x) = -\int_0^\infty t\partial_t G(x, t)dt = \int_0^\infty G(x, t)dt,$$

provided $tG(x, t) \to 0$ as $t \to \infty$, which is a condition for $\mathbb{E}T(x)$ to exist. Now apply $\mathcal{L}$ to both sides of the equation to get

$$\mathcal{L}T_1 = \int_0^\infty \mathcal{L}G(x, t)dt = \int_0^\infty \partial_t G dt = -1.$$

We have just shown that T_1, if it exists, solves an elliptic equation

(11.5) $\mathcal{L}T_1(x) = -1$ $(x \in D)$, $T_1(x) = 0$ $(x \in \partial D)$.

Example 11.1 (Brownian motion on a line). How long does it take a Brownian motion starting at the origin to exit the interval $[-R, R]$?

The generator of Brownian motion is $\mathcal{L} = \frac{1}{2}\partial_{xx}$, so we must solve

$$\frac{1}{2}\partial_{xx}T_1 = -1, \qquad T_1(-R) = T_1(R) = 0.$$

The solution is $T_1(x) = -x^2 + R^2$, so the MFPT starting at $x = 0$ is $T_1 = R^2$. Notice that to find the MFPT from the origin, we have to find it for all starting points x.

Exercise **11.1.** Suppose in the example above that the Brownian motion is reflected at $-R$. What is the MFPT for it to reach R from the origin?

Example 11.2 (Arrhenius formula for reaction rate (**Gardiner, 2009**); (**Pavliotis, 2014**, Section 7.3)). One is often interested in calculating the transition rate between meta-stable states; for example, a molecule transitions from one conformation to another with a given rate, a protein denatures with some rate, the Ising model at low temperature has rare transitions between the +1 state and the -1 state. One model to calculate the transition rate between metastable states is to consider the overdamped Langevin equation for a process X moving on an energy surface with two deep minima. We consider here a one-dimensional equation,

(11.6) $dX_t = -U'(X_t)dt + \sqrt{2D}dW_t.$

Here, D is the diffusion coefficient and $U(x)$ is the potential energy. Suppose that $U(x)$ has two deep wells at $x = a, c$, and a saddle point in between at $x = b$, as shown in

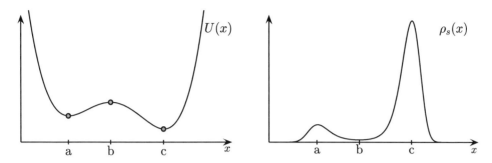

FIGURE 11.1. (Left) Schematic of a potential energy function $U(x)$ with two metastable states at $x = a, c$ with a saddle point at $x = b$ in between. (Right) the corresponding stationary distribution $\rho_s(x) = e^{-U(x)/T}$ at low temperature T. Most of the probability is concentrated near a, c. One is interested in calculating the rate of transition between a and c.

Figure 11.1. The stationary distribution is

$$\rho_s(x) = Z^{-1}e^{-U(x)/D}.$$

For small D, the stationary distribution is concentrated near each of the local minima with low probability everywhere else. We expect the system to spend a long time near a or c, and occasionally jump between them. What is the MFPT to go from a to c?

The MFPT from some point x to some point z solves

$$-U'\partial_x T_1 + D\partial_{xx} T_1 = -1, \qquad T_1'(-\infty) = 0, \quad T_1(z) = 0.$$

The boundary condition at $-\infty$ is the adjoint of the no-flux condition for the Fokker–Planck equation at $-\infty$. Solving the ODE above gives

(11.7)
$$T_1(x) = \frac{1}{D} \int_x^z dy \left[e^{U(y)/D} \int_{-\infty}^y e^{-U(s)/D} ds \right].$$

We would like to evaluate this expression with $x = a$, with z near c but slightly before it, i.e., such that $b < z < c$. We do not put the absorbing point exactly at c, because when the process gets close to c, it spends a long time wandering around in the flat part of the potential energy landscape before it actually hits c, and we only care about the time to reach the basin of c, not to reach the point c itself.

Expression (11.7) is exact but it does not tell us much about how T_1 depends on the parameters of the problem. Let us try to find a simpler expression by approximating it when D is small. The function $e^{-U(s)/D}$ is only large near $s = a$; for $a < s < c$ it is close to zero, so its contribution to the inner integral can be neglected. Therefore, we can approximate the integral using Laplace asymptotics: Taylor-expand $U(s)$ near $s = a$, and then send the limits of integration to ∞. For $y > a$,

$$\int_{-\infty}^y e^{-U(s)/D} ds \approx \int_{-\infty}^\infty e^{-\frac{1}{D}(U(a) + \frac{1}{2}U''(a)(s-a)^2)} ds = \sqrt{\frac{2\pi D}{|U''(a)|}} e^{-U(a)/D}.$$

Now, we can pull this factor out of the outer integrand in (11.7), since it is constant with respect to y. We can do a similar approximation for the outer integrand, since the first exponential factor is sharply peaked near $y = b$. Therefore we can approximate, for $x < b$,

$$\int_x^z e^{U(y)/D} dy \approx \int_{-\infty}^{\infty} e^{\frac{1}{D}(U(b) - \frac{1}{2}U''(b)(y-b)^2)} dy = \sqrt{\frac{2\pi D}{|U''(b)|}} e^{U(b)/D}.$$

Putting this together gives

$$(11.8) \qquad T_1(a \to c) \sim \frac{2\pi}{\sqrt{|U''(a)||U''(b)|}} e^{(U(b) - U(a))/D} \qquad \text{as} \quad D \to 0.$$

This is the *Arrhenius formula*; the rate of the reaction is approximated as $1/T_1$. The most important feature is the exponential dependence on the energy barrier, $U(b) - U(a)$, which shows that even a modest change in energy barrier, such as doubling it, will cause the MFPT to change by orders of magnitude.

Exercise 11.2. Suppose a particle moves following (11.6) in a double-well potential $U(x) = \frac{1}{4}(x^2 - 1)^2 = x^4 - \frac{1}{2}x^2 + \frac{1}{4}$, which has local minima at $x = -1, +1$ and a saddle point at $x = 0$. Find an expression for the mean time it takes the particle to travel from -1 to $+1$ when the diffusion coefficient D is small.

11.2. Boundary-value problems

Consider the PDE for a function $u : D \subset \mathbb{R}^n \to \mathbb{R}$:

$$(11.9) \qquad \mathcal{L}u = f \quad \text{in } D, \qquad u = g \quad \text{on } \partial D,$$

where $\mathcal{L} = b(x) \cdot \nabla + a(x) : \nabla^2$, and $D \subset \mathbb{R}^n$ is open and bounded. This is similar to equation (11.5) for the MFPT, but with a more general source term and boundary condition. Can we similarly express its solution with a stochastic process of the form (11.1)?

We aim to express the solution using a stochastic process X that is stopped at the boundary ∂D. To this end, let τ_D be the first-passage time to ∂D. Our main result is the following.

THEOREM 11.3 (Boundary-value problem). *Suppose $D \subset \mathbb{R}^n$ is open and bounded, $\mathcal{L}$ is uniformly elliptic in D, f, a_{ij}, b_i are bounded and Lipschitz continuous in D, g is continuous on ∂D, and ∂D is C^2. Then the solution to (11.9) can be written as*

$$(11.10) \qquad u(x) = \mathbb{E}^x \left(g(X_{\tau_D}) - \int_0^{\tau_D} f(X_t) dt \right),$$

where τ_D is the first-passage time to D, X_{τ_D} is the first exit point and X solves (11.1).

See, e.g., (**Koralov and Sinai, 2007**, Theorem 21.11) and (**Friedman, 2006**, Theorem 5.1.1).

REMARK 11.4. The assumptions in this theorem ensure there is a unique strong solution $u \in C^2(D) \cap C(\overline{D})$. Given slightly stronger conditions we obtain a solution $u \in C^2(\overline{D})$. We may weaken the conditions to obtain a solution that is less smooth. See Section A.A.5 for a summary of the relevant PDE theorems.

Before proving (11.10) we must first introduce the concept of integrals up to a random time τ_D. This is possible for random times which are *stopping times*. The definition and some properties of stopping times are reviewed in Section A.A.4; here, we only need to know that a first-passage time is a stopping time, and if τ is a stopping time, then so is $\tau \wedge T$ for any finite $T > 0$.

Given a stopping time τ, the indicator function $1_{\{t \leq \tau\}}$ is adapted, so we can define a stochastic integral with τ in the limits of integration as

$$(11.11) \qquad \int_0^\tau f(t,\omega)dW_t \equiv \int_0^\infty 1_{\{t \leq \tau\}} f(t,\omega)dW_t \,.$$

We would like the nonanticipating property to still hold. The following lemma tells us when it does.

LEMMA 11.5 (Dynkin's formula). *If τ is a stopping time with $\mathbb{E}^x \tau < \infty$, and $f \in C_0^2(\mathbb{R}^n)$ (twice differentiable with compact support), and X solves SDE (11.1) whose coefficients satisfy the conditions required for existence and uniqueness (Theorem 8.1), then*

$$(11.12) \qquad \mathbb{E}^x f(X_\tau) = f(x) + \mathbb{E}^x \int_0^\tau \mathcal{L}f(X_s)ds \,.$$

PROOF. Given a function $f \in C_0^2(\mathbb{R}^n)$, Itô's formula in integral form applied to f and then evaluated at $\tau \wedge T$ (see (11.11)), where $T > 0$ is a fixed time, gives

$$f(X_{\tau \wedge T}) - f(X_0) = \int_0^{\tau \wedge T} \mathcal{L}f\, ds + \int_0^{\tau \wedge T} \nabla f^T \sigma\, dW_s \,.$$

Taking the expectation and using the nonanticipating property of the Itô integral shows that

$$(11.13) \qquad \mathbb{E}^x f(X_{\tau \wedge T}) - f(x) = \mathbb{E}^x \int_0^{\tau \wedge T} \mathcal{L}f\, ds \,.$$

By the conditions on f and the coefficients of $\mathcal{L}$, we have that $|\mathcal{L}f| \leq M$ for some $M > 0$, so

$$\mathbb{E}^x \left| \int_0^T 1_{\{t \leq (\tau \wedge T)\}} \mathcal{L}f \right| \leq M\mathbb{E}(\tau \wedge T) \leq M\mathbb{E}\tau < \infty \,.$$

Applying the dominated convergence theorem to (11.13) gives (11.12). $\qquad \square$

REMARK 11.6. The condition $\mathbb{E}\tau < \infty$ is critical. See the exercises for a case where this fails.

REMARK 11.7. Alternative conditions on f are possible for (11.12) to hold. The proof only required that $\mathcal{L}f$ be bounded in the domain of X_t, which is also possible for example if f has bounded derivatives and the coefficients of $\mathcal{L}$ are bounded.

We would like to apply Dynkin's formula to the function $u(X_t)$ in (11.9). To do so we must show $\mathbb{E}^x \tau_D$ is finite.

LEMMA 11.8. *Given the assumptions in Theorem 11.3,*

$$(11.14) \qquad \sup_{x \in \overline{D}} \mathbb{E}^x \tau_D < \infty \,.$$

PROOF. (**Friedman, 2006**, part of the proof of Theorem 6.5.1) Let $h(x) = -Ae^{\lambda x_1}$. We can choose A, λ large enough so that

$$\mathcal{L}h = -a_{11}A\lambda^2 e^{\lambda x_1} - b_1 A\lambda e^{\lambda x_1} \leq -1 \quad \text{in } D.$$

Therefore, by Dynkin's formula,

$$\mathbb{E}^x h(X_{\tau_D \wedge T}) - h(x) = \mathbb{E}^x \int_0^{\tau_D \wedge T} \mathcal{L}h(X_s)ds \leq -\mathbb{E}^x(\tau_D \wedge T).$$

Since $|h(x)| \leq K$ in D for some $K > 0$, using the triangle inequality we obtain $\mathbb{E}^x(\tau_D \wedge T) \leq 2K$. Take $T \to \infty$ and use the monotone convergence theorem to obtain $\mathbb{E}^x \tau_D \leq 2K$. □

REMARK 11.9. The proof above did not require very many assumptions. In particular, it did not require the uniform ellipticity of a nor any smoothness conditions on ∂D nor on the coefficients of $\mathcal{L}$. The proof only required that $a_{11} > 0$ in $\overline{D}$, and that the coefficients of $\mathcal{L}$ be Lipschitz continuous in D to ensure that a unique process X exists.

REMARK 11.10. The key part of the proof was to construct a function h satisfying $\mathcal{L}h \leq -1$. An alternative proof could choose h to be the solution to $\mathcal{L}h = -1$, which is known to exist under the assumptions given. However, a subtlety is that this equation is usually only guaranteed to hold in D and not (without further assumptions) at ∂D. Therefore, one has to either extend the solution to a larger domain $D' \supset \overline{D}$, arguing that the PDE has sufficient regularity that one can do so, or else consider a sequence of domains $D_\epsilon \subset D$ and consider the result in the limit $\bigcup_\epsilon D_\epsilon$. See (**Koralov and Sinai, 2007**, Theorem 21.11) for the former approach, and (**Friedman, 2006**, Section 6.5) for the latter.

Finally, we are ready to show our main result.

PROOF OF THEOREM 11.3. (**Koralov and Sinai, 2007**, Theorem 21.11) If $u \in C^2(\overline{D})$, then it can be extended to a C^2 function with compact support on $\mathbb{R}^n$ (see Appendix A.A.5). We may apply Dynkin's formula using the first-passage time τ_D, since $\mathbb{E}^x \tau_D < \infty$:

$$\mathbb{E}^x u(X_{\tau_D}) - u(x) = \mathbb{E}^x \int_0^{\tau_D} \mathcal{L}u(X_t)dt.$$

Solving for $u(x)$, and noting that $\mathcal{L}u(X_t) = f(X_t)$ for $X_t \in D$ and $u(X_{\tau_D}) = g(X_{\tau_D})$, gives the desired result.

If $u \notin C^2(\overline{D})$, then we cannot apply Dynkin's formula directly since it may not hold up to the boundary, but a technical trick gives the same conclusion. Construct a sequence of domains $D_1 \subset D_2 \subset \cdots \subset D$ with smooth boundaries, such that $\overline{D}_n \subset D$ and $\bigcup_n D_n = D$. Let τ_n be the stopping times corresponding to domains D_n. Then $\lim_{n \to \infty} \tau_n = \tau_D$ almost surely. We may apply Dynkin's formula to u in each D_n (by extending u to a C_0^2 function in a slightly larger domain as before), to obtain (11.10) with τ_n instead of τ_D, and then apply the dominated convergence theorem to obtain (11.10) (see (**Koralov and Sinai, 2007**) for more details). □

Example 11.11 (MFPT). Let $f(x) = -1, g(x) = 0$. Then, by Theorem 11.3,

$$u(x) = \mathbb{E}^x \int_0^{\tau_D} 1dt = \mathbb{E}^x \tau_D.$$

We recover (11.5), the equation we derived in the previous section for the MFPT.

Example 11.12 (Mean value theorem for harmonic functions). Suppose $u : \mathbb{R}^n \to \mathbb{R}$ is harmonic: $\Delta u = 0$. Recall the mean value theorem, which says that

$$u(x) = \frac{1}{\text{Area}(\partial B(x,r))} \int_{\partial B(x,r)} u(y) dS(y),$$

where $B(x,r)$ is the ball of radius r centered at x, $\partial B(x,r)$ is its boundary, and $dS(y)$ is the surface measure on $\partial B(x,r)$. Let us show this theorem using stochastic processes. Let $dX_t = dW_t$ so that $\mathcal{L}u = \frac{1}{2}\Delta u$. By Theorem 11.3,

$$u(x) = \mathbb{E}^x u(X_{\tau_B}),$$

where τ_B is the first hitting time of $\partial B(x,r)$ for X_t. Since Brownian motion is spatially isotropic, the distribution of first hitting points $\{X_{\tau_B}\}$ is uniform on $\partial B(x,r)$, so

$$\mathbb{E}^x u(X_{\tau_B}) = \frac{1}{\text{Area}(\partial B(x,r))} \int_{\partial B(x,r)} u(y) \, dS(y).$$

REMARK 11.13. It is possible to mix boundary conditions, for example, to let $u(x) = g(x)$ on $\Gamma \subset \partial D$, $u_x(x) = 0$ on $\partial D\backslash\Gamma$. This corresponds to stopping the process at Γ and reflecting it at $\partial D\backslash\Gamma$. The stopping time must be τ_Γ, the first time the process hits Γ (**Evans, 2013**).

11.3. Feynman–Kac formula

Consider the following PDE for a function $v(x,t) : \mathbb{R}^n \times \mathbb{R} \to \mathbb{R}$:

(11.15) $$\partial_t v = \mathcal{L}v - c(x)v, \qquad v(x,0) = f(x),$$

where $\mathcal{L}v = b(x) \cdot \nabla v + a(x) : \nabla^2 v$. We ask that $c(x) \geq 0$ (more generally that it is bounded below), which helps ensure the existence of a unique weak solution to (11.15) (Appendix A.A.5, (**Evans, 2010**)). This is similar to the backward equation, but with an extra term $-c(x)v$. We expressed the solution to the backward equation using an ensemble of trajectories of a diffusion process. Can we similarly express v using an ensemble of trajectories? Let's examine some special cases first.

- Without the term $-c(x)v$, (11.15) is simply the backward equation, whose solution can be represented as

(11.16) $$v(x,t) = \mathbb{E}^x f(X_t),$$

  where X_t solves the SDE (11.1).
- Without the diffusion term $a : \nabla^2 v$, (11.15) is a first-order PDE

  $$\partial_t v = b(x) \cdot \nabla v - c(x)v, \qquad v(x,0) = f(x).$$

  This equation can be solved by the method of characteristics. A characteristic $x(s)$ starting at point x_0 solves the ODE

  $$\frac{dx}{ds} = b(x), \qquad x(0) = x_0.$$

  Let $t > s$ and define $z(s) = v(x(s), t - s)$. This function evolves as

  $$\frac{dz}{ds} = -\partial_t v + b(x) \cdot \nabla v = c(x)z, \qquad z(0) = v(x,t).$$

The solution is $z(t) = z(0)e^{\int_0^t c(s)ds}$. Using that $z(t) = f(x(t))$ gives

$$(11.17) \qquad v(x,t) = z(0) = e^{-\int_0^t c(x(s))ds} f(x(t)).$$

From this expression for the solution along each characteristic $x(s)$, we can piece together the solution anywhere in space.

When all the terms are included, we get a combination of (11.16), (11.17), called the Feynman–Kac formula.

THEOREM 11.14 (Feynman–Kac, time-homogeneous). (**Friedman, 2006**, Theorem 6.5.3) *Let $\mathcal{L}$ satisfy (A1) and (A3) from Chapter 10. Suppose c is bounded and uniformly Lipschitz continuous, and f is continuous and grows at most polynomially, $|f(x)| \le A(1 + |x|^k)$. The solution to the PDE (11.15) is given by*

$$(11.18) \qquad v(x,t) = \mathbb{E}^x \left[e^{-\int_0^t c(X_s)ds} f(X_t) \right],$$

where X_t solves the SDE (11.1).

PROOF. This proof is very similar to our proof of the backward equation. Let $v(x,t)$ be the solution to the PDE (11.15), which exists under the conditions of the theorem and is twice differentiable. Let

$$Z_1(s) = e^{-\int_0^s c(X_r)dr}, \qquad Z_2(s) = v(X_s, t-s).$$

From the Itô product rule, we have $d(Z_1 Z_2) = Z_1 dZ_2 + Z_2 dZ_1 + dZ_1 dZ_2$. We calculate (all functions are evaluated at $(X_s, t-s)$):

$$dZ_1(s) = -Z_1 c\, ds,$$

$$dZ_2(s) = (-v_t + b \cdot \nabla v + a : \nabla^2 v)ds + \sigma \nabla v \cdot dW_s = (-v_t + \mathcal{L}v)ds + \sigma \nabla v \cdot dW_s,$$

$$dZ_1(s)dZ_2(s) = 0.$$

Therefore,

$$d(Z_1(s)Z_2(s)) = Z_1 \underbrace{(-v_t + \mathcal{L}v - vc)}_{=0,\text{ since }v\text{ solves (11.15)}} ds + Z_1 \sigma \nabla v \cdot dW_s = Z_1 \sigma \nabla v \cdot dW_s.$$

Integrating in time and taking the expectation gives

$$\mathbb{E}^x(Z_1(t)Z_2(t)) = \mathbb{E}^x Z_1(0)Z_2(0).$$

But $Z_1(0)Z_2(0) = v(x,t)$ and $Z_1(t)Z_2(t) = e^{-\int_0^t c(X_r)dr} v(X_t, 0) = e^{-\int_0^t c(X_r)dr} f(X_t)$. Therefore,

$$\mathbb{E}^x[e^{-\int_0^t c(X_r)dr} f(X_t)] = \mathbb{E}^x(Z_1(t)Z_2(t)) = \mathbb{E}^x Z_1(0)Z_2(0) = v(x,t). \qquad \square$$

As we saw for the backward equation, trajectories of a diffusion process can be thought of as characteristics for the second-order parabolic equation (11.18).

***Exercise* 11.3.** Derive the time-dependent Feynman–Kac formula. Let X_t be a time-inhomogeneous diffusion process with generator $\mathcal{L}u = b(x,t) \cdot \nabla u + a(x,t) : \nabla^2 u$. Show that the solution to the PDE

$$(11.19) \qquad u_t + \mathcal{L}u - c(x,t)u = 0, \quad (0 < t < T), \qquad u(x,T) = f(x),$$

can be expressed as

$$u(x,t) = \mathbb{E}^{X_t = x} \left[e^{-\int_t^T c(X_s, s)ds} f(X_T) \right].$$

Hint: Consider the evolution of $Z_s = e^{-\int_t^s c(X_\tau)d\tau} u(X_s, s)$.

The full set of conditions required for this result to be valid are the same as for Theorem 11.14 but over the domain $\mathbb{R}^n \times [0, T]$ (**Friedman, 2006**, Theorem 6.5.3).

In the PDE (11.15), what does $c(x)$ represent physically? We claim it represents the "killing rate," i.e., the rate at which trajectories disappear, given they are at x. Physically, this could happen by chemicals being adsorbed to a surface with a rate depending on location, gamblers being kicked out of a casino with a rate that depends on how much money they have, etc. To see why this interpretation is reasonable, suppose that we kill the process X_t at rate $c(x)$, so

$$P(X_t \text{ is killed in } [t, t + h]) = c(X_t)h + o(h).$$

Then, by dividing the time interval $[0, t]$ into a fine partition $\{t_0, t_1, \ldots\}$ with $t_i = ih$ for h small, we estimate

$$P(X_t \text{ survives until } t) \approx (1 - c(X_{t_1})h)(1 - c(X_{t_2})h) \cdots (1 - c(X_{t_n})h)$$

$$\to \quad e^{-\int_0^t c(X_s)ds} \quad \text{as } h \to 0.$$

Therefore,

$$v(x, t) = \mathbb{E}^x \left[f(X_t)P(X_t \text{ is alive at time } t) \right] = \mathbb{E}^x \left[f(X_t)1_{[0,\xi)}(t) \right],$$

where $\xi(D)$ is the random time at which $X_t(D)$ is killed. The function $v(x, t)$ is the average of $f(X_t)$, weighted by the probability that the trajectory is still alive at time t (**Øksendal, 2003**, Section 8.2), (**Evans, 2013**, Section 6.B).

The Feynman–Kac formula was first developed in quantum mechanics to evaluate functionals of Brownian motion. It was constructed heuristically by Feynman and then rigorously by Kac, after he saw a lecture by Feynman and realized they were thinking about the same thing in different languages. Now, it is also heavily used in finance, especially the time-dependent version, where it has found use in pricing financial instruments, for example, via the Black–Scholes equation.

11.4. Additional exercises

Exercise 11.4. Consider the double-well potential from Exercise 11.2, and suppose you approximate it with a piecewise constant potential

$$V(x) = \begin{cases} 0 & x \in [-1, -\alpha], \\ 1/4 & x \in [-\alpha, \alpha], \\ 0 & x \in [\alpha, 1], \\ \infty & x \notin [-1, 1]. \end{cases}$$

The local minima and saddle point have the same height as $U(x)$ and $\alpha > 0$ is a parameter governing the width of the attractive well. Writing $V(x) = \infty$ means there is a reflecting boundary condition. Use (11.7) to evaluate the MFPT from -1 to 1, and determine the leading order contribution when D is small. Compare this leading order contribution to the result of Exercise 11.2 and determine which value of α gives the best fit. Does this have a reasonable interpretation? (Hint: α should depend in some way on D.)

Exercise 11.5. Suppose q solves the equation

$$\Delta q = 0 \quad \text{in } D, \qquad \begin{cases} q = 1 & \text{on } \Gamma_1 \subset \partial D, \\ q = 0 & \text{on } \Gamma_2 \subset \partial D, \end{cases}$$

where $D \subset \mathbb{R}^n$ is a bounded domain with smooth boundary ∂D and $\Gamma_1 \cup \Gamma_2 = \partial D$. Use the boundary value theorem to show that $q(x) = P(\text{Brownian motion hits } \Gamma_1 \text{ before } \Gamma_2)$. Such a function q is called the *committor function*.

Note that you may apply the boundary value theorem even though $g(x)$ is not continuous. To show this rigorously, you would mollify g by some small amount measured by ϵ to make it smooth, obtain a family of solutions q^ϵ, and argue that the stochastic interpretation remains valid as $\epsilon \to 0$.

Exercise 11.6. The aim of this question is to construct an example to show what can happen in Dynkin's formula when $\mathbb{E}\tau = \infty$. Suppose W_t is a Brownian motion starting at $W_0 = 0$. Let τ_n be the first time it exits $[-n, 1]$ and let τ_∞ be the first time it hits 1, i.e., the first time it exits $(-\infty, 1]$.
   (i) Calculate $\mathbb{E}\tau_n$, for each n.
   (ii) Use the result of question (1) to calculate the probability that a path exits $[-n, 1]$ at $-n$.
   (iii) Verify that $\mathbb{E}W_{\tau_n} = 0$ using the result of (b).
      (This has to be true by Dynkin's theorem, since $W_{\tau_n} = \int_0^{\tau_n} dW_s$, but you should check this directly for this particular case.)
   (iv) Explain why $\mathbb{E}\tau_\infty = \infty$.
   (v) Explain why τ_∞ is almost-surely finite.
   (vi) Show that $\mathbb{E}W_{\tau_\infty} \neq 0$.
   This is related to the *gambler's ruin* paradox—a gambler playing a fair game with a finite amount of money cannot quit when he is ahead and earn a positive amount of money on average. If there is a maximum amount of money he can bet, his expected winnings are always zero. If he has an infinite amount of money, then he will eventually win a fixed amount of money with probability 1, but it will take an infinite amount of time on average.

Exercise 11.7. Let $T_n(x) = \mathbb{E}^x T^n$ be the nth moment of the first-passage time T, for some diffusion process X_t starting at $x \in D$. Show that, provided $t^n G(x, t) \to 0$ as $t \to \infty$, T_n satisfies the equation

$$\mathcal{L}T_n = -nT_{n-1}, \qquad T_n(\partial D) = 0.$$

Exercise 11.8. Consider a time-dependent PDE with prescribed boundary behavior

$$\begin{aligned} u_t &= \mathcal{L}u & \text{in } D, \\ u(x, t) &= g(x) & \text{on } \partial D, \\ u(x, T) &= \phi(x), \end{aligned}$$

where $\mathcal{L} = b(x) \cdot \nabla + a(x) : \nabla^2$ and $D \subset \mathbb{R}^n$ is open and bounded. Derive an expression for the solution $u(x, t)$ in terms of expectations of functionals of a diffusion process.

Hint: Break up the solution as $u(x,t) = v(x) + w(x,t)$, where v solves the time-independent boundary value problem $\mathcal{L}v = 0$, $v|_{\partial D} = g$, and w solves the time-dependent PDE with Dirichlet boundary conditions $w|_{\partial D} = 0$.

Exercise 11.9. Consider a process $X_t \in \mathbb{R}$ that solves

$$dX_t = -U'(X_t)dt + \sqrt{2D}\, dW_t\,,$$

where $U(x)$ is a bistable potential with one local maximum at $x = b$ and two local minima at $x = a, c$, with $a < b < c$. Suppose you model the dynamics of X_t as a two-state continuous-time Markov chain on state space $S = \{a, c\}$, with rates $k_{a \to c} = \tau_{a \to c}^{-1}$ and $k_{c \to a} = \tau_{c \to a}^{-1}$, where $\tau_{a \to c}$ is the MFPT from a to c and $\tau_{c \to a}$ is the MFPT from c to a. If you approximate $\tau_{a \to c}, \tau_{c \to a}$ using the Arrhenius formula, then what is the stationary distribution of the continuous-time Markov chain? Is it a good approximation to the true stationary distribution of X_t? Explain.

Exercise 11.10. Given the PDE

$$v_t = xv_x + yv_y + 2v_{xx} + 2v_{xy} + v_{yy} - v\sqrt{x^2 + y^2}, \qquad v(x, y, 0) = e^{-\frac{1}{2}(x^2 + y^2)}.$$

Explain how you could estimate $v(x, y, t)$ by simulating trajectories of a stochastic process.

CHAPTER 12

Detailed Balance, Symmetry, and Eigenfunction Expansions

Consider a time-homogeneous diffusion $dX_t = b(X_t)dt + \sigma(X_t)dW_t$ on a domain $\Omega \subset \mathbb{R}^n$, which could be bounded or unbounded. Recall that the generator and its adjoint are

$$\mathcal{L}f = b(x) \cdot \nabla f + a(x) : \nabla^2 f, \quad \mathcal{L}^*p = -\nabla \cdot (b(x)p) + \nabla \cdot \nabla \cdot (a(x)p),$$

where $a(x) = \frac{1}{2}\sigma(x)\sigma^T(x)$. Throughout this chapter we assume conditions (A1), (A2), and (A3) from Chapter 10, to simplify our calculations. Recall that a stationary distribution π solves

$$(12.1) \qquad \nabla \cdot j_s = 0, \quad \text{with} \quad j_s = b\pi - \nabla \cdot (a\pi),$$

with boundary conditions that $j_s \cdot \hat{n} = 0$ in a bounded domain, or $j_s \to 0$ as $|x| \to \infty$ sufficiently quickly in an unbounded domain; we refer to both of these as reflecting boundary conditions. We saw in Chapter 10 that sometimes the flux vanishes in steady-state:

$$(12.2) \qquad j_s = 0.$$

Condition (12.2) implies (12.1) but is stronger because it involves n equations, whereas (12.1) is only one equation. Therefore (12.2) should not be expected to hold in general. When does it hold? And what does it imply or require about the physics of the process?

In this chapter we will formally show the following relations:

$$(12.3) \qquad j_s = 0 \iff \mathcal{L} \text{ is symmetric in } L_\pi^2(\Omega) \iff X \text{ satisfies detailed balance.}$$

Thus we provide a link between the vanishing of the steady-state flux—to the symmetry of the generator in a particular function space—to the time-reversibility of the stochastic process. We will then consider a system where (12.3) holds and use eigenfunctions of $\mathcal{L}$ to solve for quantities like the transition probability, correlation functions, and mean first-passage times. All of these generalize the same relationships and calculations we found for Markov chains in Chapter 3.

Let us now explain the vocabulary and notation used in (12.3). The space $L_\pi^2(\Omega)$ is a weighted inner product space, which uses a locally stationary distribution π (see below) as a weight for the inner product:

$$(12.4) \qquad \langle f, g \rangle_\pi = \int_\Omega f(x)g(x)\pi(x)dx.$$

We retain the notation $\langle f, g \rangle = \int_\Omega fg\,dx$ to mean the regular L^2 inner product in Ω. Hereafter, we will suppress Ω in our notation and simply write $L_\pi^2 = L_\pi^2(\Omega)$, $\int = \int_\Omega$.

A *locally stationary distribution* is a bounded positive function solving $\mathcal{L}^*\pi = 0$ with reflecting boundary conditions. Sometimes π is a stationary distribution, when one exists, but when it does not we may still find a solution to $\mathcal{L}^*\pi = 0$ that is not normalizable, as in Example 12.1. We assume throughout this chapter that such a locally stationary distribution exists. Its existence is easiest to show under the assumptions listed at the beginning of this chapter, plus some suitable integrability conditions on a, b in an unbounded domain (**Khas' minskii, 1960**) or sufficient smoothness of $\partial\Omega$ in a bounded domain; however, it can be shown to exist under a variety of weaker conditions (**Veretennikov, 1999; Bogachëv and Rëkner, 2000; Huang et al., 2015**).

Example 12.1. Consider Brownian motion on $\mathbb{R}$. A locally stationary distribution solves $\frac{1}{2}\partial_{xx}\pi = 0$; a solution is $\pi(x) = 1$. This is not a stationary distribution, since it is not normalizable on $\mathbb{R}$.

We define *detailed balance* in Section 12.12.3 as the property that the system is time-reversible. That is, the probability density for the process to go from x to y in some amount of time is the same as the probability density for the process to go from y to x: $\pi(x)p(y, t|x, s) = \pi(y)p(x, t|y, s)$. When constructing a model of a physical system, it is important to keep in mind whether the system is time-reversible or not. Not only should the model have the correct stationary distribution, but if the system is time-reversible the model should have this property too. If it does not, then by (12.3), $j_S \neq 0$, and in an isolated system we could extract energy indefinitely out of this steady-state flux! A nonzero steady-state flux is only possible when a system is subject to *external forcing*, such as active systems like particles that propel themselves by chemical reactions, bacteria that swim, etc., and many biological systems like molecular motors, where energy is input via ATP consumption.

12.1. When does the steady-state flux vanish?

We start by asking what conditions on $b(x), a(x)$ are required for $j_S = 0$ to hold. First consider a one-dimensional process $X_t \in \mathbb{R}$. Equation (12.1) implies that $j_S = cst$. Consider different possibilities for Ω.

- If $\Omega = [a, b]$ and the boundaries are reflecting, then $j_S = 0$ everywhere since $j_S = 0$ at the boundary.
- If $\Omega = \mathbb{R}$ then the probability and flux must decay at $\pm\infty$, so similarly $j_S = 0$.
- If $\Omega = [a, b]$ and the boundaries are periodic, then it is possible to have $j_S \neq 0$.

Therefore, $j_S = 0$ should hold for reflecting boundary conditions, but for periodic boundary conditions it does not necessarily have to hold.

Exercise 12.1. Find conditions on the drift and diffusion that ensure $j_S = 0$ for periodic boundary conditions.

Now consider a process $X \in \mathbb{R}^n$ and suppose $j_S = 0$, so that

$$(12.5) \qquad a(x)\,\nabla\pi(x) = \pi(x)(b(x) - \nabla \cdot a(x)).$$

Here $\nabla\cdot$ is applied along rows of the matrix a. Since $a(x)$ is uniformly elliptic it is invertible, so

$$(12.6) \qquad \nabla \log \pi(x) = Q(x), \quad \text{where} \quad Q(x) = a^{-1}(x)(b(x) - \nabla \cdot a(x)).$$

In components, $Q_i = \sum_k a_{ik}^{-1}(b_k - \sum_j \frac{\partial}{\partial x_j} a_{kj})$. Notice that this implies Q is a perfect gradient: $Q(x) = -\nabla\Phi(x)$ for some scalar function $\Phi : \Omega \to \mathbb{R}$. (It is conventional to define Q to be the negative of the gradient.)

We can express π in terms of Φ as

$$(12.7) \qquad \pi(x) = Z^{-1}e^{-\Phi(x)}, \qquad \text{with} \quad \Phi(x) = -\int_{x_0}^x Q(x')dx'.$$

Here Z is a normalizing constant (which could be absorbed into the definition of Φ) and x_0 is some arbitrary fixed point; changing it changes $\Phi(x)$ by a constant. Note that it does not matter which path is taken in the integral since $Q(x)$ is a perfect gradient.

Equation (12.7) gives a general expression for the stationary density when $j_s = 0$. This expression is similar to the Boltzmann distribution $e^{-U(x)}$ that we encountered in Example 12.5, showing that Φ plays the role of a potential energy; it is sometimes called a generalized potential.

REMARK 12.2. A necessary and sufficient condition for Q to be a perfect gradient is that its curl is zero:

$$\frac{\partial Q_i}{\partial x_j} - \frac{\partial Q_j}{\partial x_i} = 0 \qquad \text{for all } i \neq j.$$

Given a, b but not π, one can compute the curl above to verify whether $j_s = 0$.

Example 12.3. Suppose the noise is additive so the diffusivity is constant: $a_{ij}(x) = A_{ij}$, where A_{ij} are constants and $A_{ij} = A_{ji}$. Then $\nabla \cdot a(x) = 0$, so $A^{-1}b(x) = -\nabla\Phi$ or equivalently,

$$b(x) = -\nabla\phi(x)$$

for some scalar function $\phi = A\Phi$.

This is an important result: given constant diffusivity, the flux in steady-state vanishes if and only if the drift is a perfect gradient. If the drift has any curl component, then the flux cannot vanish in steady-state.

Example 12.4. If $a(x) \neq cst$, then using (12.5) we solve for the drift in terms of a, Φ, as $b = -a\nabla\Phi + \nabla \cdot a$, and obtain

$$(12.8) \qquad \mathcal{L}^*\rho = -\nabla \cdot (-a\nabla\Phi\, \rho + (\nabla \cdot a)\rho - \nabla \cdot (a\rho)).$$

This corresponds to an SDE

$$(12.9) \qquad dX_t = -a\nabla\Phi\, dt + \nabla \cdot a\, dt + \sqrt{2}a^{\frac{1}{2}}\, dW_t,$$

where $a^{\frac{1}{2}}$ means any matrix such that $a^{\frac{1}{2}}(a^{\frac{1}{2}})^T = a$. This shows the dynamics of a diffusion with zero flux in steady-state are fully prescribed by two ingredients: the generalized potential Φ and the diffusivity tensor a.

Equation (12.9) is the most general form of the overdamped Langevin equation. Compared to the overdamped Langevin equation in Example 10.30, we have introduced a varying diffusivity matrix $a(x)$ and an additional drift $\nabla \cdot a$. If we want an equation with stationary distribution $e^{-\Phi}$, then the additional drift compensates for the nonconstant diffusivity matrix, pushing the system toward regions of high diffusivity (recall Example 10.29).

Exercise 12.2. Consider the one-dimensional diffusion $dX_t = (\sin X_t + 2)dW_t$ with periodic boundary conditions on $[-\pi, \pi]$. Solve for the stationary distribution. Then determine the drift one would have to add to ensure the stationary distribution is constant.

Exercise 12.3. Use Example 12.4 to show that if $j_s = 0$, then $\mathcal{L}^*$ and its adjoint can be written as

$$\mathcal{L}^* \rho = \nabla \cdot \left(\pi a \nabla \left(\rho \pi^{-1} \right) \right), \qquad \mathcal{L}f = \pi^{-1} \nabla \cdot (\pi a \nabla f),$$

where $\pi = Z^{-1} e^{-\Phi}$ is the stationary distribution.

Example 12.5 (Brownian dynamics). Consider a system of N small particles in a fluid, with positions contained in vector $x \in \mathbb{R}^N$ (x could also include other variables characterizing the system's configuration, such as orientations, bond angles, etc.). At scales small enough that the fluid is best described by Stokes's flow but where fluctuations matter—typically scales of $O(1\mu)$ or smaller—the particles evolve according to the equations of *Brownian dynamics* (**Delong et al., 2014**):

$$(12.10) \qquad dx_t = M(x_t)f(x_t) + k_B T \nabla \cdot M(x_t) + \sqrt{2k_B T} M^{\frac{1}{2}}(x_t)dW_t.$$

Here $W_t \in \mathbb{R}^N$ is an N-dimensional Brownian motion, T is the temperature, k_B is Boltzmann's constant, and $f : \mathbb{R}^N \to \mathbb{R}^N$ is the set of forces acting on the system, which could be equal to the gradient of a potential if the forces are conservative: $f(x) = -\nabla U(x)$ for some potential $U : \mathbb{R}^N \to \mathbb{R}$. The matrix $M(x) \in \mathbb{R}^{N \times N}$ is the *mobility tensor*, a symmetric positive semidefinite matrix which gives a linear relationship between the forces acting on the system and its subsequent velocity, and which captures the effect of the hydrodynamic interactions. In fact, the mobility tensor is the inverse of the friction tensor $M(x) = \Gamma^{-1}(x)$, which gives a linear relationship between velocities and forces, and which can be determined by considering Stokes's flow, without fluctuations. The matrix $M^{\frac{1}{2}}$ is any square root of M (not necessarily square), i.e., any matrix which satisfies $M^{\frac{1}{2}}(M^{\frac{1}{2}})^T = M$.

One can see that, by substituting $a(x) = k_B T M(x)$ and $\Phi = U(x)/k_B T$, the Fokker–Planck equation corresponding to (12.10) is exactly (12.9). The stationary distribution is $\pi(x) = Z^{-1} e^{-U(x)/k_B T}$, which we recognize as the Boltzmann distribution. This distribution involves only the potential energy; it is not affected by hydrodynamic interactions. The diffusivity matrix $a(x)$ is typically a nontrivial function of r because as particles move they drag fluid with them, which then pushes on surrounding particles.

Example 12.6 (Two particles in Brownian dynamics). As a simple example of a system with a nontrivial diffusivity matrix, consider a pair of spheres with radius a and positions $x_1, x_2 \in \mathbb{R}^3$ in a fluid with dynamic viscosity η. Suppose we are only interested in the relative separation of the spheres $r = x_2 - x_1 \in \mathbb{R}^3$. The relative diffusivity tensor is, for large enough separations (**Batchelor, 1976**),

$$(12.11) \qquad D(r) = D_0 \left(G(|r|/a)\frac{rr^T}{|r|^2} + H(|r|/a)\left(I - \frac{rr^T}{|r|^2}\right) \right).$$

Here,

$$D_0 = \frac{2k_B T}{6\pi \eta a}$$

is the Stokes–Einstein–Sutherland equation for the single-particle diffusivity (multi-plied by 2, because there are 2 particles moving relative to each other), and the nondi-mensional diffusivities for spheres moving normal to each other and tangent to each other are, respectively,

$$G(\rho) = 1 - \frac{3}{2\rho} + \frac{1}{\rho^3} - \frac{15}{4\rho^4} + O(\rho^{-6}), \qquad H(\rho) = 1 - \frac{3}{4\rho} - \frac{1}{2\rho^3} + O(\rho^{-6}).$$

How shall we interpret (12.11)? The diffusion coefficient along a particular direc-tion with unit vector $v \in \mathbb{R}^3$ is $v^T D(r) v$. As $|r| \to \infty$ both $G(|r|/a), H(|r|/a) \to 1$, so $D(r) \to D_0 I_3$, where I_3 is the 3×3 identity matrix. Since $v^T D_0 I_3 v = D_0$ for any unit vector v, the relative separation diffuses at the same rate in all directions, with diffusion coefficient twice the diffusion coefficient of a single particle.

For finite $|r|$, the diffusivity depends on the direction of motion. In the normal direction, where particles move directly towards or away from each other, $v = r/|r|$, the diffusion coefficient is $v^T D(r) v = D_0 G(|r|/a)$. In the tangential direction, i.e., the set of directions v that are perpendicular to r, the diffusion coefficient is $v^T D(r) v = D_0 H(|r|/a)$. Since $G(|r|/a) < H(|r|/a)$, the spheres diffuse the slowest when they move toward or away from each other. Physically, this is because such motion requires dis-placing or entraining the fluid between the particles.

Computing the diffusivity tensor efficiently for a large collection of particles (not just 2 particles, as in Example 12.5) is an ongoing research problem (**Sprinkle et al., 2020**).

12.2. Symmetry of $\mathcal{L}$

This section argues formally that

$$\mathcal{L} \text{ is symmetric in } L^2_\pi(\Omega) \quad \Longleftrightarrow \quad j_s = 0.$$

For simpler notation we assume that Ω is bounded but the results below follow with Ω unbounded provided we choose test functions in $L^2_\pi \cap C_0^2(\mathbb{R}^n)$ (see, e.g., (**Pavliotis, 2014**, Section 4.5)).

LEMMA 12.7. *Let π be a locally stationary distribution and let $j_s = b\pi - \nabla \cdot (a\pi)$ be the associated steady-state flux. Then*

(12.12)
$$\langle \mathcal{L}f, g \rangle_\pi = -\langle a\nabla f, \nabla g \rangle_\pi - \langle f, \pi^{-1} \nabla g \cdot j_s \rangle_\pi$$

for $f, g \in L^2_\pi \cap C^2(\overline{\Omega})$ equipped with boundary conditions at $\partial\Omega$ that are either absorbing ($f = g = 0$ at $\partial\Omega$) or reflecting ($a\nabla f \cdot \hat{n} = a\nabla g \cdot \hat{n} = 0$).

PROOF. This follows from multiple integration by parts. In detail,

$$\langle \mathcal{L}f, g \rangle_\pi = \int b \cdot \nabla f g \pi + \int (a : \nabla^2 f) g \pi.$$

Consider each of the terms on the right-hand side separately. We have

$$\int b \cdot \nabla f g \pi = \int \underbrace{\nabla \cdot (f g \pi b)}_{\text{boundary}} - \int \underbrace{f \pi b \cdot \nabla g}_{A} - \int \underbrace{f g \nabla \cdot (b\pi)}_{B}.$$

We also have

$$\int (a : \nabla^2 f) g\pi = \int \nabla \cdot (a(\nabla f) g\pi) - \int a\nabla f \cdot (\nabla g)\pi - \int ((\nabla f)g) \cdot \nabla \cdot (a\pi)$$

$$= \int \underbrace{\nabla \cdot (a(\nabla f) g\pi)}_{\text{boundary}} - \langle a\nabla f, \nabla g\rangle_\pi - \int \underbrace{\nabla \cdot (fg\nabla \cdot (a\pi))}_{\text{boundary}}$$

$$+ \int \underbrace{f\nabla g \cdot \nabla \cdot (a\pi)}_{A} + \int \underbrace{fg\nabla \cdot \nabla \cdot (a\pi)}_{B}.$$

The terms labeled "A" combine to give $- \int f\nabla g \cdot j_s = -\langle f, \pi^{-1}\nabla g \cdot j_s\rangle_\pi$.

The terms labeled "B" combine to give $- \int fg\nabla \cdot j_s = 0$.

The terms labeled "boundary" combine to give $\int \nabla \cdot (fgj_s + a(\nabla f)g\pi)$. Using the divergence theorem, the reflecting condition on j_s, and either an absorbing condition on g or a reflecting condition on f, gives that this term vanishes. We are left with (12.12). □

PROPOSITION 12.8. $j_s = 0$ if and only if $\mathcal{L}$ is symmetric in L_π^2 when equipped with either absorbing or reflecting boundary conditions.

PROOF. Suppose $j_s = 0$. Let $f, g \in L_\pi^2 \cap C^2(\overline{\Omega})$. Then by Lemma 12.7,

$$\langle \mathcal{L}f, g\rangle_\pi = \langle a\nabla f, \nabla g\rangle_\pi, \quad \text{and} \quad \langle f, \mathcal{L}g\rangle_\pi = \langle a\nabla g, \nabla f\rangle_\pi = \langle a\nabla f, \nabla g\rangle_\pi,$$

so $\langle \mathcal{L}f, g\rangle_\pi = \langle f, \mathcal{L}g\rangle_\pi$. Now suppose that $\mathcal{L}$ is symmetric in L_π^2. Then from Lemma 12.7,

$$\int f\nabla g \cdot j_s - g\nabla f \cdot j_s = 0$$

for all $f, g \in L_\pi^2 \cap C^2(\overline{\Omega})$. This is only possible if $j_s = 0$ (for example, take $f = cst$). □

Here is another useful relationship when $j_s = 0$ or, equivalently, (12.5) holds.

LEMMA 12.9. If $j_s = 0$, then for $g \in C^2(\Omega)$,

$$(12.13) \qquad\qquad \mathcal{L}^*(g\pi) = \pi\mathcal{L}g.$$

This relationship is independent of the boundary conditions on $\mathcal{L}, \mathcal{L}^*$.

PROOF. Calculate:

$$\mathcal{L}^*(g\pi) = -\nabla \cdot (bg\pi) + \nabla \cdot \nabla \cdot (ag\pi)$$
$$= -\nabla \cdot (bg\pi) + \nabla \cdot (g(\nabla \cdot a)\pi + ga\nabla\pi + \pi a\nabla g) \qquad \text{expanding } \nabla\cdot$$
$$= -\nabla \cdot (bg\pi) + \nabla \cdot (bg\pi + \pi a\nabla g) \qquad\qquad \text{using (12.5)}$$
$$= \nabla \cdot (\pi a\nabla g).$$

This representation is useful in itself (see Exercise 12.3). Continue expanding this expression:

$$\mathcal{L}^*(g\pi) = a\nabla\pi \cdot \nabla g + \pi\nabla \cdot a\nabla g + \pi a : \nabla^2 g$$
$$= \pi b \cdot \nabla g + \pi a : \nabla^2 g \qquad\qquad\qquad \text{using (12.5)}$$
$$= \pi\mathcal{L}g.$$

□

Exercise **12.4.** Use Lemma 12.9 to show that $\mathcal{L}$ is symmetric in L^2_π.

Exercise **12.5.** Let the probability density be $\rho(x, t) = g(x, t)\pi(x)$, so that g is the density of ρ with respect to π. Use Lemma 12.9 to show that if $j_s = 0$ and ρ solves the forward equation $\partial_t \rho = \mathcal{L}^* \rho$, then g solves the backward equation $\partial_t g = \mathcal{L} g$.

12.3. Detailed balance

Our goal is to show that

$$(12.14) \qquad \mathcal{L} \text{ is symmetric in } L^2_\pi \quad \Longleftrightarrow \quad X_t \text{ satisfies detailed balance.}$$

Recall that a Markov chain satisfies detailed balance if $\pi_i P_{ij} = \pi_j P_{ji}$. Advancing this equation by n steps in time shows that $\pi_i P_{ij}^{(n)} = \pi_j P_{ji}^{(n)}$ for all n, where $P^{(n)}$ is the n-step transition matrix. These ideas are generalized to a continuous Markov process as follows.

DEFINITION 12.10. A continuous Markov process satisfies *detailed balance* or is *reversible* if, for all $x, y \in \Omega$ and all $s < t$,

$$(12.15) \qquad \pi(x)p(y, t | x, s) = \pi(y)p(x, t | y, s).$$

One can show that detailed balance is equivalent to the process $(X_t | X_0 \sim \pi)_{0 \le t \le T}$ and the time-reversed process $(X_{T-t} | X_0 \sim \pi)_{0 \le t \le T}$ having the same probability law, including the same finite-dimensional distributions (**Pavliotis, 2014**, Section 4.6 Theorem 4.5).

Our arguments to show (12.14) will be purely formal. We will make frequent use of the operator $e^{\mathcal{L}t} = I + \mathcal{L}t + \frac{1}{2}\mathcal{L}^2 t^2 + \cdots$, which is such that if $u(x, t)$ solves the PDE $\partial_t u = \mathcal{L}u$, $u(x, 0) = f(x)$, then $u(x, t) = e^{\mathcal{L}t}f(x)$, with a similar definition for $e^{\mathcal{L}^* t}$. In particular, we have the representation

$$(12.16) \qquad p(y, t | x, s) = e^{\mathcal{L}^*_y (t-s)}\delta(x - y).$$

We write $\mathcal{L}^*_y$ with a subscript y to remind the reader that this operator acts on the y-variables. One can show that the adjoint of $e^{\mathcal{L}t}$ is $e^{\mathcal{L}^* t}$, and, similarly, that $\mathcal{L}$ is symmetric in L^2_π if and only if $e^{\mathcal{L}t}$ is too.

To show the $\Leftarrow$ implication in (12.14), suppose X satisfies detailed balance, multiply both sides of (12.15) by $f(x), g(y) \in L^2_\pi$, and integrate over x, y:

$$(12.17) \qquad \int \pi(x)f(x)g(y)p(y, t | x, s)dxdy = \int \pi(y)f(x)g(y)p(x, t | y, s)dxdy.$$

The stochastic interpretation of the left-hand side is

$$\mathbb{E}[f(X_s)g(X_t) | X_s \sim \pi] = \mathbb{E}^\pi[f(X_0)g(X_T)] \quad \text{for} \quad T = t - s,$$

and the stochastic interpretation of the right-hand side is

$$\mathbb{E}[f(X_t)g(X_s) | X_s \sim \pi] = \mathbb{E}^\pi[f(X_T)g(X_0)].$$

The left-hand side of (12.17) is

$$\int \pi(x)f(x)g(y)e^{\mathcal{L}_y^*(t-s)}\delta(x-y)dxdy = \int \pi(x)f(x)\delta(x-y)e^{\mathcal{L}_y(t-s)}g(y)dxdy$$

$$= \int \pi(y)f(y)e^{\mathcal{L}_y(t-s)}g(y)dy$$

$$= \langle f, e^{\mathcal{L}_y(t-s)}g\rangle_\pi.$$

The right-hand side of (12.17) is—changing the dummy variables $x \leftrightarrow y$ and following the same steps as above—

$$\int \pi(x)f(y)g(x)p(y,t|x,s)dxdy = \int \pi(x)f(y)g(x)e^{\mathcal{L}_y^*(t-s)}\delta(x-y)dxdy$$

$$= \int \pi(x)g(x)\delta(x-y)e^{\mathcal{L}_y(t-s)}f(y)dxdy$$

$$= \int \pi(y)g(y)e^{\mathcal{L}_y(t-s)}f(y)dy$$

$$= \langle g, e^{\mathcal{L}_y(t-s)}f\rangle_\pi.$$

Putting together the pieces above shows that

(12.18) $$\langle f, e^{\mathcal{L}_y(t-s)}g\rangle_\pi = \langle g, e^{\mathcal{L}_y(t-s)}f\rangle_\pi.$$

Therefore, $e^{\mathcal{L}t}$ is symmetric in L_π^2; differentiate in t at $s = t$ to show that $\mathcal{L}$ is symmetric in L_π^2.

Conversely, suppose that $\mathcal{L}$ is symmetric in L_π^2. Then (12.18) holds, so working backwards in the derivation above shows that (12.17) holds. Since it holds for all test functions f, g, (12.15) holds, and we are done.

12.4. Eigenfunction methods

Recall that for Markov chains which satisfied detailed balance, we symmetrized the transition matrix by the similarity transformation $D^{1/2}PD^{-1/2}$, where $D_{ij} = \pi_i \delta_{ij}$ is the matrix with the stationary distribution on its diagonal. We used this to argue that P has real eigenvalues and a complete orthonormal basis of eigenvectors, and then we expanded many quantities of interest in terms of these eigenvectors. We will perform the same expansion for a reversible diffusion process, although because we are working in infinite-dimensional vector spaces, the arguments to justify an eigenvector expansion are more subtle and we do not provide precise conditions under which they hold.

We consider a uniformly elliptic operator $\mathcal{L}$ that is symmetric in the L_π^2 inner product. The symmetry implies that the eigenvalues of $\mathcal{L}$ are real. Under mild additional conditions one can show its eigenfunctions are countable and form a complete orthonormal basis of L_π^2; we will assume this is true going forward (one can always check it holds for a particular problem).

REMARK 12.11. See (**Evans, 2010**, Theorem 6.5.1) for a proof of the completeness of the eigenfunctions of the operator $\mathcal{L}u = \nabla \cdot (a\nabla u)$ on a bounded domain Ω with Dirichlet boundary conditions, assuming $a_{ij} \in C^\infty(\overline{\Omega})$ and a is symmetric and uniformly elliptic. From the representation in Exercise 12.3, we expect this argument can be adapted to the situation here. For an unbounded domain Ω one needs a Poincaré inequality to hold, which requires imposing growth conditions on the generalized potential Φ in (12.7) (**Pavliotis, 2014**). These arguments are based on the spectral theory of linear operators, which says that for a compact, symmetric, linear operator A on a separable Hilbert space H, the eigenvalues of A are real and their only accumulation point is 0, and there is an orthonormal basis for H consisting of eigenvectors of A (e.g., (**Lax, 2002**, Theorem 28.3), (**Evans, 2010**, Theorem D.6.7)). This theory is applied not to $\mathcal{L}$ but rather to its inverse $\mathcal{L}^{-1}$.

Let us write $\{\lambda_i\}_{i=1}^\infty$ for the eigenvalues of $\mathcal{L}$ and $\mathcal{L}^*$, $\{\phi_i\}_{i=1}^\infty$ for the eigenfunctions of $\mathcal{L}$, and $\{\psi_i\}_{i=1}^\infty$ for the eigenfunctions of $\mathcal{L}^*$. The eigenfunctions and eigenvalues must satisfy the same boundary conditions imposed on the operators they are associated with; changing the boundary conditions will change both the eigenvalues and eigenfunctions. The eigenvalues are ordered as $\lambda_1 > \lambda_2 \geq \lambda_3 \geq \cdots$, and can be shown to satisfy $\lambda_i \to -\infty$ as $i \to \infty$. We have by orthonormality of eigenfunctions that $\int \phi_i \phi_j \pi dx = \delta_{ij}$, where δ is the Kronecker delta. Here are some additional facts about the eigenvalues and eigenfunctions that we can show directly, writing $\mu_0 > 0$ for the minimum eigenvalue of $a(x)$.

(1) $\mathcal{L}$ is negative semi-definite, so the eigenvalues of $\mathcal{L}$ are nonpositive, $\lambda_i \leq 0$.

PROOF. Since $j_s = 0$, Lemma 12.7 implies that

$$\langle \mathcal{L}f, f \rangle_\pi = \int \pi f \mathcal{L}f = -\int \pi (\nabla f)^T a \nabla f \leq -\mu_0 \|\nabla f\|_\pi \leq 0. \qquad \square$$

(2) If $\mathcal{L}$ has reflecting boundary conditions, then its null space is one-dimensional and contains only constants. Therefore the largest eigenvalue is $\lambda_1 = 0$ with multiplicity 1, and the corresponding eigenfunctions are $\phi_0 = 1, \psi_0 = \pi$.

PROOF. Suppose $\mathcal{L}f = 0$. By the calculations above,

$$0 = \langle \mathcal{L}f, f \rangle_\pi \leq -\mu_0 \|\nabla f\|_\pi \leq 0.$$

The only way this is possible is if $\nabla f = 0$, so $f = cst$. Notice that this one-dimensional space of solutions does satisfy the reflecting boundary condition.
$\square$

(3) If $\mathcal{L}$ has absorbing boundary conditions, then all eigenvalues are strictly negative.

PROOF. This follows from the calculations above because there is no nontrivial solution satisfying $f|_{\partial\Omega} = 0$.
$\square$

(4) The left and right eigenfunctions are related by a factor of π:

(12.19) $$\psi_i(x) = \pi(x)\phi_i(x).$$

Recall this same relation was true for Markov chains.

PROOF. Calculate, using Lemma 12.9 applied to an eigenfunction ϕ_i,

$$\mathcal{L}^*(\pi\phi_i) = \pi\mathcal{L}\phi_i = \lambda_i\pi\phi_i.$$

Therefore if ϕ_i is an eigenfunction of $\mathcal{L}$ with eigenvalue λ_i, then $\pi\phi_i$ is an eigenfunction of $\mathcal{L}^*$ with the same eigenvalue.
$\square$

(5) ϕ_i, ψ_i form a bi-orthogonal set in L^2 (the nonweighted inner product space):

(12.20) $$\langle \phi_i, \psi_j \rangle = \delta_{ij},$$

where δ is the Kronecker delta.

PROOF. This follows from the orthonormality of $\{\phi_i\}$ in L^2_π. $\qquad\square$

Many quantities can be expressed using eigenfunctions.

Example 12.12 (Transition probability). Let us solve for the transition probability using separation of variables. Expand the transition probability in eigenfunctions of $\mathcal{L}^*_x$ as

$$p(x,t|y,0) = \sum_{i=1}^{\infty} a_i g_i(t)\psi_i(x)$$

where $a_i \in \mathbb{R}$ are unknown coefficients and $g_i(t)$ are unknown functions. Substitute into the forward equation $p_t = \mathcal{L}^*_x p$ to find

$$\sum_{i=1}^{\infty} a_i g'_i(t)\psi_i(x) = \sum_{i=1}^{\infty} a_i g_i(t)\lambda_i \psi_i(x).$$

Taking the L^2 inner product with ϕ_i and using (12.20) shows that $g_i(t) = e^{\lambda_i t}$. To find the coefficients a_i use the initial condition $p(x,0|y,0) = \delta(x-y)$ and take the L^2 inner product of $p(x,0|y,0)$ with ϕ_i to get

$$a_i = \langle p(x,0|y,0), \phi_i(x)\rangle = \langle \delta(x-y), \phi_i(x)\rangle = \phi_i(y).$$

Putting this all together shows the transition probability can be written as

(12.21) $$p(x,t|y,0) = \sum_{i=1}^{\infty} \phi_i(y)\psi_i(x)e^{\lambda_i t}.$$

Example 12.13 (Stationary covariance matrix). We derive an expression for the covariance matrix of a stationary diffusion process. Note that the process must have reflecting boundary conditions to be stationary. We have

$$\mathbb{E}^\pi X_t X_0^T = \iint xy^T p(x,t|y,0)\pi(y)dxdy$$

$$= \iint xy^T \pi(y) \sum_{k=1}^{\infty} \phi_k(y)\psi_k(x)e^{\lambda_k t}dxdy$$

$$= \sum_{k=1}^{\infty} \left(\int x\psi_k(x)dx\right)\left(\int x\psi_k(x)dx\right)^T e^{\lambda_k t} \qquad \text{using (12.19)}$$

(12.22) $$= \sum_{k=1}^{\infty} C^{(k)}e^{\lambda_k t},$$

where $C^{(k)}$ is a matrix constructed as

$$C^{(k)} = \overline{x}^{(k)} \otimes \overline{x}^{(k)} = \overline{x}^{(k)}(\overline{x}^{(k)})^T, \qquad \text{with} \quad \overline{x}^{(k)} = \int x\psi_k(x)dx.$$

That is, the ijth element is $C^{(k)}_{ij} = (\int x_i\psi_k(x)dx)(\int x_j\psi_k(x)dx)$. We also have, remembering that $\lambda_1 = 0$, $\psi_1 = \pi$ for a process with reflecting boundary conditions,

$$\mathbb{E}^\pi X_t = \int x\pi(x)dx = \int x\psi_1(x)e^{\lambda_1 t}dx.$$

Therefore, the stationary covariance function is

$$(12.23) \qquad C(t) = \mathbb{E}^\pi X_t X_0^T - (\mathbb{E}^\pi X_t)^2 = \sum_{k=2}^{\infty} C^{(k)} e^{\lambda_k t}.$$

Exercise 12.6. Consider Brownian motion on an interval $[0,1]$ with reflecting boundary conditions. Calculate the eigenvalues and eigenfunctions. Suppose you start the process with initial condition $\rho(x,0) = 2 \cdot 1_{x \in [0,\frac{1}{2}]}$. Write down an expression for the probability density $\rho(x,t)$ at time t. Estimate how quickly this decays to the stationary distribution.

Example 12.14 (Ornstein–Uhlenbeck process, 1D). The generator and its adjoint are

$$\mathcal{L}f = -\alpha x f_x + \frac{1}{2}\sigma^2 f_{xx}, \qquad \mathcal{L}^* p = \partial_x(\alpha x p) + \frac{1}{2}\sigma^2 \partial_{xx} p.$$

The eigenfunctions of the generator solve

$$\phi_\lambda'' - \frac{2\alpha x}{\sigma^2}\phi_\lambda' - \frac{2\lambda}{\sigma^2}\phi_\lambda = 0$$

with appropriate decay conditions at $\pm\infty$. Let $y = x\sqrt{\frac{2\alpha}{\sigma^2}}$. The eigenfunction equation becomes

$$\phi_\lambda'' - y\phi_\lambda' - \frac{\lambda}{\alpha}\phi_\lambda = 0.$$

This is the eigenvalue equation for the Hermite polynomials[1] (with eigenvalues scaled by α), which are defined as:

$$H_n(x) = (-1)^n e^{x^2/2} \frac{d^n}{dx^n} e^{-x^2/2}, \qquad H_n = \{1,\ x,\ x^2 - 1,\ x^3 - 3x,\ x^4 - 6x^2 + 3, \ldots\}.$$

Therefore, with normalizing constants chosen so that $\|\phi_n\|_\pi = 1$, we have

$$\phi_n(x) = (n!)^{-1/2} H_n(x\sqrt{2\alpha/\sigma^2}), \qquad \lambda_n = -n\alpha, \qquad n = 0, 1, \ldots.$$

The probability density at time t, assuming initial density $X_0 \sim \rho_0$, is

$$\rho(x,t) = \frac{1}{\sqrt{2\pi\sigma^2/2\alpha}} e^{-\frac{x^2\alpha}{\sigma^2}} \sum_n A_n (n!)^{-1/2} H_n(x\sqrt{2\alpha/\sigma^2}) e^{-n\alpha t},$$

where the coefficients are

$$A_n = \frac{1}{\sqrt{n!}} \langle \rho_0(x), H_n(x\sqrt{2\alpha/\sigma^2}) \rangle.$$

The probability density relaxes to the stationary probability exponentially quickly, with a rate governed by the smallest nonzero eigenvalue $\lambda_1 = \alpha$.

Let us calculate the stationary covariance function. Using our earlier calculations,

$$C(t) = \sum_{n=0}^{\infty} c_n^2 e^{-n\alpha t}, \qquad \text{where } c_n = \langle x, \psi_n \rangle.$$

---

[1]This is the "probabilist's" definition of Hermite polynomials. You may also encounter the "physicist's" definition: $H_n^p(x) = (-1)^n e^{x^2} \frac{d^n}{dx^n} e^{-x^2}$, which differs from the probabilist's definition by a rescaling; $H_n^p(x) = 2^{n/2} H_n(\sqrt{2}x)$.

Note that $x = \sqrt{\sigma^2/2\alpha}\phi_1(x)$, and $\langle \phi_1, \psi_j \rangle = 0$ if $j \neq 1$. Therefore, $c_1 = \sqrt{\sigma^2/2\alpha}$, and $c_n = 0$ for $n \neq 1$. Putting this together gives

$$C(t) = \frac{\sigma^2}{2\alpha}e^{-\alpha t}.$$

Let us pause to point out that the covariance function is just a single exponential, instead of a sum of exponentials as is more often the case. This is because we are computing the covariance of $f(X_t)$ with $f(x) = x$, and the function $f(x) = x$ is itself an eigenfunction of the generator.

Example 12.15 (Mean first-passage time). Let Ω be bounded, and let us calculate the mean first-passage time $T(x)$ to $\partial\Omega$ from $x \in \Omega$, using an eigenfunction expansion. Expand the mfpt as

$$T(x) = \sum_{i=1}^{\infty} a_i\phi_i(x),$$

where ϕ_i are eigenfunctions for $\mathcal{L}$ with absorbing boundary conditions. Substituting into the equation $\mathcal{L}T = -1$ and taking the inner product with ψ_i gives

$$\sum_{i=1}^{\infty} a_i\lambda_i\phi_i(x) = -1 \quad \Rightarrow \quad a_i\lambda_i = \langle -1, \psi_i \rangle.$$

Therefore,

$$T(x) = \sum_{i=1}^{\infty} \frac{1}{|\lambda_i|}\phi_i(x) \int \psi_i(y)dy.$$

Suppose the smallest eigenvalue (in absolute value) is a lot smaller than all the others: $|\lambda_1| \ll |\lambda_i|$ for $i > 1$. Then the series above can be approximated by its first term. Furthermore, $\mathcal{L}\phi_1 = \lambda_1\phi_1 \approx 0$, since $|\lambda_1|$ is small. Therefore, $\phi_1 \approx K$, a constant, away from the boundary, so $1 = \int \psi_1(x)\phi_1(x) \approx K \int \psi_1(x)$. We obtain the approximation

$$T(x) \approx \frac{1}{|\lambda_1|}.$$

That is, the smallest absolute eigenvalue gives the inverse timescale for reaching the boundary. These approximations can be made systematic using asymptotic methods, see (**Gardiner, 2009**, Section 6.6.1, p. 166) and (**Gardiner, 2009**, Chapter 14).

Example 12.16 (Two-dimensional Brownian motion in a square (**Gardiner, 2009**, Section 6.6.1, p. 166)). Consider a two-dimensional Brownian motion with constant diffusivity D in a square E with corners $(0,0), (0,1), (1,0), (1,1)$ and let $T(x)$ be the mean first-passage time to the boundary, ∂E. T solves

$$\frac{D}{2}(\partial_{xx}T + \partial_{yy}T) = -1, \qquad T(\partial E) = 0.$$

The eigenfunctions and eigenvalues for this problem are

$$\psi_{n,m}(x,y) = \sin(n\pi x)\sin(m\pi y),$$
$$\phi_{n,m}(x,y) = 4\sin(n\pi x)\sin(m,\pi y),$$
$$\lambda_{n,m} = \frac{\pi^2 D}{2}(n^2 + m^2),$$

with $n, m = 1, 2, \ldots$. One can work out that $a_{n,m} = 0$ if either of n, m are even, and $a_{n,m} = \frac{4}{mn\pi^2}$ if both n, m are odd. Therefore,

$$T(x, y) = \frac{1}{D} \sum_{n,m \text{ odd}} \frac{32}{\pi^2 nm(m^2 + n^2)} \sin(n\pi x) \sin(m\pi y).$$

12.5. Even versus odd variables

Our discussion so far applies to physical systems where all variables are *even*: they "look" the same forward and backward in time. For example, if you watch a movie of a car driving down the road, and you stop the movie halfway through and start playing it backwards, the car's position does not change the instant you start playing the movie backwards. If you only observe the car's position instantaneously, you cannot tell if the movie is playing forwards or backwards—position is an even variable. However, the car's velocity *does* change when you play the movie backwards—the velocity reverses sign. Based on the instantaneous velocity, you *can* tell whether the movie is playing forward or backward in time. Velocity is an example of an *odd* variable—it changes sign if time starts going backward.

In general, each physical variable x_i is classified as either *even* or *odd* depending on how it transforms under time reversal: $x_i \rightarrow \epsilon_i x_i$, with $\epsilon_i = +1(-1)$ for an even (odd) variable respectively. Examples of even variables include position, acceleration, force, voltage, energy, and electric polarization. Examples of odd variables include velocity, angular and linear momentum, magnetic field, density of electric current, etc.

The previous results that link reversibility to a zero steady-state flux do not apply to systems with odd variables. For example, we saw in Exercise 10.8 that in the Langevin equations—which contain velocities—the steady-state flux is not zero. These equations are used to model equilibrium systems all the time. How then should the concept of reversibility be generalized to such systems?

As an example, consider a gas of particles with positions contained in vector x and velocities contained in vector v, and remember that $\frac{dx}{dt} = v$. Suppose the system moves from state $(x, v) \rightarrow (x', v')$ in some time interval of length Δt. This is *not* the same as moving from $(x', v') \rightarrow (x, v)$ backward in time, because if you change the direction of time, then the velocities of each particle must change sign. What it *is* physically equivalent to is moving from $(x', -v') \rightarrow (x, -v)$ in the same time interval Δt. Indeed, to go from $x \rightarrow x'$ in a small time Δt requires $v \approx (x' - x)/\Delta t$, and to go from $x' \rightarrow x$ requires $v' \approx (x - x')/\Delta t = -v$.

Therefore, for this gas of particles, detailed balance or time-reversibility should be written as

$$p(r', v', \tau | r, v, 0)\pi(r, v) = p(r, -v, \tau | r', -v', 0)\pi(r', v').$$

The most general principle of detailed balance requires that
(12.24)
$$P(x \rightarrow y, \text{ forward in time}) = P(y \rightarrow x, \text{ backward in time}), \qquad \text{in steady-state,}$$

i.e., the probability of making some transition forward in time equals the probability of making the reverse transition backward in time when the system is in steady-state, and where all variables change sign in the appropriate way. This principle comes from microscopic reversibility: Newton's laws are time-reversible, so if we coarse-grain them we want the stochastic system to preserve the same property. The condition for detailed balance becomes

(12.25) $$p(y, t|x, s)\pi(x) = p(\epsilon x, t|\epsilon y, s)\pi(y).$$

Conditions on the coefficients $b(x)$, $a(x)$ of a time-homogeneous SDE that are both necessary and sufficient for detailed balance to be satisfied are (**Gardiner, 2009**, Section 6.3.5)

(i) $\epsilon_i b_i(\epsilon x)\pi(x) = -b_i(x)\pi(x) + \sum_j \partial_j(2a_{ij}(x)\pi(x))$
(ii) $\epsilon_i\epsilon_j a_{ij}(\epsilon x) = a_{ij}(x)$.

When all variables are even, these conditions reduce to the condition $j_s = 0$.

12.6. Additional exercises

Exercise 12.7. For each of the following, compute the stationary distribution (up to a normalizing constant) and determine if the process satisfies detailed balance.

(i) A process (X_t, Y_t) on $[0, 1]^2$ with reflecting boundary conditions.

$$dX_t = -(X_t - Y_t)dt + \sigma dW_t^{(1)}$$
$$dY_t = -(Y_t - X_t)dt + \sigma dW_t^{(2)}$$

(ii) A process (X_t, Y_t) on $[0, 2\pi]^2$ with periodic boundary conditions.

$$dX_t = \sin Y_t dt + dW_t^{(1)}$$
$$dY_t = \sin X_t dt + dW_t^{(2)}$$

(iii) A process (X_t, Y_t) on $D = [-R, R] \times [1, 2]$, and $R > 0$ is some constant, with reflecting boundary conditions on ∂D.

$$dX_t = -X_t dt + \frac{1}{Y_t^2}dW_t^{(1)}$$
$$dY_t = -2Y_t^3 dt + \frac{1}{\sqrt{X_t^2 + 1}}dW_t^{(2)}$$

Exercise 12.8. Consider Brownian motion W_t on the interval $[0, 1]$ with a reflecting boundary condition at 1 and an absorbing boundary condition at 0.

(i) Calculate the eigenvalues and eigenfunctions of the generator.
(ii) Suppose you start a trajectory at $y \in (0, 1)$. What is the probability density for the trajectory to be found at x at time t? Express this in terms of the eigenfunctions.
(iii) Estimate the rate of decay of $P_{tot}^{x_0}(t)$, the total probability for a trajectory starting at x_0 to be found in the domain at time t. Do this by finding an exponential bound α (independent of x_0) such that $P_{tot}^{x_0}(t) \leq Ce^{-\alpha t}$ for large enough t, where C is some constant.

Exercise 12.9. Given a reversible diffusion X_t and a smooth function $g(x)$. Find an expression for the covariance function of $Y_t = g(X_t)$ in steady-state, using the eigenfunctions of the generator.

Exercise 12.10. Use the previous exercise to calculate the covariance function of $Y_t = X_t^3$ in steady-state, where X_t is an Ornstein–Uhlenbeck process with generator $\mathcal{L}f = -\alpha x f_x + \frac{1}{2}\sigma^2 f_{xx}$. Hint: You should end up with a finite sum of terms as an answer.

Exercise 12.11. Recall that the *Rayleigh process* describes the evolution of the amplitude of a 2D Ornstein–Uhlenbeck process with independent identical components (Example 7.19, Exercise 10.3):

$$dA_t = \left(-\gamma A_t + \frac{\mu}{A_t}\right)dt + \sqrt{2\mu}\,dW_t, \qquad A_t \in (0, \infty).$$

(i) Find the stationary distribution p_s, and find the eigenfunctions of the generator of this process. Write these in terms of the Laguerre polynomials.

(ii) Write down an expression for the transition probability density $p(x, t|x_0, 0)$, in terms of the Laguerre polynomials.

(iii) Show that the covariance function in steady-state is

$$C(t) = \frac{2\mu\pi}{4\gamma} \sum_{n=1}^{\infty} \binom{1/2}{n}^2 e^{-2n\gamma t}.$$

Some useful information:

- Laguerre polynomials $L_n(x)$ are solutions to the following differential equation:

$$xy'' + (1 - x)y' + ny = 0.$$

   The first few are $\{1, -x + 1, \frac{1}{2}(x^2 - 4x + 2), \frac{1}{6}(-x^3 + 9x^2 - 18x + 6), \dots\}$.
- $\int_0^\infty z^\alpha e^{-z} L_n(z)dz = (-1)^n \Gamma(\alpha + 1)\binom{\alpha}{n}$.
- $\binom{x}{y} = \frac{\Gamma(x+1)}{\Gamma(y+1)\Gamma(x-y+1)}$.
- $\binom{1/2}{k} = \binom{2k}{k}\frac{(-1)^{k+1}}{2^{2k}(2k-1)}$.

CHAPTER 13

Asymptotic Analysis of SDEs

Sometimes an SDE will contain a parameter which is much smaller or larger than the others, for example, if it models a systems with dynamics on widely separated time-scales. Averaging over the fast scales leads to dynamics on longer scales which are often simpler to analyze. This chapter will introduce one technique to do this, based on performing a singular perturbation analysis on the generator of the process. We will consider three examples: an ODE driven by a coloured noise that converges to a white noise, the overdamped limit of the Langevin equation, and an ODE driven by a continuous-time Markov chain. The latter example mixes techniques for discrete and continuous Markov processes.

13.1. White noise limit of a colored noise

Consider the equation

$$(13.1) \qquad \frac{dx^\epsilon}{dt} = b(x^\epsilon) + \sigma(x^\epsilon)\frac{y^\epsilon(t)}{\epsilon},$$

where $y^\epsilon(t)$ is a stationary stochastic process (depending on parameter ϵ) that has a nonzero correlation time, i.e., it is a *coloured noise*. If the correlation time of $y^\epsilon(t)$ is very short, then we might expect $y^\epsilon(t)/\epsilon$ to behave approximately as a white noise, so that (13.1) is approximately an SDE. But recall there is more than one way to interpret the noise term when the noise is multiplicative—we could interpret it in an Itô sense, a Stratonovich sense, or some other version of the stochastic integral. Let us determine which of these is the best interpretation in the limit when $y^\epsilon(t)/\epsilon$ approaches a white noise.

As a model, let y^ϵ be an Ornstein–Uhlenbeck process, solving

$$(13.2) \qquad dy^\epsilon = -\frac{y^\epsilon}{\epsilon^2}dt + \frac{1}{\epsilon}dW_t.$$

The correlation time of y^ϵ is proportional to ϵ^2 but the variance of y^ϵ is constant. Indeed, the steady-state covariance function of y^ϵ and the corresponding power spectrum are

$$C_{y^\epsilon}(t) = \frac{1}{2}e^{-\frac{|t|}{\epsilon^2}}, \qquad \hat{C}_{y^\epsilon}(\omega) = \frac{1}{2\pi}\frac{\epsilon^2}{(1+\epsilon^4\omega^2)}.$$

We are interested in $\epsilon \ll 1$, so the correlation time of y^ϵ is very short. If we rescale the process by considering y^ϵ/ϵ, then $C_{y^\epsilon/\epsilon}(t) \to 0$ for $t \neq 0$, and $\int_{-\infty}^{\infty} C_{y^\epsilon/\epsilon}(t)dt = 1$. Thus, we obtain a process whose stationary covariance function approaches a delta-function as $\epsilon \to 0$:

$$C_{y^\epsilon/\epsilon}(t) = \frac{1}{2\epsilon^2}e^{-\frac{|t|}{\epsilon^2}} \quad \xrightarrow{\epsilon\to 0} \quad \delta(t).$$

Since the covariance function for white noise is $\delta(t)$, we expect y^ϵ/ϵ to behave like a white noise in the limit.

To derive the limit of the process (x^ϵ, y^ϵ) described by (13.1) and (13.2) as $\epsilon \to 0$, consider the generator of the process:

$$\mathcal{L}^\epsilon = \frac{1}{\epsilon^2}\left(-y\partial_y + \frac{1}{2}\partial_{yy}\right) + \frac{1}{\epsilon}\sigma(x)y\partial_x + b(x)\partial_x.$$

The backward equation is

(13.3)
$$\frac{\partial u^\epsilon}{\partial t} = \left(\frac{1}{\epsilon^2}\mathcal{L}_0 + \frac{1}{\epsilon}\mathcal{L}_1 + \mathcal{L}_2\right)u^\epsilon,$$

where $\mathcal{L}_0 = -y\partial_y + \frac{1}{2}\partial_{yy}$, $\mathcal{L}_1 = \sigma(x)y\partial_x$, $\mathcal{L}_2 = b(x)\partial_x$. This equation is equipped with no-flux boundary conditions at infinity.

We analyze this equation using a technique called *singular perturbation theory*. Expand u^ϵ in an asymptotic expansion, as

$$u^\epsilon(x, y, t) = u_0(x, y, t) + \epsilon u_1(x, y, t) + \epsilon^2 u_2(x, y, t) + \cdots.$$

Now substitute this ansatz into the backward equation (13.3) and equate terms of each order:

(13.4)
$$\begin{array}{lll} O(\frac{1}{\epsilon^2}): & \mathcal{L}_0 u_0 = & 0 \\ O(\frac{1}{\epsilon}): & \mathcal{L}_0 u_1 = & -\mathcal{L}_1 u_0 \\ O(1): & \mathcal{L}_0 u_2 = & -(\mathcal{L}_1 u_1 + \mathcal{L}_2 u_0 - \frac{\partial u_0}{\partial t}) \end{array}$$

Let us solve these equations, order by order. At $O(\frac{1}{\epsilon^2})$, we have

$$-y\partial_y u_0 + \frac{1}{2}\partial_{yy}u_0 = 0.$$

This is an operator only in y. We call y the "fast" variable because it evolves very quickly, on timescale $O(1/\epsilon^2)$, whereas x evolves on a slower timescale. We are interested in the dynamics of x on the slowest timescale, of $O(1)$, so we want to average over the fast variables in some way.

The solution which satisfies no-flux boundary conditions at infinity is $u_0 = $ constant (in y), so

(13.5)
$$u_0 = u_0(x, t),$$

At $O(\frac{1}{\epsilon})$, we have

$$-y\partial_y u_1 + \frac{1}{2}\partial_{yy}u_1 = -y\sigma(x)\partial_x u_0.$$

We can solve—for example, by separation of variables—to get

(13.6)
$$u_1(x, y, t) = y\sigma(x)\partial_x u_0 + \Psi_1(x, t),$$

where Ψ_1 is some unknown function. Note that we could drop it, since it is in the null space of $\mathcal{L}_0$ so we could absorb it in u_0, but we will keep it anyway and show it does not matter in the end.

At $O(1)$, we have

(13.7)
$$\mathcal{L}_0 u_2 = -\mathcal{L}_1 u_1 - \mathcal{L}_2 u_0 + \frac{\partial u_0}{\partial t}.$$

In order for this equation to have a solution u_2, the RHS must satisfy the *Fredholm alternative*: if π is in the null space of $\mathcal{L}_0^*$, i.e., $\mathcal{L}_0^*\pi = 0$, then $\langle \pi, RHS \rangle = 0$, where we use the regular L^2 inner product $\langle f, g \rangle = \int f(y)g(y)dy$. To see why, take the inner product of π with (13.7):

$$\langle \pi, \mathcal{L}_0 u_2 \rangle = \langle \mathcal{L}_0^* \pi, u_2 \rangle = 0 \quad \Rightarrow \quad \langle \pi, RHS \rangle = 0.$$

Therefore, we must have

$$\int \pi(y) \left(\frac{\partial u_0}{\partial t} - \mathcal{L}_1 u_1 - \mathcal{L}_2 u_0 \right) dy = 0.$$

Now we substitute the ingredients we have solved for into the equation above. We solved for u_0, u_1 in (13.5) and (13.6). Clearly, $\pi(y)$ is the stationary distribution for the process with generator $\mathcal{L}_0$, which is the generator for an Ornstein–Uhlenbeck process in the y-variables, so $\pi(y) = \frac{1}{\sqrt{\pi}} e^{-y^2}$. Therefore

$$\frac{\partial u_0}{\partial t} = \int \pi(y) \left[y\sigma(x)\partial_x \left(y\sigma(x)\partial_x u_0(x,t) + \Psi_1(x,t) \right) + b(x)\partial_x u_0(x,t) \right] dy$$

$$= \sigma(x)\partial_x(\sigma(x)\partial_x u_0) \underbrace{\int y^2 \pi(y)dy}_{\mathbb{E}^\pi y^2} + \sigma(x)\partial_x \Psi_1(x,t) \underbrace{\int y\pi(y)dy}_{\mathbb{E}^\pi y} + b(x)\partial_x u_0.$$

Now, we use the fact that $\mathbb{E}^\pi y^2 = 1/2$, $\mathbb{E}^\pi y = 0$ to write the above as

$$\frac{\partial u_0}{\partial t} = \frac{1}{2}\sigma(x)\partial_x(\sigma(x)\partial_x u_0) + b(x)\partial_x u_0.$$

Alternatively, separating the drift and diffusion terms,

$$\frac{\partial u_0}{\partial t} = \left(b(x) + \frac{1}{2}\sigma(x)\partial_x \sigma(x) \right)\partial_x u_0 + \frac{1}{2}\sigma^2(x)\partial_{xx} u_0.$$

This is the backward equation for the *Stratonovich* SDE

(13.8) $$dX_t = b(X_t) + \sigma(X_t) \circ dW_t.$$

Hence, the correct interpretation of the colored noise in the limit as it approaches a white noise is in the Stratonovich sense.

REMARK 13.1. We computed the limiting process—using formal asymptotics—by showing that the generator of the process (x^ϵ, y^ϵ) given in (13.1) and (13.2) approaches the generator of the Stratonovich process (13.8). It is possible to strengthen this result; see (**Pavliotis and Stuart, 2008**) for a range of applications of this technique, as well as stronger convergence results. We considered an Ornstein–Uhlenbeck process for the noise but the same result holds with a wide range of other choices, provided the noise is one-dimensional. When the noise is higher-dimensional, the limit is not necessarily a Stratonovich SDE but rather could contain an extra drift term, the so-called Levy area correction (**Pavliotis, 2014**, Section 5), (**Pavliotis and Stuart, 2008**, Section 11.7.7).

In general, to make these asymptotics work for a backward equation of the form (13.3), we need the following assumptions (**Papanicolaou, 1977**):

   (i) $\mathcal{L}_0$ is the generator of a stationary Markov process and it depends only on the fast variables, y.
   (ii) $\mathcal{L}_0$ is ergodic: it has only constants in its null space and the semigroup $T_t = e^{\mathcal{L}_0 t}$ converges to $\mathcal{P}$ as $t \to \infty$, where $\mathcal{P}$ is the projection operator onto the null space of $\mathcal{L}_0$, defined by $(\mathcal{P}u)(x) = \int u(x,y)\pi(y)dy$. The function $\pi(y)$

is the stationary distribution for the y-variables with x held fixed, satisfying $\mathcal{L}_0^* \pi = 0$.

(iii) The Fredholm alternative holds for $\mathcal{L}_1$: $\mathcal{P}\mathcal{L}_1\mathcal{P} = 0$, or, in other words, $\langle \pi, \mathcal{L}_1 u \rangle = 0$ for all $u \in \text{Null}(\mathcal{L}_0)$.

(iv) Consistency in the initial condition: $\mathcal{P}u|_{t=0} = u|_{t=0}$ (otherwise we must consider the initial layer problem).

If these conditions hold, we can find a a PDE for the evolution of the leading-order term u_0:

$$\frac{\partial u_0}{\partial t} = (\mathcal{P}\mathcal{L}_2\mathcal{P} - \mathcal{P}\mathcal{L}_1\mathcal{L}_0^{-1}\mathcal{L}_1\mathcal{P})u_0 .$$

Here, $\mathcal{L}_0^{-1}f$ means the function u such that $f = \mathcal{L}_0 u$.

13.2. Overdamped limit of the Langevin equation

Next, we consider the one-dimensional Langevin equation:

$$(13.9) \qquad m\frac{d^2x}{dt^2} = -\partial_x U(x) - \gamma\frac{dx}{dt} + \sqrt{2k_B T\gamma}\,\eta(t).$$

This represents, for example, the position x of a particle of mass m subject to a random forcing. It comes from Newton's second law: the mass times the acceleration equals the sum of forces acting on the particle. The forces include a force from the external potential $-\partial_x U(x)$, a friction force $-\gamma\frac{dx}{dt}$ with friction coefficient γ, and a fluctuating force $\sqrt{2k_B T\gamma}\eta(t)$, where $\eta(t)$ is a white noise. The latter two forces arise naturally after coarse-graining a solvent's degrees of freedom, using Mori–Zwanzig theory (**Zwanzig, 2001; Hijón et al., 2010**). They capture the effect of the discreteness of the solvent molecules, without explicitly represent these molecules.

We will show that in a certain limit, the Langevin equation approaches the overdamped Langevin equation:

$$(13.10) \qquad \frac{dx}{dt} = -\gamma^{-1}\partial_x U(x) + \sqrt{2k_B T\gamma^{-1}}\eta(t).$$

Notably, the overdamped equation does not depend on the mass of the particle—momentum has been damped to nonexistence, hence the terminology.

One way this limit arises is when the mass is small, by using the rescaling $m \to \epsilon^2 m$ with $\epsilon \ll 1$. (Another way is with large friction and long times, under the rescaling $\gamma \sim 1/\epsilon, t \sim 1/\epsilon$; see Exercise 13.2.) Heuristically, setting the left-hand side of (13.9) to 0 and solving for $\frac{dx}{dt}$ gives (13.10). This is *not*, however, a correct derivation—it gives the correct result as a convenient accident when γ is constant, but it will not give the correct result when $\gamma = \gamma(x)$ (see Exercise 13.3). The reason this heuristic is wrong is that when a perturbation applies to the highest order derivative in the equation—in this case the second derivative—the mathematical nature of the equation can change in ways that one has to account for in the derivation.

To derive (13.10) properly we use singular perturbation theory. Substitute $m \to \epsilon^2 m$, define $p = \epsilon m\frac{dx}{dt}$ to be proportional to the system's momentum, and write (13.9) as a pair of SDEs:

$$dx = \frac{p}{\epsilon m}dt, \qquad dp = \left(-\frac{\partial_x U}{\epsilon} - \frac{\gamma p}{\epsilon^2 m}\right)dt + \frac{\sqrt{2k_B T\gamma}}{\epsilon}dW_t.$$

The backward equation corresponding to this system is

$$(13.11) \qquad \partial_t u = \frac{1}{\epsilon}\underbrace{\left(\frac{p}{m}\partial_x u - \partial_x U \partial_p u\right)}_{\mathcal{L}_1 u} + \frac{1}{\epsilon^2}\underbrace{\left(-\frac{\gamma p}{m}\partial_p u + k_B T \gamma \partial_{pp} u\right)}_{\mathcal{L}_0 u}.$$

We have defined operators $\mathcal{L}_1, \mathcal{L}_0$ as before. This equation has no-flux boundary conditions at infinity. From the definition of $\mathcal{L}_0$, we see that p is our "fast" variable and x is our "slow" variable.

Assuming an ansatz $u(x,p,t) = u_0(x,p,t) + \epsilon u_1(x,p,t) + \epsilon^2 u_2(x,p,t)$ as before and expanding (13.11) in powers of ϵ leads to the same formal system of equations (13.4), which we again solve order by order. At $O(1/\epsilon^2)$ we have

$$-\frac{\gamma p}{m}\partial_p u_0 + k_B T \gamma \partial_{pp} u_0 = 0$$

whose solution (with no-flux boundary conditions)[1] is constant in p: $u_0(x,t)$. At $O(1/\epsilon)$ we have

$$-\frac{\gamma p}{m}\partial_p u_1 + k_B T \gamma \partial_{pp} u_1 = -\frac{p}{m}\partial_x u_0,$$

whose solution is $u_1(x,p,t) = \frac{p}{\gamma}\partial_x u_0(x,t)$ (we ignore the term in $\text{Null}(\mathcal{L}_0)$). At $O(1)$ we have

$$\mathcal{L}_0 u_2 = -\mathcal{L}_1 u_1 + \partial_t u_0.$$

Again, requiring the solvability condition $\langle \pi, RHS \rangle = 0$—where π solves $\mathcal{L}_0^* \pi = 0$, $\int \pi(p)dp = 1$—leads to

$$\partial_t u_0 = \int \pi(p)\left(\frac{p^2}{\gamma m}\partial_{xx} u_0 - \partial_x U \frac{\partial_x u_0}{\gamma}\right)dp.$$

The stationary distribution in the fast variable p is

$$\pi(p) = \frac{1}{\sqrt{2\pi m k_B T}}e^{-\frac{p^2}{2m k_B T}},$$

from which we calculate $\langle \pi, p^2 \rangle = m k_B T$. So, $u_0(x,t)$ evolves as

$$\partial_t u_0 = -\frac{\partial_x U(x)}{\gamma}\partial_x u_0 + \frac{k_B T}{\gamma}\partial_{xx} u_0.$$

This is the backward equation corresponding to (13.10).

We make one final remark on the physical interpretation of this derivation. The derivation above, while mathematically correct, is physically inappropriate because mass is a dimensional quantity, so we may only compare it to something with the same dimensions. The physically appropriate way to coarse-grain the equations is to first nondimensionalize them and then identify the scalings of the nondimensional parameters.

---

[1]The general solution is $u_0(x,t) + C(x,t)\int e^{\frac{1}{2}p^2/k_B T m}dp$; however, we must have $C(x,t) = 0$ to satisfy the no-flux boundary conditions.

To this end, suppose $x = L\tilde{x}, t = T\tilde{t}, m = M\tilde{m}$, and $U = \beta^{-1}\tilde{U}$ (writing $\beta^{-1} = k_B T$) where L, T, M are characteristic length, time, and mass scales, respectively, and variables with a tilde are nondimensional. Then (13.9) becomes (noting that the dimensions of $\frac{dW}{dt}$ are (time)$^{-1/2}$):

$$\frac{ML}{T^2}\tilde{m}\frac{d^2\tilde{x}}{d\tilde{t}^2} = -\frac{\beta^{-1}}{L}\partial_{\tilde{x}}\tilde{U} - \frac{\gamma L}{T}\frac{d\tilde{x}}{d\tilde{t}} + \sqrt{\frac{2\beta^{-1}\gamma}{T}}\frac{dW}{d\tilde{t}}.$$

Rearranging the parameters and removing the tildes for clarity, we can write this as

$$\overline{M}m\frac{d^2x}{dt^2} = -\partial_x U(x) - \overline{\Gamma}\frac{dx}{dt} + \overline{B}\sqrt{2}\frac{dW}{dt},$$

where we defined nondimensional parameters

$$\overline{M} = \frac{ML^2\beta}{T^2}, \qquad \overline{\Gamma} = \frac{\gamma L^2\beta}{T}, \qquad \overline{B} = \frac{\sqrt{\beta\gamma}L}{\sqrt{T}}.$$

Our previous scaling arose from assuming $\overline{M} = \epsilon^2, \overline{\Gamma}, \overline{B} = O(1)$ for $\epsilon \ll 1$. Because these parameters are nondimensional, it is appropriate to compare them. There are several combinations of the dimensional parameters that produce this scaling. Proceeding with this scaling ansatz in exactly the same way as above leads to the overdamped equation (13.10).

13.3. A random walk converging to a diffusion process

In our final example, we will consider a process driven by a noise that is a continuous-time Markov chain. Over long times where the ctMC behaves approximately as a white noise, the process will converge to a multiple of a Brownian motion. Consider the equation

$$(13.12) \qquad \frac{dx^\epsilon}{dt} = \frac{y^\epsilon(t)}{\epsilon},$$

where $y^\epsilon(t)$ is a continuous-time Markov chain, which take values $\pm\alpha$, and jumps between them with rate β/ϵ^2. The generator of y^ϵ is

$$A^\epsilon = \frac{1}{\epsilon^2}\begin{pmatrix} -\beta & \beta \\ \beta & -\beta \end{pmatrix}.$$

The process x^ϵ moves with velocity $\pm\alpha$ for a random time Δt and then repeats. Hence, it performs a random walk with steps of size $\Delta x = \pm(\alpha/\epsilon)\Delta t$ and at time intervals with average duration $\mathbb{E}\Delta t = \epsilon^2/\beta$. Since $\mathbb{E}\Delta x^2/\mathbb{E}\Delta t = \alpha^2/\beta$, we expect the process at long times to look like a Brownian motion scaled by $\alpha/\sqrt{\beta}$.

Let us show this using an asymptotic analysis of the generator. Define a $u(x, y, t) = \mathbb{E}^{(x,y)}f(x^\epsilon(t), y^\epsilon(t))$ for some function $f(x, y)$. Considering the two different values for y^ϵ, we can write

$$u(x, y, t) = \begin{pmatrix} u_+(x, t) \\ u_-(x, t) \end{pmatrix}, \qquad \text{where} \quad u_+(x, t) = u(x, \alpha, t), \quad u_-(x, t) = u(x, -\alpha, t).$$

We similarly write $f_+(x) = f(x, \alpha), f_-(x) = f(x, -\alpha)$.

We will analyze the backward equation describing the evolution of u. Since the process is a mix of a continuous and a discrete process, we first briefly describe how to obtain its generator. Recall that the generator $\mathcal{L}$ is defined by

$$(\mathcal{L}f)(x,y) = \lim_{t \to 0+} \frac{1}{t}(\mathbb{E}^{x,y}f(x^\epsilon(t), y^\epsilon(t)) - f(x,y)).$$

We compute $\mathbb{E}^{x,y}f(x^\epsilon(t), y^\epsilon(t))$ for small t by Taylor-expanding up to $O(t)$ and approximating the jump probability in y using its infinitesimal generator A^ϵ:

$$\mathbb{E}^{x,\alpha}f(x^\epsilon(t), y^\epsilon(t)) = f(x,\alpha) + \partial_x f(x,\alpha)\mathbb{E}\Delta X + f(x,\alpha)A_{11}^\epsilon t + f(x,-\alpha)A_{12}^\epsilon t$$

$$= f^+(x) + \partial_x f^+(x)\frac{\alpha}{\epsilon}t - f^+(x)\frac{\beta}{\epsilon^2}t + f^-(x)\frac{\beta}{\epsilon^2}t,$$

$$\mathbb{E}^{x,-\alpha}f(x^\epsilon(t), y^\epsilon(t)) = f(x,-\alpha) + \partial_x f(x,-\alpha)\mathbb{E}\Delta X + f(x,\alpha)A_{12}^\epsilon t + f(x,-\alpha)A_{22}^\epsilon t$$

$$= f^-(x) + \partial_x f^-(x)\frac{-\alpha}{\epsilon}t + f^+(x)\frac{\beta}{\epsilon^2}t - f^-(x)\frac{\beta}{\epsilon^2}t.$$

Subtracting off $f(x,y)$, dividing by t, and letting $t \to 0$ gives generator

$$\mathcal{L}\begin{pmatrix} f^+ \\ f^- \end{pmatrix} = \begin{pmatrix} \frac{\alpha}{\epsilon}\partial_x f^+ \\ \frac{-\alpha}{\epsilon}\partial_x f^- \end{pmatrix} + A^\epsilon \begin{pmatrix} f^+ \\ f^- \end{pmatrix}.$$

Now, using the generator we may write the time-homogeneous backward equation as

$$(13.13) \qquad \frac{\partial}{\partial t}\begin{pmatrix} u_+ \\ u_- \end{pmatrix} = \mathcal{L}\begin{pmatrix} u_+ \\ u_- \end{pmatrix} = \frac{1}{\epsilon}\begin{pmatrix} \alpha & 0 \\ 0 & -\alpha \end{pmatrix}\frac{\partial}{\partial x}\begin{pmatrix} u_+ \\ u_- \end{pmatrix} + \frac{1}{\epsilon^2}\begin{pmatrix} -\beta & \beta \\ \beta & -\beta \end{pmatrix}\begin{pmatrix} u_+ \\ u_- \end{pmatrix},$$

with initial condition $u_\pm(x,0) = f_\pm(x)$. We could now perform the asymptotic analysis on (13.13) using singular perturbation theory, as in Section 13.13.1. We will not do this; instead we will change variables to make (13.13) simpler to analyze (**Papanicolaou, 1977; E et al., 2019**).

Let

$$w = u_+ + u_-, \quad v = u_+ - u_-.$$

Take one more time derivative of (13.13) and substitute the change of variables. Then w evolves as

$$(13.14) \qquad \begin{aligned} \epsilon^2 \frac{\partial^2 w}{\partial t^2} &= \alpha^2 \frac{\partial^2 w}{\partial x^2} - 2\beta \frac{\partial w}{\partial t}, \\ w(x,0) &= f_+(x) + f_-(x), \\ \frac{\partial w}{\partial t}(x,0) &= \frac{\alpha}{\epsilon}\frac{\partial}{\partial x}(f_+ - f_-). \end{aligned}$$

This equation is almost decoupled from that of v; the only coupling enters through the initial condition. Suppose $f_+(x) = f_-(x) = f(x)$. Then $\frac{\partial w}{\partial t}(x,0) = 0$, so there is no initial transient layer; the equations are fully decoupled.

Now we can consider an asymptotic analysis of (13.13.3). Let $w = w_0 + \epsilon w_1 + \epsilon^2 w_2 + \ldots$. Substitute this ansatz into (13.13.3) and equate terms of different orders. At $O(1)$, we have

$$(13.15) \qquad \frac{\partial w_0}{\partial t} = \frac{\alpha^2}{2\beta}\frac{\partial^2 w_0}{\partial x^2}, \qquad w_0(x,0) = 2f(x).$$

This is the generator of the diffusion

(13.16)
$$dX_t = \frac{\alpha}{\sqrt{\beta}} dW_t.$$

This shows that at long times, $x^\epsilon(t)$ behaves as the scaled Brownian motion $\frac{\alpha}{\sqrt{\beta}} W_t$.

13.4. Additional exercises

Exercise 13.1. Consider the system

$$\frac{dx}{dt} = \frac{xy}{\epsilon}, \qquad dy = \frac{-y}{\epsilon^2} dt + \frac{\sqrt{2\lambda}}{\epsilon} dW_t.$$

(i) Derive an SDE for $x(t)$ as $\epsilon \to 0$ using singular perturbation theory.
(ii) Solve this SDE to obtain a solution X_t.
(iii) Solve the original system analytically for fixed ϵ. Verify that the solution converges to X_t as $\epsilon \to 0$.
    Hint: Solve for x by integrating an appropriate quantity, then substitute a known expression for y.

Exercise 13.2. Verify that the overdamped equation (13.10) may alternatively be derived from the Langevin equation (13.9) under the rescalings $\gamma \to \gamma/\epsilon$, $t \to t/\epsilon$. Remember that the dimensions of $\eta(t) = \frac{dW}{dt}$ are $1/\sqrt{\text{time}}$.

Exercise 13.3. Consider the Langevin equation with a position-varying friction coefficient:

$$m\frac{d^2x}{dt^2} = -\partial_x U(x) - \gamma(x)\frac{dx}{dt} + \sqrt{2k_B T\gamma(x)}\,\eta(t).$$

Use singular perturbation theory to derive the corresponding overdamped Langevin equation:

$$\frac{dx}{dt} = -\gamma^{-1}(x)\partial_x U(x) + k_B T\partial_x\gamma^{-1}(x) + \sqrt{2k_B T\gamma^{-1}(x)}\,\eta(t).$$

Comment: Notice the connection to a general reversible diffusion process, Example 12.4. In fact, this is exactly the equations of Brownian dynamics; see Example 12.5.

Appendix

A.1. A brief review of probability theory

This is a brief review of some of the key concepts from probability theory that the reader is expected to be familiar with. To learn these concepts properly, the reader is invited to consult one of the many excellent textbooks on the subject, e.g., (**Grimmett and Stirzaker, 2001**).

A.1.1. Probability spaces, random variables, and expectation.

DEFINITION A.1. A *probability space* is a triple $(\Omega, \mathcal{F}, P)$, where
   (1) Ω is the *sample space*, i.e., the set of all possible outcomes of a random experiment. Each element $\omega \in \Omega$ is a *sample point*. A subset $A \subset \Omega$ is an *event*.
   (2) $\mathcal{F}$ is a σ-field of subsets of Ω, i.e., it satisfies[1]
       (a) $\Omega \in \mathcal{F}, \emptyset \in \mathcal{F}$;
       (b) $A \in \mathcal{F} \Rightarrow A^c \in \mathcal{F}$;
       (c) $A_1, A_2, \ldots \in \mathcal{F} \Rightarrow \cup_{n=1}^{\infty} A_n \in \mathcal{F}$.
   (3) P is a *probability measure*, i.e., a set function defined on subsets of Ω, which satisfies
       (a) $P(\emptyset) = 0, P(\Omega) = 1$;
       (b) If $A_1, A_2, \ldots$ are pairwise disjoint ($A_i \cap A_j = \emptyset$ if $i \neq j$), then $P(\cup_{n=1}^{\infty} A_n) = \sum_{n=1}^{\infty} P(A_n)$.

We will not worry too much about $\mathcal{F}$ in this course; we will assume it allows us to speak about what we want, which is almost always true in applications. A common σ-algebra that we refer to below is the *Borel sets* $\mathcal{B}$, which is the σ-algebra generated by open intervals of $\mathbb{R}$.

Examples A.2.
   (1) Toss a fair coin n times. Then

$$\Omega = \{HH\ldots H, HH\ldots, T, \ldots, TT\ldots T\} = \{H, T\}^n = \text{all strings of H,T of length } n,$$

$$\mathcal{F} = \text{all subsets of } \Omega,$$

$$P(A) = \frac{|A|}{2^n}.$$

For example, for $n = 4$ and $A = \{HHHT, HHTH, HHTT\}$, we have $P(A) = 3/16$.

---

[1] If you do not know what a σ-field is, do not worry; it is included merely for completeness. In applications, you can think of $\mathcal{F}$ as the set of all events that you might possibly dream of asking about.

(2) Spin a top, and measure its angle with North when it falls. Then

$$\Omega = [0, 2\pi),$$

$$\mathcal{F} = \text{Borel sets} \cap [0, 2\pi),$$

$$P(A) = \frac{\mu(A)}{2\pi}, \quad \text{where } \mu \text{ is the Lebesgue measure, i.e. } \mu([a, b]) = b - a..$$

DEFINITION A.3. A *random variable* is a function $X : \Omega \to S \subset \mathbb{R}$ such that X is $\mathcal{F}$-measurable,[2] i.e., $X^{-1}(B) \in \mathcal{F}$ for all Borel sets $B \subset \mathbb{R}$. The set of possible values S is called the *state space*.

A random variable X induces a probability measure μ on $\mathbb{R}$, given by

$$\mu(B) = P(X \in B) = P(X^{-1}(B)).$$

Because of this, we often just work with random variables and the measure they induce, and forget about the probability space underlying them.

Examples A.4. Some random variables for each of Example A.2, and the measures they induce, include

(1) $X(\omega) = $ number of Heads in ω. This induces a binomial distribution on the integers $\{0, 1, \ldots, n\}$, $\mu_X(k) = \binom{n}{k}/2^n$.
$Y(\omega) = 1$ if the first coin in ω was Heads. This induces a probability measure on $\{0, 1\}$ with $\mu_Y(0) = 1/2$, $\mu_Y(1) = 1/2$.

(2) $X(\omega) = \begin{cases} 1 & \omega \in [0, \pi/2] \\ 0 & \text{otherwise} \end{cases}$. This induces a probability measure on $\{0, 1\}$ with $\mu_X(0) = 1/4$, $\mu_Y(1) = 3/4$.
$Y(\omega) = \omega^2$. This induces a probability measure on $[0, 4\pi^2)$ with probability density $\mu_Y([y, y + dy]) = 1/(4\pi\sqrt{y})$.

DEFINITION A.5. The *distribution function* or *cumulative distribution function* of a random variable X is the function $F : \mathbb{R} \to [0, 1]$ given by $F(x) = P(X \leq x)$.

Recall that a distribution function satisfies; (i) $\lim_{x \to -\infty} F(x) = 0$, $\lim_{x \to \infty} F(x) = 1$, (ii) $F(x)$ is monotonically increasing, and (iii) $F(x)$ is right-continuous, i.e., $\lim_{h \to 0} F(x + h) = F(x)$.

DEFINITION A.6. X is *discrete* if it takes values in some countable subset $S = \{x_1, x_2, \ldots\}$ of $\mathbb{R}$. A discrete random variable has a *probability mass function* (pmf) $f : \mathbb{R} \to [0, 1]$ given by $f(x) = P(X = x)$. The probability of event $A \in \mathcal{F}$ is $P(X \in A) = \sum_{x_i \in A} f(x_i)$.

DEFINITION A.7. X is *continuous* if there is an integrable function $f : \mathbb{R} \to [0, \infty)$ such that $F(x) = \int_{-\infty}^{x} f(u)du$. The function f is called the *probability density function* (pdf) of X. The probability of an event $A \in \mathcal{F}$ is $P(X \in A) = \int_A f(u)du$.

REMARK A.8. Not all random variables are continuous or discrete. They can be a mixture, or they can have a singular part, as for the Cantor measure. The full classification is given by Lebesgue's decomposition theorem.

---

[2] Again, if you have not seen this before it does not matter.

DEFINITION A.9. The *expectation* of a random variable X is defined as

$$(A.1) \qquad \mathbb{E}X = \int_\Omega X(\omega)\, P(d\omega) = \int_\mathbb{R} x\, dF(x) = \begin{cases} \int_\mathbb{R} x f(x) dx & X \text{ is continuous,} \\ \sum_{x \in S} x f(x) & X \text{ is discrete.} \end{cases}$$

This definition extends naturally to functions of X as $\mathbb{E}h(X) = \int h(x)dF(x)$.

Note that the definition above uses the notation $\int h(x)dF(x)$ to represent both a continuous integral and a discrete sum. This notation is convenient because we do not need to worry about whether the random variable under consideration is continuous or discrete. If you are not familiar with this kind of integral, you should review Section A.A.2 and references within.

DEFINITION A.10. The *variance* of X is

$$\mathrm{Var}(X) \equiv \mathbb{E}(X - \mathbb{E}X)^2 = \mathbb{E}X^2 - (\mathbb{E}X)^2.$$

These definitions extend naturally to collections of random variables, as we summarize briefly below.

DEFINITION A.11. $X = (X_1, \ldots, X_n)^T \in \mathbb{R}^n$ is a *random vector* or *vector-valued random variable* if each component is a random variable defined on the same probability space $(\Omega, \mathcal{F}, P)$. Then we define
   (i) The mean: $\mathbb{E}X = (\mathbb{E}X_1, \ldots, \mathbb{E}X_n)^T$;
   (ii) The covariance matrix: $\mathrm{cov}(X, X) = \mathbb{E}(X - \mathbb{E}X)(X - \mathbb{E}X)^T$.

The covariance matrix has components

$$\mathrm{cov}(X, X)_{ij} = \mathrm{cov}(X_i, X_j) = \mathbb{E}(X_i - \mathbb{E}X_i)(X_j - \mathbb{E}X_j)^T,$$

which is the covariance between the random variables X_i, X_j. For example, if $X = (X_1, X_2)^T$, then

$$B = \mathrm{cov}(X, X) = \begin{pmatrix} \mathrm{var}(X_1) & \mathrm{cov}(X_1, X_2) \\ \mathrm{cov}(X_1, X_2) & \mathrm{var}(X_2) \end{pmatrix}.$$

The covariance matrix B is positive semi-definite, a property we will exploit heavily in lectures to come.

DEFINITION A.12. The *joint distribution function* is $F(x_1, \ldots, x_n) = P(X_1 \le x_1, \ldots, X_n \le x_n)$. A continuous vector-valued random variable has a *probability density function* (pdf) $f(x_1, \ldots, x_n)$, which is such that $P(X \in A) = \int_A f(x_1, \ldots, x_n)dx$; and a discrete vector-valued random variable has a *probability mass function* (pmf), defined in a similar way. Sometimes these are called joint pdfs or joint pmfs to emphasize that they describe the distribution of several random variables jointly.

DEFINITION A.13. Given a continuous random vector $X = (X_1, \ldots, X_n)$, the *marginal pdf* of a component X_i is

$$f_{X_i}(x_i) = \int f(x_1, \ldots, x_n) dx_1 \cdots dx_{i-1} dx_{i+1} \cdots dx_n.$$

That is, we integrate the joint pdf over all variables except the variable of interest. A similar definition holds for the *marginal pmf* of a discrete random vector, with the integral replaced by a sum.

A.1.2. Conditional probability and independence.

DEFINITION A.14. Two events $A, B \in \mathcal{F}$ are *independent* if $P(A \cap B) = P(A)P(B)$. Two random variables X, Y are *independent* if, for all Borel sets $A, B \subset \mathbb{R}$, the events $X^{-1}(A)$ and $Y^{-1}(B)$ are independent, i.e., $P(X^{-1}(A) \cap Y^{-1}(B)) = P(X^{-1}(A))P(Y^{-1}(B))$. A collection of random variables $X_1, \ldots, X_n$ is independent if, for any Borel sets B_j, $P\left(\cap_{j=1}^n X_j^{-1}(B_j) \right) = \prod_{j=1}^n P(X_j^{-1}(B_j))$.

REMARK A.15. Continuous or discrete random variables X, Y are independent if and only if the joint pdf or pmf factors, as $f(x, y) = f_X(x)f_Y(y)$. A similar statement is true for a larger collection of random variables.

DEFINITION A.16. Given events A, B, the *conditional probability of A given B* is

$$(A.2) \qquad\qquad P(A|B) \equiv \frac{P(A \cap B)}{P(B)}.$$

REMARK A.17. Events A, B are independent iff $P(A|B) = P(A)$.

A very useful theorem is the following.

LAW OF TOTAL PROBABILITY (LOTP). Let $B_1, \ldots, B_k$ be a sequence of events that form a *partition* of the sample space: they are disjoint, $B_i \cap B_j = \emptyset$ for all $i \neq j$, and their union is the whole space, $\cup_i B_i = \Omega$. Then, for any event A,

$$(A.3) \qquad\qquad P(A) = \sum_{i=1}^k P(A \cap B_i) = \sum_{i=1}^k P(A|B_i)P(B_i).$$

Example A.18. According to the Pew Research Center (**Faverio, 2022**), 61% of US adults age 65 and older own a smartphone, while 91% of adults age 18-64 own a smartphone. About 22% of US adults are age 65 and over. You stop an adult at random on the street. What is the probability they own a smartphone?

Solution. Let S be the event a person owns a smartphone, and let A be the event they are 65 or older. By the LOTP,

$$P(S) = P(S|A)P(A) + P(S|A^c)P(A^c) = (0.61)(0.22) + (0.91)(0.78) = 0.844.$$

The probability a random adult owns a smartphone is about 84%.

We will use various other versions of conditional probability. Often we will need to condition on the value of a random variable, for example as $P(Y \in A|X = x)$ where $A \subset S$ is some event in the state space. When X is discrete this is not a problem as we can simply define the conditional probability mass function to be

$$(A.4) \qquad\qquad f(y|x) \equiv \frac{P(Y = y \cap X = x)}{P(X = x)} = \frac{f(x, y)}{f_X(x)},$$

for all x such that $P(X = x) \neq 0$, and define it to be 0 otherwise. Here $f(x, y)$ is the joint pmf, and $f_X(x) = \sum_y f(x, y)$ is the marginal pmf of X. We can then calculate the desired conditional probability using $f(y|x)$ as the pmf.

For a continuous random variable X this is a problem because $P(X = x) = 0$ for all x. However, we can define the conditional density to be

$$(A.5) \qquad\qquad f(y|x) = \frac{f(x, y)}{f_X(x)},$$

where $f_X(x) = \int f(x,y)dy$ is the marginal density of X. This definition is equivalent to (A.4) in a limiting sense, if we take an appropriate decreasing sequence of sets that shrink to the sets $\{X = x\}$, $\{Y = y\}$. For example, let us define $B_n = \{x \leq X \leq x + h_n\}$, $C_n = \{y \leq Y \leq y + h_n\}$, where $h_n \to 0$ as $n \to \infty$. Then the conditional probability $P(Y \in C_n | X \in B_n)$ approaches (A.5) as $n \to \infty$. We can then use $f(y|x)$ as a pdf when calculating probabilities of the form $P(Y \in A | X = x)$.

One must be careful when performing this limiting procedure as not all sequences of shrinking sets will give the same answer. To be fully rigorous we should condition on a σ-algebra, not a random variable. That is, we need to define the conditional expectation $\mathbb{E}(X|\mathcal{G})$ where $\mathcal{G}$ is a σ-algebra. Then we can define the random variable $\mathbb{E}(Y|X)$ to be the random variable one obtains by conditioning on the σ-algebra generated by X. Such considerations are beyond the scope of this book; when we need to condition on a continuous random variable we will use (A.5) unless otherwise noted.

A.1.3. Some useful distributions.

UNIFORM ON $[a, b]$ (continuous).

$$f(x) = \frac{1}{b-a}1_{[a,b]}(x), \qquad F(x) = \begin{cases} 0 & x \leq a \\ \frac{b-a}{x} & a \leq b \leq x \\ 1 & x > b \end{cases}$$

A uniform distribution on a discrete state space is defined in a similar way.

BERNOULLI DISTRIBUTION, PARAMETER p (discrete). A Bernoulli random variable is like the result of a coin toss which comes up heads with probability p (a "success"), and tails with probability $1 - p$ ("failure"):

$$f(0) = 1 - p, \quad f(1) = p, \qquad \mathbb{E}X = p, \quad \mathrm{Var}(X) = p(1 - p).$$

BINOMIAL DISTRIBUTION, PARAMETERS n, p (discrete). This gives the probability of getting a certain number of heads in n independent coin tosses with parameter p, i.e., the probability of each number of successes in a sequence of n independent Bernoulli trials:

$$f(k) = \binom{n}{k}p^k(1 - p)^{n-k}, \quad k = 0, 1, \ldots, n; \qquad \mathbb{E}X = np, \quad \mathrm{Var}(X) = np(1 - p).$$

POISSON DISTRIBUTION, PARAMETER λ (discrete). This models the number of events that occur in an interval of time, when the events occur completely independently of each other. E.g., the number of radioactive atoms that decay in an hour, the number of meteorites that hit the earth in a millenium, the number of deaths by horse kicks per year in the Prussian army, etc.

$$f(k) = \frac{\lambda^k e^{-\lambda}}{k!}, \quad k = 0, 1, 2, \ldots; \qquad \mathbb{E}X = \lambda, \quad \mathrm{Var}(X) = \lambda.$$

EXPONENTIAL DISTRIBUTION, PARAMETER λ (continuous). Often used to model the waiting time between events that occur independently of each other, such as the time between which two atoms decay radioactively.

$$f(x) = \lambda e^{-\lambda x}, \quad x \geq 0. \qquad \mathbb{E}X = \lambda, \quad \mathrm{Var}(X) = \lambda.$$

The exponential distribution is the only continuous distribution which describes a random variable X that is *memoryless*: $P(X > s + t | X > t) = P(X > s)$ for all $s, t > 0$.

GAUSSIAN DISTRIBUTION, PARAMETERS μ, σ (continuous). Also called the normal distribution. This arises as the distribution of occurs a sum of a large number of (roughly) independent random variables, by the central limit theorem.

$$f(x) = \frac{1}{\sqrt{2\pi\sigma^2}} e^{-\frac{1}{2\sigma^2}(x-\mu)^2}, \quad x \in \mathbb{R}. \qquad \mathbb{E}X = \mu, \quad \text{Var}(X) = \sigma^2.$$

A.1.4. Convergence of random variables. There are various ways that random variables can converge. We review some key definitions here.

DEFINITION A.19. A sequence of random variables $X_1, X_2, \ldots$, *converges almost surely* or *converges with probability 1* to another random variable X, written $X_n \overset{a.s.}{\longrightarrow} X$ if $P(\lim_{n \to \infty} X_n = X) = 1$.

DEFINITION A.20. A sequence of random variables $X_1, X_2, \ldots$, *converges in mean-square* to another random variable X, written $X_n \overset{m.s.}{\longrightarrow} X$ or m. s. $\lim_{n \to \infty} X_n = X$, if $\mathbb{E}|X_n - X|^2 \to 0$ as $n \to \infty$.

DEFINITION A.21. A sequence of random variables $X_1, X_2, \ldots$, *converges in probability* to another random variable X, if for all $\epsilon > 0$, $\lim_{n \to \infty} P(|X_n - X| > \epsilon) \to 0$.

DEFINITION A.22. A sequence of random variables $X_1, X_2, \ldots$, with cumulative distribution functions $F_1, F_2, \ldots$, *converges in distribution* to another random variable X with cumulative distribution function F if $\lim_{n \to \infty} F_n(x) = F(x)$ at each $x \in \mathbb{R}$ where F is continuous.

Convergence in mean-square implies convergence in probability, which in turn implies convergence in distribution. Convergence in mean-square does *not* imply almost sure convergence or vice versa. Convergence in probability implies that there is a subsequence which converges almost surely. Hence, convergence in mean-square implies there is a subsequence that converges almost surely.

Almost sure convergence implies convergence in probability and hence convergence in distribution.

A.2. Integration with respect to a measure

We will occasionally need to integrate a function with respect to a measure, such as when we calculate the expectation of a random variable, $\mathbb{E}X = \int x \, dF(x)$ as in (A.1), where the measure is $\mu(dx) = dF(x)$. Here is a brief review of how to define such an integral. More details can be found in (**Durrett, 2019**, Appendix A.4), including proofs that the integral is well defined.

Let $(\Omega, \mathcal{F}, \mu)$ be a measure space with (σ-finite) measure μ and let $f : \Omega \to \mathbb{R}$ be a measurable function defined on the sample space. We wish to define the integral

(A.6)
$$\int f \, d\mu,$$

for a suitable class of measurable functions f. (Sometimes we write this as $\int f(x)\mu(dx)$.) Let us first consider some examples of measures μ and the corresponding integral (A.6). For all of the items below we will assume that $\Omega = \mathbb{R}$ and $\mathcal{F}$ is the Borel sets.

- μ is the Lebesgue measure, i.e., $\mu(dx) = dx$. Then (A.6) becomes

$$\int f d\mu = \int f(x) dx,$$

where the second integral is the Lebesgue integral.

- μ is absolutely continuous with respect to the Lebesgue measure. Then we can write either $\mu(dx) = g(x)dx$ for some function $g \in L^1(\mathbb{R})$, or equivalently $\mu(dx) = dG(x)$ where $G(x) = \int^x g dx$ is the antiderivative of g. Then again (A.6) is the Lebesgue integral

$$\int f d\mu = \int f dG = \int f(x) g(x) dx.$$

- μ is supported on a countable set of points $\{x_1, x_2, \ldots\}$, so we can formally write $\mu(dx) = b_1 \delta(x - x_1) dx + b_2 \delta(x - x_2) dx + \cdots$, where $b_i > 0$. The integral (A.6) is

$$\int f d\mu = b_1 f(x_1) + b_2 f(x_2) + \cdots .$$

- μ is a probability measure associated with a random variable X with cumulative distribution function G. Then $\mu([a, b]) = G(b) - G(a)$; formally, we write $\mu(dx) = dG(x)$. If G is differentiable, then $\mu(dx) = G'(x)dx$. The integral (A.6) is (recall (A.1))

$$\int f d\mu = \int f dG = \mathbb{E} f(X).$$

Roughly, this integral can be approximated by a discrete sum over a partition $x_0, x_1, \ldots, x_N$ as

$$\int_{\mathbb{R}} f(x) \, dG(x) \quad \approx \quad \sum_i f(x_i)(G(x_{i+1}) - G(x_i))(x_{i+1} - x_i).$$

To properly define the integral in (A.6) there are four steps, outlined below.

(1) Let a *simple function* be a function of the form $\phi(x) = \sum_{i=1}^n a_i 1_{A_i}(x)$, where $a_i \in \mathbb{R}$, and $A_i \in \mathcal{F}$ are disjoint measurable sets such that $\mu(A_i) < \infty$. The function $1_A(x)$ is an indicator function, i.e., $1_A(x) = 1$ if $x \in A$, $1_A(x) = 0$ if $x \notin A$. Define the integral for a simple function to be

$$\int \phi(x) \mu(dx) = \sum_{i=1}^n a_i \mu(A_i).$$

One can verify the integral above satisfies the following properties (see **(Durrett, 2019)** for the proofs):

(i) If $\phi \geq 0$ a.e.[3] then $\int \phi d\mu \geq 0$.

(ii) For any $a \in \mathbb{R}$, $\int a\phi d\mu = a \int \phi d\mu$.

(iii) $\int(\phi + \psi)d\mu = \int \phi d\mu + \int \psi d\mu$.

(iv) If $\phi \leq \psi$ a.e., then $\int \phi d\mu \leq \int \psi d\mu$.

(v) If $\phi = \psi$ a.e., then $\int \phi d\mu = \int \psi d\mu$.

(vi) $|\int \phi d\mu| \leq \int |\phi| d\mu$.

(2) Let f be a bounded function that is nonzero only on a set $E \subset \Omega$ with $\mu(E) < \infty$. Define

$$\int f d\mu = \sup_{\substack{\phi \leq f \\ \phi \text{ simple}}} \int \phi d\mu = \inf_{\substack{\psi \geq f \\ \psi \text{ simple}}} \int \psi d\mu \,.$$

To show this is well defined, one must show the sup and inf are equal. To do this one uses the properties (i)–(vi) above. Then one can show that properties (i)–(vi) still hold for bounded functions.

(3) Let $f \geq 0$. Define

$$\int f d\mu = \sup\{\int h d\mu : 0 \leq h \leq f, \ h \text{ is bounded}\} \,.$$

This is well defined already; we do not need to check anything. One can then show properties (i)–(vi) hold for nonnegative functions.

(4) Suppose $\int |f| d\mu < \infty$. Let

$$f^+(x) = f(x) \vee 0 \quad \text{and} \quad f^-(x) = (-f(x)) \vee 0 \,,$$

where $a \vee b = \max(a, b)$. Then $f(x) = f^+(x) - f^-(x)$, and $|f(x)| = f^+(x) + f^-(x)$. Define

$$\int f d\mu = \int f^+ d\mu - \int f^- d\mu \,.$$

This is well defined since $f^+, f^- \leq |f|$; and by property (iv). One can then show properties (i)–(vi) hold for integrable functions.

A.3. Multivariate Gaussian random variables

Here are some useful facts about multivariate Gaussian random variables.

(1) Let X be a multivariate Gaussian random vector, let $A \in \mathbb{R}^{m \times n}$ with $m \leq n$ be a constant matrix, and let $Y = AX$. Then Y is also a multivariate Gaussian random vector, with $Y \sim N(\mu, A\Sigma A^T)$.

PROOF. This is an exercise is multivariable calculus. Transform the density using the correct Jacobian **(Grimmett and Stirzaker, 2001**, Theorem 4.9.6, p. 117). $\square$

(2) The marginal distributions are Gaussian, with mean and covariance given by dropping the relevant rows and columns in the mean vector and covariance matrix.

---

[3] Almost everywhere, i.e., with probability 1.

PROOF. Another exercise in calculus: integrate the joint density over a subset of variables and show it has the correct form. □

(3) If (X, Y) is a multivariate Gaussian, and if X, Y are uncorrelated, then X, Y are independent.

Note that uncorrelated $\Rightarrow$ independent is *only* true for jointly Gaussian random variables; for other distributions this is not true in general. This is one reason why calculations with Gaussians are significantly more tractable than with other kinds of distributions.

PROOF. This follows directly from the form of the probability density function. If X, Y are uncorrelated then the covariance matrix has the form

$$\Sigma = \begin{pmatrix} \sigma_1^2 & 0 \\ 0 & \sigma_2^2 \end{pmatrix}.$$

We can substitute this form into (5.3) and find the density factors in a product of marginals, as

$$f(x, y) = f_x(x) f_y(y) = \frac{1}{\sqrt{2\pi}\sigma_1} e^{-\frac{(x-\mu_1^2)}{2\sigma_1^2}} \frac{1}{\sqrt{2\pi}\sigma_2} e^{-\frac{(y-\mu_2^2)}{2\sigma_2^2}}.$$

Therefore X, Y are independent. □

Here is a general expression for the pdf of a bivariate Gaussian. If (X, Y) is a multivariate Gaussian and the correlation coefficient between X, Y is ρ, then the pdf has the form

$$f(x, y) = \frac{1}{2\pi\sigma_1\sigma_2\sqrt{1-\rho^2}} \exp\left\{-\frac{\frac{(x-\mu_1^2)}{\sigma_1^2} - \frac{2\rho(x-\mu_1)(y-\mu_2)}{\sigma_1\sigma_2} + \frac{(y-\mu_2)^2}{\sigma_2^2}}{2(1-\rho^2)}\right\}.$$

(4) The conditional distributions are Gaussian. For example, if $X = (X_1, \ldots, X_n)$ and $Y = (X_m, \ldots, X_n)$, then the random vector $Z = (X|Y)$, whose probabilities are calculated as $P(Z \in A) = P(X \in A|Y)$, is a multivariate Gaussian. The mean and covariance may also be calculated using calculus and algebra; the formulas are somewhat more complicated than for the marginals involving Schur complements.

Note that it is not true that if random variables X, Y are separately Gaussian, then the random vector (X, Y) is a multivariate Gaussian. For a counterexample, see Exercise A.1.

Exercise A.1. Let $X \sim N(0, 1)$, let $a > 0$, and let $Y = X$ if $|X| < a$, and $Y = -X$ if $|X| \geq a$. Show that $Y \sim N(0, 1)$ but that the random variable (X, Y) does not have a bivariate normal distribution. (Hint: Calculate the covariance of X, Y.)

A.4. Stopping times

DEFINITION A.23. A random variable $\tau : D \to [0, \infty]$ is called a *stopping time* with respect to a Brownian motion $(W_t)_{t \geq 0}$ if the event $\{\tau \leq t\}$ can be decided using only the values of $(W_s)_{0 \leq s \leq t}$.

REMARK A.24. The rigorous definition is that τ is a stopping time with respect to the filtration $\{\mathcal{F}_t\}$ if $\{\tau \leq t\} \in \mathcal{F}_t$ for all $t \geq 0$.

THEOREM A.25 (Properties of stopping times). *Let* τ_1, τ_2 *be two stopping times. Then*

(i) $\{\tau_i = t\} \in \mathcal{F}_t$, *for all times* $t \geq 0$.
(ii) $\tau_1 \wedge \tau_2 = \min(\tau_1, \tau_2)$ *and* $\tau_1 \vee \tau_2 = \max(\tau_1, \tau_2)$ *are both stopping times.*

PROOF.

(i) $\{\tau_i = t\} = \{\tau_i \leq t\} - \{\tau_i < t\}$, both of which are measurable in $\mathcal{F}_t$ (Exercise: Show that $\{\tau_i < t\}$ is $\mathcal{F}_t$-measurable, by writing it as a countable union of measurable sets.)
(ii) $\{\tau_1 \wedge \tau_2 \leq t\} = \{\tau_1 \leq t\} \cup \{\tau_2 \leq t\} \in \mathcal{F}_t$. Similar calculations hold for the max.

$\square$

Here are some examples of random times that are or are not stopping times.

(1) $\tau = c$, where c is a constant, is a stopping time.
(2) Let X_t the the solution to an SDE and let E be a nonempty open or closed subset of $\mathbb{R}^n$. Then

$$(A.7) \qquad \tau = \inf\{t \geq 0 \mid X_t \in E\}$$

is a stopping time. (Set $\tau = \infty$ for sample paths that never hit E.) For a proof, see (**Evans, 2013**, Section 6.A). This is called the *first-passage time* to set E.
(3) If τ_E is a first-passage time and $T > 0$ is a real number, then $\tau_E \wedge T$ is a stopping time. This is a technique used to construct stopping times with finite expected values.
(4) The random variable

$$\sigma = \sup\{t \geq 0 \mid X_t \in E\},$$

representing the last time that X_t hits E, is *not* a stopping time. Heuristically, this is because $\{\sigma \leq t\}$ depends on the whole future of the process, so it cannot depend on only X_s for $s \leq t$ (it cannot be $\mathcal{F}_t$-measurable).

A.5. Collected results about PDEs

This section collects some theorems regarding the well-posedness of PDEs that we refer to in the text. The theorems concern an operator

$$(A.8) \qquad Lu = \sum_{i,j=1}^{n} a_{ij}(x,t)\frac{\partial^2 u}{\partial x_i \partial x_j} + \sum_{i=1}^{n} b_i(x,t)\frac{\partial u}{\partial x_i} + c(x,t)u.$$

The matrix $a = (a_{ij})$ is assumed to be symmetric, i.e., $a_{ij} = a_{ji}$. The operator acts on functions $u : D \times [0,T] \to \mathbb{R}$, where $D \subset \mathbb{R}^n$ could be bounded or unbounded. Let $\Omega = D \times [0,T]$.

We say that L is *elliptic at* (x,t) if $y^T a(x,t)y > 0$ for all $y \in \mathbb{R}^d$, and it is *uniformly elliptic in* Ω if $y^T a(x,t)y \geq \lambda_0$ for all $(x,t) \in \Omega$, $y \in \mathbb{R}^d$ with $|y| = 1$, and for some $\lambda_0 > 0$.

REMARK A.26. Recall that a function f defined on a bounded closed set $\subset \mathbb{R}^n$ is *Hölder continuous with exponent α in S (for $0 < \alpha < 1$) if*

$$(A.9) \qquad |f(x) - f(y)| \leq A(x-y)^\alpha \qquad \text{for all } x, y \in S.$$

If S is unbounded (and its intersection with every bounded closed set B is closed), then f is Hölder continuous with exponent α if (A.9) holds in $S \cap B$ for every bounded closed set B; the constant A may depend on B. If A is independent of B then f is *uniformly Hölder continuous in S*. If S is open then f is *locally Hölder continuous* if (A.9) holds in every bounded closed set $B \subset S$, with A which may depend on B; if A is independent of B then f is uniformly Hölder continuous.

If (A.9) holds with $\alpha = 1$, then f is *Lipschitz continuous*, with a similar definition of uniformly Lipschitz continuous.

A.5.1. Parabolic PDEs on an unbounded domain. Let $D = \mathbb{R}^n$ and $\Omega = \mathbb{R}^n \times [0, T]$. We are interested in the solution to the *Cauchy problem*

$$(A.10) \qquad Lu(x,t) - \frac{\partial u}{\partial t}(x,t) = f(x,t) \quad \text{in } \mathbb{R}^n \times (0,T], \qquad u(x,0) = \phi(x) \text{ on } \mathbb{R}^n.$$

The *fundamental solution* to the Cauchy problem in Ω (also called the *Green's function*) is the function $\Gamma(x,t|\xi,s)$ defined for $(x,t),(\xi,s) \in \Omega$ with $t > s$, which satisfies

(i) For fixed (ξ,s) it satisfies in (x,t) the equation

$$L\Gamma - \frac{\partial \Gamma}{\partial t} = 0 \quad \text{for } x \in \mathbb{R}^n, \ s < t \leq T.$$

(ii) For every continuous function $\phi : \mathbb{R}^n \to \mathbb{R}$, it satisfies

$$\lim_{t \searrow s} \int_{\mathbb{R}^n} \Gamma(x,t|\xi,s)\phi(\xi)d\xi = \phi(x).$$

The following theorem is due to (**Friedman, 1964**, Chapter 1, Theorem 12), with help from Theorems 9 & 10 regarding the smoothness of the solution and Equations 6.12 & 6.13 for decay bounds; see also (**Friedman, 2006**, Chapter 6, Theorems 4.5 and 4.6).

THEOREM A.27. *Suppose that L is uniformly elliptic in Ω, the coefficients of L are bounded, continuous functions in Ω, and the coefficients are uniformly Lipchistz continuous in the spatial variable in Ω. Let $f(x,t)$ be Lipschitz continuous in Ω and let $\phi(x)$ be continuous in $\mathbb{R}^n$, such that $|f(x,t)| \leq cst \cdot e^{h|x|^2}$, $|\phi(x)| \leq cst \cdot e^{h|x|^2}$, where h is any positive constant such that $h < \bar{\lambda}_0/4T$ and $\bar{\lambda}_0 > 0$ is a lower bound on the minimum eigenvalue of a^{-1} in Ω. Then there exists a fundamental solution $\Gamma(x,t|\xi,s)$ to the Cauchy problem satisfying*

$$(A.11) \qquad |D_x^m \Gamma(x,t|\xi,s)| \leq C(t-s)^{-(n-|m|)/2} e^{-c\frac{|x-\xi|^2}{t-s}},$$

for $|m| = 0, 1$, where C, c are positive constants. The functions $D_x^m\Gamma(x,t|\xi,s)$ $(0 \leq |m| \leq 2)$ and $D_t\Gamma(x,t|\xi,s)$ are continuous in $\Omega \times \Omega$ for $t > s$. Furthermore, the function

$$(A.12) \qquad u(x,t) = \int_{\mathbb{R}^n} \Gamma(x,t|\xi,0)\phi(\xi)d\xi - \int_0^t \int_{\mathbb{R}^n} \Gamma(x,t|\xi,s)f(\xi,s)d\xi ds$$

is a solution of the Cauchy problem (A.10), such that $u, \partial_i u, \partial_{ij} u, \partial_t u$ are continuous in $\mathbb{R}^n \times (0,T]$, and

$$|u(x,t)| \leq cst \cdot e^{k|x|^2}$$

where k is a constant depending only on h, λ_0, T. Finally, u is the unique solution satisfying $|u(x,t)| \leq Be^{\beta|x|^2}$ for some positive constants B, β.

Given stronger bounds on f, ϕ, we may obtain stronger bounds on u using its representation (A.12) and the bounds (A.11) on the derivatives of Γ. For example, if f, ϕ are bounded, then $u, \partial_i u$ are also bounded. Alternatively, if $|f(x, t)|, |\phi(x)| \leq A e^{-\alpha |x|^2}$ for some positive constants A, α, then we find that $|u(x, t)| \leq G t^{-n/2} e^{-\gamma |x|^2}, |\partial_i u(x, t)| \leq G t^{-(n-1)/2} e^{-\gamma |x|^2}$ for some positive constants G, γ.

A.5.2. Elliptic PDEs on a bounded domain. We next consider the solution to the boundary-value problem

(A.13) $$Lu = f \quad \text{in } D, \qquad u = g \quad \text{on } \partial D,$$

where $D \subset \mathbb{R}^n$ is open and bounded and all coefficients of L are independent of t.

Let $C^{2,1}(D)$ be the space of functions on D which are twice continuously differentiable and whose derivatives up to 2nd order are Lipschitz continuous. We say a boundary ∂D is C^2 or $C^{2,1}$ if each point of ∂D has a neighborhood which is the graph of a C^2 or $C^{2,1}$ function with $n - 1$ variables. Recall that D satisfies the *exterior sphere condition* if, for each $\xi \in \partial D$, there exists a ball $B = B_R(y)$ such that $\bar{B} \cap \bar{D} = \xi$. If ∂D is C^2, it satisfies this condition.

THEOREM A.28 ((**Gilbarg and Trudinger, 1977**), Theorem 6.13). *Let D be an open bounded domain which satisfies the exterior sphere condition. Suppose L is uniformly elliptic on D, with $c \leq 0$. Further suppose f and the coefficients of L are bounded and Lipschitz continuous in D, and g is continuous on ∂D. Then there is a unique solution $u \in C^{2,1}(D) \cap C(\bar{D})$ to (A.13).*

By strengthening the conditions on the coefficients, we obtain a solution that is twice continuously differentiable up to the boundary.

THEOREM A.29 ((**Gilbarg and Trudinger, 1977**), Theorem 6.14). *Given an open bounded domain D which is a $C^{2,1}$ domain. Suppose $\mathcal{L}$ is uniformly elliptic on D with $c \leq 0$. Further suppose f and the coefficients of L are Lipschitz continuous on $\bar{D}$ and $g \in C^{2,1}(\bar{D})$. Then there is a unique solution $u \in C^{2,1}(\bar{D})$ to (11.9).*

Given a solution up to the boundary, it can be extended a little bit beyond the boundary.

THEOREM A.30 ((**Gilbarg and Trudinger, 1977**), Lemma 6.37). *Let D be a $C^{2,1}$ domain and let D' be an open set containing $\bar{D}$. Suppose $u \in C^{2,1}(\bar{D})$. Then there exists a function $w \in C^{2,1}(D')$ such that $w = u$ in D.*

Bibliography

Aldous, D. and P. Diaconis. 1986. *Shuffling cards and stopping times*, Amer. Math. Monthly **93**, no. 5, 333–348, DOI 10.2307/2323590. MR841111

Austin, D. 2010. *How many times do I have to shuffle this deck?*, http://www.ams.org/samplings/feature-column/fcarc-shuffle.

Batchelor, G. K. 1976. *Brownian diffusion of particles with hydrodynamic interaction*, J. Fluid Mech. **74**, no. 1, 1–29, DOI 10.1017/S0022112076001663. MR406082

Bogachëv, V. I. and M. Rëkner. 2000. *A generalization of Khas′minskiĭ's theorem on the existence of invariant measures for locally integrable drifts* (Russian, with Russian summary), Teor. Veroyatnost. i Primenen. **45**, no. 3, 417–436, DOI 10.1137/S0040585X97978348; English transl.,. 2000, Theory Probab. Appl. **45**, no. 3, 363–378. MR1967783

Bou-Rabee, N. and M. Holmes-Cerfon. 2020. *Sticky Brownian motion and its numerical solution*, SIAM Review **62**, no. 1, 164–195.

Bou-Rabee, N. and E. Vanden-Eijnden. 2018. *Continuous-time random walks for the numerical solution of stochastic differential equations*, Mem. Amer. Math. Soc. **256**, no. 1228, v+124, DOI 10.1090/memo/1228. MR3870359

Breiman, L. 1992. *Probability*, Classics in Applied Mathematics, vol. 7, Society for Industrial and Applied Mathematics (SIAM), Philadelphia, PA. Corrected reprint of the 1968 original, DOI 10.1137/1.9781611971286. MR1163370

Coifman, R. R. 2005. *Perspectives and challenges to harmonic analysis and geometry in high dimensions: geometric diffusions as a tool for harmonic analysis and structure definition of data*, Perspectives in analysis, Math. Phys. Stud., vol. 27, Springer, Berlin, pp. 27–35, DOI 10.1007/3-540-30434-7_3. MR2206766

Cowles, M. K. and B. P. Carlin. 1996. *Markov chain Monte Carlo convergence diagnostics: A comparative review*, J. Amer. Statist. Assoc. **91**, no. 434, 883–904, DOI 10.2307/2291683. MR1395755

Delong, S., F. B. Usabiaga, R. Delgado-Buscalioni, B. E. Griffith, and A. Donev. 2014. *Brownian dynamics without green's functions*, J. Chem. Phys. **140**, no. 13.

Diaconis, P. 2009. *The Markov chain Monte Carlo revolution*, Bull. Amer. Math. Soc. (N.S.) **46**, no. 2, 179–205, DOI 10.1090/S0273-0979-08-01238-X. MR2476411

Diaconis, P., S. Holmes, and R. Montgomery. 2007. *Dynamical bias in the coin toss*, SIAM Rev. **49**, no. 2, 211–235, DOI 10.1137/S0036144504446436. MR2327054

Durrett, R. 1996. *Stochastic calculus*, Probability and Stochastics Series, CRC Press, Boca Raton, FL. A practical introduction. MR1398879

Durrett, R. 2019. *Probability—theory and examples*, Cambridge Series in Statistical and Probabilistic Mathematics, vol. 49, Cambridge University Press, Cambridge. Fifth edition of [MR1068527], DOI 10.1017/9781108591034. MR3930614

E, W., T. Li, and E. Vanden-Eijnden. 2019. *Applied stochastic analysis*, Graduate Studies in Mathematics, vol. 199, American Mathematical Society, Providence, RI, DOI 10.1090/gsm/199. MR3932086

Einstein, A. 1905. *Über die von der molekularkinetischen theorie der wärme geforderte bewegung von in ruhenden flüssigkeiten suspendierten teilchen*, Annalen der physik **322**, no. 8, 549–560.

Evans, L. C. 2010. *Partial differential equations*, 2nd ed., Graduate Studies in Mathematics, vol. 19, American Mathematical Society, Providence, RI, DOI 10.1090/gsm/019. MR2597943

Evans, L. C. 2013. *An introduction to stochastic differential equations*, American Mathematical Society, Providence, RI, DOI 10.1090/mbk/082. MR3154922

Faverio, M. 2022. *Share of those 65 and older who are tech users has grown in the past decade*, https://www.pewresearch.org/short-reads/2022/01/13/share-of-those-65-and-older-who-are-tech-users-has-grown-in-the-past-decade/.

Frenkel, D. and A. J. Ladd. 1984. *New Monte Carlo method to compute the free energy of arbitrary solids: Application to the fcc and hcp phases of hard spheres*, J. Chem. Phys. **81**, no. 7, 3188–3193.

Friedman, A. 2006. *Stochastic differential equations and applications*, Dover Publications, Inc., Mineola, NY. Two volumes bound as one; Reprint of the 1975 and 1976 original published in two volumes. MR2295424

Friedman, A. 1964. *Partial differential equations of parabolic type*, Prentice-Hall, Inc., Englewood Cliffs, NJ. MR181836

Frisch, U. 1995. *Turbulence: The legacy of A. N. Kolmogorov*, Cambridge University Press, Cambridge. MR1428905

Gardiner, C. 2009. *Stochastic methods: A handbook for the natural and social sciences*, 4th ed., Springer Series in Synergetics, Springer-Verlag, Berlin. MR2676235

Roberts, G. O., A. Gelman, and W. R. Gilks. 1997. *Weak convergence and optimal scaling of random walk Metropolis algorithms*, Ann. Appl. Probab. **7**, no. 1, 110–120, DOI 10.1214/aoap/1034625254. MR1428751

Gelman, A., G. O. Roberts, and W. R. Gilks. 1996. *Efficient Metropolis jumping rules*, Bayesian statistics, 5 (Alicante, 1994), Oxford Sci. Publ., Oxford Univ. Press, New York, pp. 599–607. MR1425429

Gikhman, I. I. and A. V. Skorokhod. 2004. *The theory of stochastic processes. I*, Classics in Mathematics, Springer-Verlag, Berlin. Translated from the Russian by S. Kotz; Reprint of the 1974 edition. MR2058259

Gilbarg, D. and N. S. Trudinger. 1977. *Elliptic partial differential equations of second order*, Grundlehren der Mathematischen Wissenschaften, Vol. 224, Springer-Verlag, Berlin-New York. MR473443

Goodman, J. and A. D. Sokal. 1989. *Multigrid Monte Carlo method: Conceptual foundations*, Physical Review D **40**, no. 6.

Goodman, J. and J. Weare. 2010. *Ensemble samplers with affine invariance*, Commun. Appl. Math. Comput. Sci. **5**, no. 1, 65–80, DOI 10.2140/camcos.2010.5.65. MR2600822

Grimmett, G. R. and D. R. Stirzaker. 2001. *Probability and random processes*, 3rd ed., Oxford University Press, New York. MR2059709

Gubernatis, J. E. 2005. *Marshall Rosenbluth and the Metropolis algorithm*, Phys. Plasmas **12**, no. 5, 057303, 5, DOI 10.1063/1.1887186. MR2146373

Hastings, W. K. 1970. *Monte Carlo sampling methods using Markov chains and their applications*, Biometrika **57**, no. 1, 97–109, DOI 10.1093/biomet/57.1.97. MR3363437

Hayes, B. 2013. *First links in the Markov chain*, American Scientist **101**.

Hida, T. and M. Hitsuda. 1993. *Gaussian processes*, Translations of Mathematical Monographs, vol. 120, American Mathematical Society, Providence, RI. Translated from the 1976 Japanese original by the authors, DOI 10.1090/mmono/120. MR1216518

Higham, D. J. 2001. *An algorithmic introduction to numerical simulation of stochastic differential equations*, SIAM Rev. **43**, no. 3, 525–546, DOI 10.1137/S0036144500378302. MR1872387

Hijón, C., P. Español, E. Vanden-Eijnden, and Delgado-Buscalioni R. 2010. *Mori–Zwanzig formalism as a practical computational tool*, Faraday Discussions **144**.

Holmes-Cerfon, M., O. Bühler, and R. Ferrari. 2011. *Particle dispersion by random waves in the rotating Boussinesq system*, J. Fluid Mech. **670**, 150–175, DOI 10.1017/S0022112010005240. MR2773677

Horn, R. A. and C. R. Johnson. 2013. *Matrix analysis*, 2nd ed., Cambridge University Press, Cambridge. MR2978290

Hou, F., J. Goodman, and D. W. Hogg, *The probabilities of orbital-companion models for stellar radial velocity data*, Preprint, arXiv:1401.6128, 2014.

Huang, W., M. Ji, Z. Liu, and Y. Yi. 2015. *Steady states of Fokker–Planck equations: I. Existence*, J. Dynam. Differential Equations **27**, no. 3-4, 721–742, DOI 10.1007/s10884-015-9454-x. MR3435129

John, F. 1978. *Partial differential equations*, 3rd ed., Applied Mathematical Sciences, vol. 1, Springer-Verlag, New York-Berlin. MR514404

Kaipio, J. and E. Somersalo. 2005. *Statistical and computational inverse problems*, Applied Mathematical Sciences, vol. 160, Springer-Verlag, New York. MR2102218

Karatzas, I. and S. E. Shreve. 1991. *Brownian motion and stochastic calculus*, 2nd ed., Graduate Texts in Mathematics, vol. 113, Springer-Verlag, New York, DOI 10.1007/978-1-4612-0949-2. MR1121940

Karlin, S. and H. M. Taylor. 1981. *A second course in stochastic processes*, Academic Press, Inc. [Harcourt Brace Jovanovich, Publishers], New York-London. MR611513

Khas' minskii, R. Z. 1960. *Ergodic properties of recurrent diffusion processes and stabilization of the solution to the cauchy problem for parabolic equations*, Theory of Probability & Its Applications **5**, no. 2, 179–196.

Kirkpatrick, S., C. D. Gelatt Jr., and M. P. Vecchi. 1983. *Optimization by simulated annealing*, Science **220**, no. 4598, 671–680, DOI 10.1126/science.220.4598.671. MR702485

Kloeden, P. E. and E. Platen. 1992. *Numerical solution of stochastic differential equations*, Applications of Mathematics (New York), vol. 23, Springer-Verlag, Berlin, DOI 10.1007/978-3-662-12616-5. MR1214374

Koralov, L. B. and Y. G. Sinai. 2007. *Theory of probability and random processes*, 2nd ed., Universitext, Springer, Berlin, DOI 10.1007/978-3-540-68829-7. MR2343262

Lax, P. D. 1997. *Linear algebra*, Pure and Applied Mathematics (New York), John Wiley & Sons, Inc., New York. A Wiley-Interscience Publication. MR1423602

Lax, P. D. 2002. *Functional analysis*, Pure and Applied Mathematics (New York), Wiley-Interscience [John Wiley & Sons], New York. MR1892228

Levental, S. and R. V. Erickson. 2003. *On almost sure convergence of the quadratic variation of Brownian motion*, Stochastic Process. Appl. **106**, no. 2, 317–333, DOI 10.1016/S0304-4149(03)00048-6. MR1989631

Lindgren, G. 2013. *Stationary stochastic processes*, Chapman & Hall/CRC Texts in Statistical Science Series, CRC Press, Boca Raton, FL. Theory and applications. MR3024784

Liu, J. S. 2001. *Monte Carlo strategies in scientific computing*, Springer Series in Statistics, Springer-Verlag, New York. MR1842342

Markowich, P. A. and C. Villani. 2000. *On the trend to equilibrium for the Fokker-Planck equation: an interplay between physics and functional analysis*, Mat. Contemp. **19**, 1–29. VI Workshop on Partial Differential Equations, Part II (Rio de Janeiro, 1999). MR1812873

Metropolis, N., A. W. Rosenbluth, M. N. Rosenbluth, A. H. Teller, and E. Teller. 1953. *Equation of state calculations by fast computing machines*, J. Chem. Phys. **21**, 1087–1092.

Norris, J. R. 1998. *Markov chains*, Cambridge Series in Statistical and Probabilistic Mathematics, vol. 2, Cambridge University Press, Cambridge. Reprint of 1997 original. MR1600720

Øksendal, B. 2003. *Stochastic differential equations*, 6th ed., Universitext, Springer-Verlag, Berlin. An introduction with applications, DOI 10.1007/978-3-642-14394-6. MR2001996

Papanicolaou, G. C. 1977. *Introduction to the asymptotic analysis of stochastic equations*, Modern modeling of continuum phenomena (Ninth Summer Sem. Appl. Math., Rensselaer Polytech. Inst., Troy, N.Y., 1975), Lectures in Appl. Math., Vol. 16, Amer. Math. Soc., Providence, RI, pp. 109–147. MR458590

Pavliotis, G. A. 2014. *Stochastic processes and applications*, Texts in Applied Mathematics, vol. 60, Springer, New York. Diffusion processes, the Fokker-Planck and Langevin equations, DOI 10.1007/978-1-4939-1323-7. MR3288096

Pavliotis, G. A. and A. M. Stuart. 2008. *Multiscale methods*, Texts in Applied Mathematics, vol. 53, Springer, New York. Averaging and homogenization. MR2382139

Petra, N., J. Martin, G. Stadler, and O. Ghattas. 2014. *A computational framework for infinite-dimensional Bayesian inverse problems, Part II: Stochastic Newton MCMC with application to ice sheet flow inverse problems*, SIAM J. Sci. Comput. **36**, no. 4, A1525–A1555, DOI 10.1137/130934805. MR3233941

Rogers, W. B., T. Sinno, and J. C. Crocker. 2013. *Kinetics and non-exponential binding of DNA-coated colloids*, Soft Matter **9**, no. 28, 6412–6417.

Rudin, W. 1976. *Principles of mathematical analysis*, 3rd ed., International Series in Pure and Applied Mathematics, McGraw-Hill Book Co., New York-Auckland-Düsseldorf. MR385023

Sharma, S. 2017. *Markov chain monte carlo methods for bayesian data analysis in astronomy*, Annual Review of Astronomy and Astrophysics **55**, 213–259.

Sokal, A. D. 1989. *Monte Carlo methods in statistical mechanics: Foundations and new algorithms.* In Cours de Troisieme Cyle de la Physique en Suisse Romande, Lausanne.

Sprinkle, B., E. B. van der Wee, Y. Luo, M. M. Driscoll, and A. Donev. 2020. *Driven dynamics in dense suspensions of microrollers,* Soft Matter **16**, no. 34, 7982–8001.

Strang, G. 1988. *Linear Algebra and its Applications,* 3rd ed., Brooks/Cole.

Stroock, D. W. 2008. *Partial differential equations for probabilists,* Cambridge Studies in Advanced Mathematics, vol. 112, Cambridge University Press, Cambridge, DOI 10.1017/CBO9780511755255. MR2410225

Stroock, D. W. and S. R. S. Varadhan. 1979. *Multidimensional diffusion processes,* Grundlehren der Mathematischen Wissenschaften, vol. 233, Springer-Verlag, Berlin-New York. MR532498

Tao, T. October 2010. *245A, Notes 6: Outer measures, pre-measures, and product measures,* https://terrytao.wordpress.com.

Taylor, G. I. 1921. *Diffusion by continuous movements,* Proc. London Math. Soc. (2) **20**, no. 3, 196–212, DOI 10.1112/plms/s2-20.1.196. MR1577363

Varadhan, S. R. S. 2007. *Stochastic processes,* Courant Lecture Notes in Mathematics, vol. 16, Courant Institute of Mathematical Sciences, New York; American Mathematical Society, Providence, RI, DOI 10.1090/cln/016. MR2354349

Veretennikov, A. Yu. 1999. *On polynomial mixing and the rate of convergence for stochastic differential and difference equations* (Russian, with Russian summary), Teor. Veroyatnost. i Primenen. **44**, no. 2, 312–327, DOI 10.1137/S0040585X97977550; English transl.,. 1999, Theory Probab. Appl. **44**, no. 2, 361–374. MR1751475

Fernandez de la Vega, W. 1974. *On almost sure convergence of quadratic Brownian variation,* Ann. Probability **2**, 551–552, DOI 10.1214/aop/1176996675. MR359029

Yaglom, A. M. 1962. *An introduction to the theory of stationary random functions,* Revised English edition, Prentice-Hall, Inc., Englewood Cliffs, NJ. Translated and edited by Richard A. Silverman. MR184289

Zappa, E., M. Holmes-Cerfon, and J. Goodman. 2018. *Monte Carlo on manifolds: sampling densities and integrating functions,* Comm. Pure Appl. Math. **71**, no. 12, 2609–2647, DOI 10.1002/cpa.21783. MR3869037

Zwanzig, R. 2001. *Nonequilibrium statistical mechanics,* Oxford University Press, New York. MR2012558

Index

SELECTED PUBLISHED TITLES IN THIS SERIES